FRIEDLINE

(232)

LESLIE E. FRIEDLINE

Numerator = 10

Denominator inches less than one

Konp = 3 - 5

P 398

Computers

Principles of
Automatic Controls

PRENTICE-HALL ELECTRICAL ENGINEERING SERIES

W. L. Everitt, Ph.D., *Editor*

Principles of

Automatic Controls

By

FLOYD E. NIXON

Chief of Simulation
The Glenn L. Martin Company

PRENTICE-HALL, INC.
Englewood Cliffs, N. J.

Library of Congress Card Catalog Number: 54–5075.

First Printing . . . . October, 1953
Second Printing . . . August, 1954
Third Printing . . September, 1955
Fourth Printing. . . August, 1956

PRINTED IN THE UNITED STATES OF AMERICA

70570

To Kitty

PREFACE

The basic aim of this book is to give the reader a reasonably complete understanding of the various principles utilized in the design of an automatic control system. Simple control systems can be defined by mathematical equations whose solutions are relatively simple. However, more complicated systems involve highly complicated, interacting equations whose solutions are very difficult by conventional methods. Therefore, the designer is vitally interested in knowing principles which are easily applied, easily interpreted, and easily understood.

This book is concerned with all aspects of linear system design and covers transient response, frequency response, stability criteria, numerical integration, automatic computers and transient analysis. The book is intended as a reference, self-study, or college level text. Accordingly, except for the appendix on the derivation of the Nyquist criterion, no mathematical background beyond first-year calculus should be required for any of the material. A first-year course in physics is assumed, and a course in electrical circuits would be helpful, but is not essential.

Chapters 1 through 11 discuss frequency and transient response methods, as well as stability criteria, proper gain adjustment, compensating methods, and the effect of noise and extraneous inputs. These chapters constitute the normal course in automatic control systems. Chapters 12 through 15 discuss further techniques and tools which the designer uses; namely, numerical integration, automatic computers, methods for analyzing transient response data, and nonlinear systems. Automatic computers have become an essential tool for control system design, and Chapter 13 serves to introduce to the reader their methods of operation. Chapter 14 discusses methods for analyzing transient response data. This chapter is intended to aid those who want to write an equation fitting a given transient. Chapter 15 is a brief introductory chapter on nonlinear systems and is aimed at challenging the reader to explore this field further. The appendix includes reference material often used in control analysis work. Particular appendix features are design data for cascaded compensating functions and a table of Laplace transform pairs.

This book is an out-growth of a company training course of The Glenn L. Martin Company, given by the author.

The author would like to express his appreciation to Noran E. Kersta for suggesting and encouraging this project. He would also like to express his gratitude to the many individuals and companies who have aided in the publication of this book. Sincere thanks are due to the following associates at The Glenn L. Martin Company: Kenneth D. Engle, Sales Development; Martin E. Hogan and Robert F. Crocker, Legal Division; Welcome W. Bender, Howard W. Merrill, James H. Bennett, Sidney Stark, Beverly McKinney, Thomas J. Anderson, Frank Baxter, Stanley Duklewski and Walter Carrier, Engineering Division. The careful reading of the manuscript and many suggestions of Sidney Stark and Beverly McKinney, and the fine preparation of the drawings by Frank Baxter merit particular mention. The author would also like to express his appreciation to those who have aided in manual numerical calculations; particular mention is due Mrs. Mildred Sando, Mrs. Muriel Bauer, Mrs. Billie Jean Istre, and Miss Helen Hilmer.

Finally, the author wishes to express his appreciation to his wife, who typed the manuscript and exhibited much patience during its preparation.

FLOYD E. NIXON

Ventura, California

CONTENTS

ix

CHAPTER 1

AUTOMATIC CONTROL SYSTEMS

1.00 Introduction

An important group (servomechanisms) of automatic control systems is that in which an output quantity is monitored and compared with a desired quantity. If any difference exists, it is used to actuate the system and cause the output to equal the desired value. The monitoring may be either continuous or intermittent. In this book we are concerned with continuous monitoring systems. Examples are plentiful. The human being possesses many control systems.

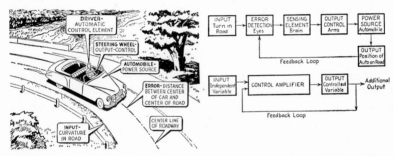

FIG. 1.00-1. Steering an automobile involves all the basic elements of an automatic control system. (From "A Basic Approach to Servomechanism Design," by Richard Herst, *Electrical Manufacturing*, December, 1949.)

In merely reaching for an object, one functions as a control system. The eyes detect the error between the object and the hands, and the arms move in the proper direction. The well-regulated temperature of the body is another example. Some automatic control systems are entirely mechanical, and do not involve any human link other than the manually turning on and off of the system. In others a human serves as one element. Steering an automobile is an excellent example of this (see Fig. 1.00-1). The eyes act as the error detection element. The brain then determines the proper command, and the arms, in response, steer the automobile.

1

This book is concerned with the design of a control system from the analytical viewpoint. A number of individuals over a period of many years have contributed to this field. Newton's physical laws and the mathematical work of Cauchy, Heaviside, and Laplace are basic fundamentals.

The analysis techniques covered in this book, however, are quite recent. In 1932 Nyquist[39]* published a description of the application of the widely-used frequency response method to feedback amplifier design. This was later extended by Black.[3] Soon after, Bode[4] demonstrated the relation between the frequency and phase responses for minimum phase functions.

In the early 1940's Hall[19] and Harris[20] demonstrated that the Nyquist analysis techniques could be applied to automatic control systems as well as to feedback amplifiers. Because of the many military applications, work in this field was highly classified during World War II. Since then a number of books and many articles have been published, and the number of applications is rapidly increasing. Extensions of the analytical techniques are continuing, the root locus method of Evans[11,12] being a significant example.

A companion field, automatic computers, has experienced a similar growth. Today the two are becoming more and more closely connected. Simulation of a control circuit by an automatic computer serves as a rapid and relatively inexpensive method of proving an automatic control system design. Also, many complex control systems now involve a computer as part of their operation. Conversely, most of the components in a computer are themselves automatic control units.

1.10 Applications

Automatic control systems may be man-made, as in an industrial machine, or they may simply exist as part of our everyday life. In a sense, the economic law of supply and demand is an automatic control system. Demand is the input, supply is the output, and the difference causes prices to fluctuate up or down. Considerable thought is being given to the application of control theory to economic problems.

Industrial applications have as their purpose safety, comfort, and/or economy. Airplane travel is safer when the plane is equipped

---

* Superior numbers refer to references in the Bibliography.

with automatic landing instruments. An elevator ride is more comfortable when the elevator starts and stops smoothly. The output of a strong laborer is equivalent to about one-tenth of one horsepower. When one considers the cost of electric power *vs.* manual power, he immediately sees the advantage of mechanization. This is not an altogether fair comparison, as the upkeep and initial investment in most machinery is much more expensive than its operating cost. Even so, the economic factor is very much on the side of mechanization. Automatic control systems provide an important means of achieving mechanization. Higher quality and greater output are other important factors.

Military applications are numerous. Automatic control systems point guns, guide aircraft, direct radar, and perform many other tasks.

In some cases an automatic control system must be employed because a human being could not respond quickly enough or even exist in the environment in question. Consider the case of the airplane. Airplane speed increased from 100 mph during World War I to 400 mph by World War II. Similarly, the best engines available during World War I produced only a few hundred horsepower at an almost prohibitive weight, while in World War II, engines with as much as 3000 hp were available in compact packages weighing less than one pound per horsepower. Meanwhile, the Germans developed the V-2 rocket which would reach an output of approximately 600,000 hp at 4000 mph. The control problem for such high-speed vehicles is tremendous, and the use of human pilots only increases the magnitude of the problem. Flights in the ultrasonic range must take place in an intensively-cold, low-pressure altitude completely devoid of oxygen. Cabin pressurization and heating for human occupants are major problems. Further, the human body can be subjected to only very low forces or g, sustained forces in excess of $3g$ being intolerable. For turns, a rocket traveling at 4000 mph would require a 70-mile radius in order not to exceed $3g$. Also the reaction time of a human is very slow. It takes the average person about 0.2 second to take his foot off the accelerator when the traffic light turns red. This is too slow for high-speed rocket control.

In other fields both the utilization of automatic control systems and the application of automatic control system analysis procedures are progressing rapidly. The automatic anesthesia system discussed in Section 1.20 is an example of a medical application. Similarly, control analysis procedures are being applied in such widely separated fields as economics, physics, psychology, aeronautics, sociology, chemistry, mathematics, philosophy, electrical engineering, etc. Much of the work has progressed in each of these fields along parallel lines. More recently, however, the similarity of the applications has become increasingly evident, and techniques used in one field are applied in another.

1.20 Control system examples

An example of a simple control system is shown in Fig. 1.20-1. The weight of the truck turns the rotor of a synchro. This causes a

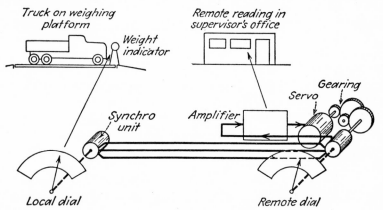

FIG. 1.20-1. Remote indication may be provided over long distances by synchro units, with a servo-motor driven by an amplifier operating the element. (From "Seven Basic Types of Servomechanisms Analyzed," by Richart Herst, *Electrical Manufacturing*, May, 1950.)

voltage at the remote station which is amplified and applied to the servomotor, resulting in a remote dial weight indication. This provides a relatively inexpensive remote-positioning control system. Additional weighing platforms could be monitored by a single office.

Figure 1.20-2 shows four typical applications. The output speed is automatically controlled in Fig. 1.20-2a at a preset value. The tachometer produces a voltage proportional to the shaft rotation. This voltage is compared with the desired speed setting, and if any difference exists, the servo changes the variable-speed drive in the proper direction. Variations in the output load, therefore, have only a minor effect on the rotation speed. The system in Fig. 1.20-2b automatically adjusts itself, so that the output voltage is constant. Should this voltage depart from its desired level, the error is detected, amplified, and applied to the servomotor, changing the

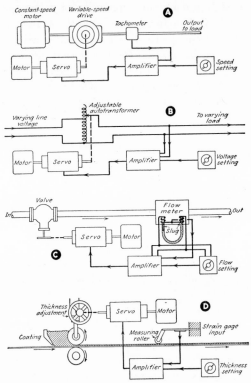

FIG. 1.20-2. Automatic control servos for four typical applications: (a) automatic speed control; (b) voltage control; (c) a similar system for controlling fluid flow; and (d) mechanical displacement. These are closed-loop systems that work to a null balance, with magnitude of correction proportional to the error and response time lags of no appreciable length. (From "Seven Basic Types of Servomechanisms Analyzed," by Richard Herst, *Electrical Manufacturing*, May, 1950.)

autotransformer setting. Fluid flow is controlled by the system in Fig. 1.20-2c. The two floating magnetic slugs in the U-tube will change their position as the pressure changes. This causes an unbalance in a bridge circuit formed by the inductance coils. Again, the error voltage actuates the servomotor, changing the valve opening. The system in Fig. 1.20-2d is used for automatic thickness control. Thickness is measured by a small roller that deflects a strain gage. Any deviation from the desired thickness is detected, and causes the servomotor to change the thickness adjustment.

Both speed and position are controlled by the system in Fig. 1.20-3. The shaft of the synchro receiver rotates in accordance with the rotation of the synchro to which it is connected. This rotation, applied to a differential gear, turns the potentiometer wiper, if the shaft rotation speeds of the two differential gear inputs are not the same. The resulting error voltage is applied to an amplifier, causing the servomotor to alter the variable-speed drive setting.

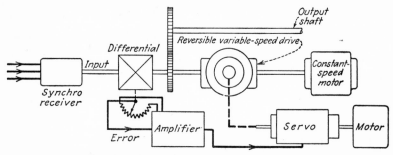

FIG. 1.20-3. Speed and position are both synchronized in this system developed for printing presses. From a synchro unit driven by the master shaft, signals are sent to the receiver; the amplifier detects deviations and drives the servo-motor to keep shafts in synchronism. (From "Seven Basic Types of Servomechanisms Analyzed," by Richard Herst, *Electrical Manufacturing*, May, 1950.)

Automatic control systems are finding widespread application in many fields. A significant example is an automatic controller for the administration of anesthesia. The anesthetist, in giving an anesthetic agent, functions as a human link in a control system, much the same as the automobile driver in Fig. 1.00-1. He receives a continuous flow of information through his eyes, ears, and hands, as shown in Fig. 1.20-4. This information is utilized to form a judgment of the patient's depth of anesthesia, which is compared with a known standard depth that the surgeon requires.

The human-link control system is subject to two defects: (1) an erroneous estimate of the anesthetic depth, and (2) a slow operator response. The first seldom occurs with an experienced anesthetist, but the second is present to some extent most of the time. Recognizing this, Bickford and his associates developed an electronic element which may be substituted for the human link. This does not replace the necessity of human supervision, of course, as any control system must be adequately monitored.

The components of the control system are shown in Fig. 1.20-5. Extensive tests have shown that the electric activity of the brain

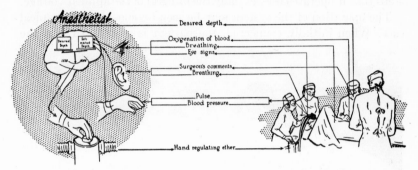

FIG. 1.20-4.　An anesthetist, in giving an anesthetic agent, functions as a human link in a control system. (Courtesy Dr. Reginald G. Bickford, Mayo Clinic.)

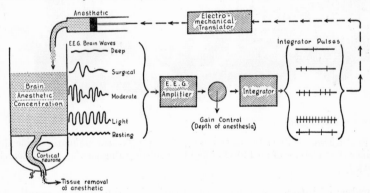

FIG. 1.20-5.　Block diagram of an automatic control system which maintains a desired level of anesthesia. (Courtesy Dr. Reginald G. Bickford, Mayo Clinic.)

undergoes a characteristic series of changes in relation to depth of anesthesia. In low concentrations most anesthetic drugs stimulate the cortical nerve cells and increase the electric output over that of a resting state. As the concentration is increased the effect changes, until in deep anesthesia the brain may become electrically inoperative. Typical patterns are shown in Fig. 1.20-5.

The electric output provides a simple index which may be used to replace the human link. The electric activity can be detected easily by small silver-disk electrodes attached to the scalp. A high-gain amplifier raises the signal level. Whenever the brain wave signal reaches a value determined by the gain control, a stepping relay turns one notch and applies one dosage of anesthesia. The stepping relay is called an integrator, because the number of notches or steps that it operates is essentially the integral of the applied voltage.

The operation of the system may be seen by considering a typical case. When initially connected, the patient is resting, so that the

Fig. 1.20-6.   ERCO F9F-2 Operational Flight Trainer simulates inside the trailer the behavior of an F9F-2 in flight. (Courtesy Engineering and Research Corp.)

number of integrator pulses (or anesthesia injections) is small. As noted previously, the first effect of anesthesia is stimulating so that more integrator pulses occur. As the effect of the anesthetic increases, the brain electric activity and the integrator pulses reduce. Thus by setting the gain control at a desired depth, an automatic control system results. If too much anesthetic is applied, the integrator does not pulse as often. If too little, the integrator functions more often.

Another example of a control system application is shown in Fig. 1.20-6. This pictures an F9F-2 Operational Flight Trainer made by the Engineering and Research Corporation for the Office of Naval Research. The trainer realistically simulates on the ground practically every flight condition the F9F-2 might encounter. A typical "flight" begins with an engine turn-up. Next the pilot calls the tower for a duty runway and taxi instructions. After lining up on the runway, the "plane" takes off on instruments. During the simulated flight, anything can happen. The trainer is complete with thunderstorms, clouds, flameouts, and radio static. Bright sunlight is projected on the translucent hood and a cloud effect moves across. The "plane" can be slow-rolled and looped. Feel in the controls is natural and varies with the speed, as does the roar of air flowing past the plane. The engine whine sounds real, and the tires screech on the runway in landing.

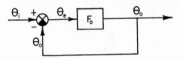

Electronic simulators provide valuable training at a considerable monetary saving, for the cost of operating a flight simulator is

Fig. 1.20-7. General block diagram of a control system.

much lower than the cost of flying. They use many automatic control circuits, each functioning to simulate a specific phase.

It should be noted that all the examples that have been discussed have some common characteristics, namely,

1. A specific function exists.

2. A desired quantity is compared with an actual quantity.

3. The error operates the controller.

Consequently the block diagram in Fig. 1.20-7 is applicable to most control systems. Here θ_i is the input or desired quantity, θ_o is the output or actual quantity, θ_e is the error signal $(\theta_i - \theta_o)$, and F_o denotes the system characteristics between the output and error.

1.30 Analysis techniques

It is often necessary to be able to predict the operation of a control system before it is used. An airplane autopilot is a clear example because of the safety factor. Similarly, in industrial applications, production should not be interrupted while a designer uses "trial and error" methods.

Control systems may contain either linear or nonlinear components. Linear components are those whose operation in a given range may be described by a linear differential equation having time as the independent variable. Nonlinear components are those whose operation cannot be expressed so simply. If a system contains only linear components, linear theory methods may be used. These methods, discussed in detail in later chapters, enable the operation of the system to be determined quickly, and provide information on how optimum operation may be obtained.

If the control system contains nonlinear elements, the analysis is much more difficult. Generally, the system is studied over very

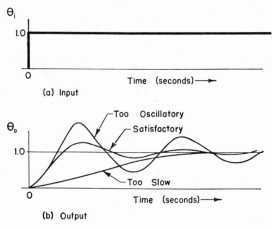

Fig. 1.30-1.   Typical system transient responses for different system gain adjustments.

small ranges in which the elements are more nearly linear, so that linear theory may be used to obtain a first picture. This often is sufficient, but sometimes a nonlinear system requires the use of an automatic computer which can simulate the characteristics accurately.

This book covers the basic principles of linear theory. Two approaches are used, the transient response and the frequency response. The transient response is the variation of the output, θ_o, vs. time when a given θ_i input signal, such as a unit step or a constant rate, is applied. Typical θ_o transient responses are shown in Fig. 1.30-1. If θ_o oscillates (or hunts) about the desired value, or if it responds too slowly for the particular application, it is considered unsatisfactory. Tests on the automatic anesthetizer described in Section 1.20 revealed that it had a response time of about three minutes. This is satisfactory for that application, but a three-minute delay time would be entirely too long in the case of driving an automobile.

The transient response of a linear system may be obtained in a straightforward manner by using an operational calculus method such as the Laplace transformation. This enables very complex (but linear) differential equations to be "transformed" into algebraic expressions which may be manipulated by conventional algebraic means until the desired form is obtained. The expression is then "transformed" back into the complete solution of the differential

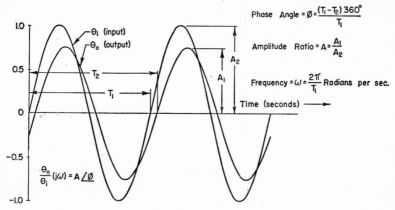

Fig. 1.30-2.   Typical frequency response waveforms of a system for one input frequency.

equation in terms of the independent variable, time. Since many equations fall into the same pattern, they have been coded with their solutions and form the table of Laplace transform pairs in Appendix 6.

The frequency response of a system is found by comparing the steady-state sinusoidal waveform of θ_o with that of θ_i for a sinusoidal θ_i input. Inputs of various frequencies are applied. A typical result for a specific frequency is shown in Fig. 1.30-2. The amplitude of θ_o is not necessarily the same as the input. Likewise, the output wave may either lead or lag (which it does in Fig. 1.30-2) the input, as indicated by $T_1 - T_2$.

The amount of lead or lag is converted into a phase angle. Thus if the lag were 0.1 second and it took 1.8 seconds for a complete cycle in Fig. 1.30-2, we say that the output lags the input by 20°. This is because there are 360° in one cycle, and the lag is $\frac{1}{18}$ of one cycle. When θ_o lags θ_i, we call the phase angle negative. A complete frequency response of a system may be represented by a continuous polar locus from zero frequency to infinite frequency, as shown in Fig. 1.30-3. The distance from the origin is the amplitude ratio (output-to-input), and the angle is the phase angle existing for that input frequency.

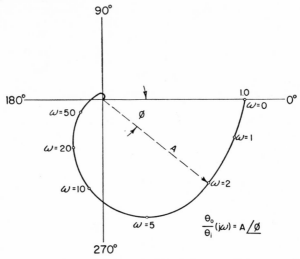

Fig. 1.30-3.   Typical complete frequency response locus of a system. Vector ratio of output to input amplitude and output to input phase as a function of input frequency are shown.

It is conventional in automatic control work to use radians per second as the frequency unit and to represent this by the Greek letter ω. Hence

$$\omega = 2\pi f \text{ radians per sec.} \qquad (1.30\text{-}1)$$

where f is in cycles per second.

The frequency response analysis method is based upon application of Nyquist's feedback amplifier theory to automatic control systems. Essentially the two are the same. In each, the output is combined with the input and applied to the amplifier or control system. Nyquist was able to show that if a system is linear, the frequency response characteristic between the output, θ_o, and error,

θ_e, is sufficient to determine the system operation. The response could be taken between the output and input instead of between the output and error. However, necessary corrective measures and proper system adjustment are more evident, and fewer calculations

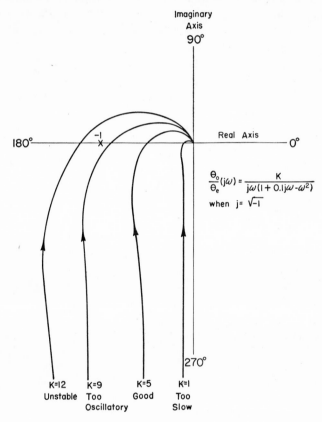

$$\frac{\theta_o}{\theta_e}(j\omega) = \frac{K}{j\omega(1 + 0.1j\omega - \omega^2)}$$

when $j = \sqrt{-1}$

K=12	K=9	K=5	K=1
Unstable	Too	Good	Too
	Oscillatory		Slow

Fig. 1.30-4.　Typical open-loop frequency response loci and their meaning for different gain settings. Arrowheads indicate direction of increasing frequency.

are required when the output-to-error relation (called the "open-loop" function) is used.

　The −1 point in the open-loop frequency response locus is very important. An example is shown in Fig. 1.30-4. A system whose open-loop locus is very near the −1 point corresponds to the highly oscillatory transient response in Fig. 1.30-1. One which never comes near the −1 point corresponds to the slow responding case. A properly adjusted system is one in which the locus comes moderately near the −1 point.

It should be noted that a mathematical equation relates the two variables in Fig. 1.30-4, while in Fig. 1.30-2, the transfer relation is obtained by comparing two waveforms. This illustrates an important feature of the frequency response method, namely, the transfer characteristics may be obtained either experimentally (by comparing waveforms) or analytically (from mathematical relations). Sometimes a combination of the two approaches is used. The designer may obtain part of the system transfer relation experimentally and the other part analytically. The two are then combined to obtain the final result. Because the two approaches may be used, one is often used as a check on the other.

It might seem that the frequency response method involves much more calculation than the transient response method. This is not the case. The calculation of a transient response for a complex system is often a tedious task. Further, while it shows how the system is operating, it does not show how its operation could be improved. On the other hand, the transient response can be approximated; and so much other vital design information may be obtained from a frequency response locus, that the frequency response method is the more popular.

PROBLEMS

(Note: The following problems involve mathematical operations used extensively in control system analysis. The problems are presented here so that the reader may become familiar with these operations.)

1-1. Express the following complex numbers in the polar and exponential forms.

(a) $5 + j3$ (e) $(5 + j3)(10 + j50)$
(b) $10 + j50$ (f) $(-8 + j6)(5 + j3)$
(c) $-8 + j6$ (g) $(5 + j3)/(-8 + j6)$
(d) $-6 - j8$

1-2. Express the following complex numbers in the rectangular and exponential forms

(a) $10∠25°$ (e) $\dfrac{10∠25°}{5∠90°}$
(b) $5∠90°$
(c) $200∠120°$ (f) $\dfrac{20∠120°}{50∠-60°}$
(d) $50∠-60°$

1-3. Calculate and plot the following functions for values of $\omega = 10, 7,$ 5, 3, 2, 1.5, 1, 0.7, 0.5, 0.3, -0.3, -0.5, -0.7, -1, -1.5, -2, -3, -5, -7, and -10.

(a) $F = \dfrac{1}{j\omega(1 + j\omega)(1 + 0.5j\omega)}$

(b) $F = \dfrac{0.5(1 + 0.5j\omega)}{j\omega(1 + j\omega)(1 + 2j\omega)}$

·1-4. Find the roots of the following equations.

(a) $s^3 + 6s^2 + 11s + 6 = 0$ (f) $s^3 + 2.75s^2 - 6.25 = 0$

(b) $s^3 + 4s^2 + 6s + 4 = 0$ (g) $s^2 + 5s + 6 = 0$

(c) $s^3 + 2s^2 + s + 2 = 0$ (h) $s^3 + 5s^2 + 6s = 0$

(d) $s^4 + 10s^3 + 59s^2 + 98s + 82 = 0$

(e) $s^4 + 22s^3 + 242s^2 + 440s + 400 = 0$

CHAPTER 2

APPLICATION OF MATHEMATICS TO CONTROL SYSTEMS

2.00 Introduction

Linear analysis of automatic control systems is largely based on:

1. Expressing the operation of such systems by linear differential equations with constant coefficients and with time as the independent variable.

2. Techniques for either solving or knowing the nature of the solution of linear differential equations.

Fortunately, most systems can be expressed in this way with reasonable approximations. Linear differential equations describe the characteristic behavior of electric, mechanical, and hydraulic systems, and of complex combinations of them. Some exceptions exist (such as saturation effects, distributed constants, coulomb friction, and mechanical play), but their effects are often minor and may be neglected in a preliminary analysis. Chapters 12 and 13 include methods for handling these effects.

2.10 Linear differential equations

A linear differential equation with time as the independent variable is one in which a variable (for example, the output) and its time derivatives are equated to a forcing function (the input). The equation is linear as long as the output and all its derivatives are raised only to the first power. Some examples of linear equations are

$$x + 3\dot{x} + 2\ddot{x} = 1 \qquad (2.10\text{-}1)$$

$$-24x - 10\dot{x} + 3\ddot{x} + \dddot{x} = 10 \qquad (2.10\text{-}2)$$

$$25x + \ddot{x} = 1 \qquad (2.10\text{-}3)$$

where
$$\dot{x} = \frac{dx}{dt}, \qquad \ddot{x} = \frac{d^2x}{dt^2}, \quad \text{etc.}$$

Some examples of differential equations in time which are not linear are

$$4x^2 - 3\ddot{x} + \ddot{x} = 0 \qquad (2.10\text{-}4)$$

$$x + \dot{x}^2 + \ddot{x} = 1 \qquad (2.10\text{-}5)$$

$$5x - 12\dot{x} + 10\ddot{x}^3 - 4\dddot{x} + \ddddot{x} = 0 \qquad (2.10\text{-}6)$$

An equation is also linear if the coefficients are functions of time; however, we are interested mainly in those with constant coefficients. It should be noted that it is not necessary for all derivatives to be present. Thus in (2.10-3) the function $\dot{x}$, the first time derivative of x, is missing; yet the equation is linear. Similarly, the sign of any of the terms may be positive or negative.

For simple systems, where the order of the differential equation is not high, the solution is not difficult. For more complicated systems, as the order of the equation becomes higher, the solution becomes exceedingly difficult; and the effect of different coefficients on the solution is not easy to determine. Control concepts are particularly valuable in simplifying the analysis of these higher order systems.

Most calculus books give the conventional methods for the solution of typical linear differential equations. The technique used is to substitute in the differential equation the operator p to denote differentiation with respect to time, p^2 for the second derivative, p^3 for the third derivative, etc. For example, (2.10-1) becomes

$$(1 + 3p + 2p^2)x = 1 \qquad (2.10\text{-}7)$$

and the term $(1 + 3p + 2p^2)$ equated to zero is called the characteristic equation. The roots of this equation are then found by factoring, so that (2.10-7) reduces to

$$(1 + p)(1 + 2p)x = 1 \qquad (2.10\text{-}8)$$

The solution consists of a "characteristic solution" and a "particular solution." The characteristic solution is determined solely by the roots of the characteristic equation. The particular solution is determined by the forcing function, which in this example is unity. The complete solution is the sum of the characteristic solution and the particular solution. In this case it is

$$x = c_1 \epsilon^{-t/2} + c_2 \epsilon^{-t} + 1 \qquad (2.10\text{-}9)$$

where c_1 and c_2 are constants determined by a specific set of initial conditions and ϵ is the Napierian constant.

The exponents of ϵ are always the roots of the characteristic equation multiplied by time. This serves to introduce the basic mathematical concept of dynamic system stability; namely, if all roots of the characteristic equation have negative real parts, which they did in (2.10-1), the characteristic contribution (transient) dies out, leaving the particular solution (steady-state). When this happens between the input and output, a system is said to be stable. Conversely, if any root of the characteristic equation had a positive real part, the characteristic contribution to the system solution would increase without bound. When and only when this happens, the system is said to be unstable.

An example of this case is (2.10-2), where the characteristic equation is

$$p^3 + 3p^2 - 10p - 24 = 0 \qquad (2.10\text{-}10)$$

The roots are

$$p = -2, +3, \text{ and } -4 \qquad (2.10\text{-}11)$$

Because of the positive root $+3$, the system which this represents would be called unstable.

A third possibility exists when the real part of a pair of complex roots is zero, leaving a positive and a negative imaginary root (these always occur as pairs). Such a case is generally undesirable, for it represents a bounded, persistent oscillation. These cases, called "neutrally stable," do not occur very often in a linear system, as it is difficult to adjust a system so that it is on the border line between stability and instability. Usually an oscillatory output is due to a saturation or nonlinearity in a system that would be unstable otherwise. An example of an equation yielding this result is (2.10-3). Here the characteristic equation is

$$p^2 + 25 = 0 \qquad (2.10\text{-}12)$$

and the roots are

$$p = \pm j5 \qquad (2.10\text{-}13)$$

where $j = \sqrt{-1}$. The solution is

$$x = c_1 \epsilon^{-j5t} + c_2 \epsilon^{+j5t} + \tfrac{1}{25} \qquad (2.10\text{-}14)$$

where c_1 and c_2 are constants depending on the particular initial conditions. If x and $\dot{x}$ were initially zero, solving (2.10-14) at $t = 0$ yields

$$0 = c_1 + c_2 + \tfrac{1}{25} \qquad (2.10\text{-}15)$$

Differentiating, (2.10-14) becomes

$$\dot{x} = -5jc_1\epsilon^{-j5t} + 5jc_2\epsilon^{+j5t} \qquad (2.10\text{-}16)$$

At $t = 0$, eq. (2.10-16) is

$$0 = -5jc_1 + 5jc_2 \qquad (2.10\text{-}17)$$

By simultaneous solution of (2.10-15) and (2.10-17),

$$c_1 = c_2 = -\tfrac{1}{50} \qquad (2.10\text{-}18)$$

Substituting this in (2.10-14) gives the result

$$x = -\tfrac{1}{50}\epsilon^{-j5t} - \tfrac{1}{50}\epsilon^{+j5t} + \tfrac{1}{25} \qquad (2.10\text{-}19)$$

Since $\qquad\qquad \epsilon^{\pm jx} = \cos x \pm j \sin x \qquad (2.10\text{-}20)$

eq. (2.10-19) can be rewritten as

$$x = -\tfrac{1}{25}\cos 5t + \tfrac{1}{25} \qquad (2.10\text{-}21)$$

This illustrates the fact that imaginary roots in the characteristic equation indicate that a persistent oscillation exists in the system.

2.20 Electric systems

The action of electric circuits composed of resistances, inductances, and capacitances can be readily expressed by linear differential equations. This follows from voltage-current relations. The voltage across a resistor is proportional to the current; the voltage across an inductance is proportional to the derivative of the current; and the voltage across a capacitance is proportional to the integral of the current. These are summarized in Table 2.20-1.

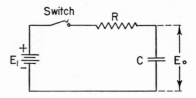

2.21 ELECTRIC CIRCUIT WITH RESISTANCE AND CAPACITANCE.

Figure 2.21-1 is an electric circuit with resistance R and capacitance

FIG. 2.21-1. Resistance-capacitance circuit.

C. A voltage of constant magnitude E_1 is suddenly applied to the circuit causing a current I. Since the applied voltage E_1 is equal to the sum of the voltage drops in the circuit, the differential equation for the relation between the voltage and current is

$$E_1 = RI + \frac{1}{C} \int I \, dt \qquad (2.21\text{-}1)$$

TABLE 2.20-1
BASIC DYNAMIC RELATIONSHIPS*

Parameter		Equation	Description
Mass		$f_1 - f_2 = M(d^2x/dt^2)$	The net force acting on a body = its mass × its acceleration with respect to an arbitrary fixed reference.
Spring		$f = KX$	The force which must be applied to each end of a spring to deflect it a distance X = the spring constant $K \times X$.
Dashpot		$f = D(dX_1/dt - dX_2/dt)$	The force which must be applied to each end of a dashpot to produce a relative motion of its two ends = the viscous damping coefficient $D \times$ the relative velocity.
Inertia		$q_1 - q_2 = J(d^2\theta/dt^2)$	The net torque acting on a body = its inertia × its angular acceleration with respect to an arbitrary fixed reference.
Torsional spring		$q = G(\theta_1 - \theta_2)$	The torque which must be applied to each end of a torsional spring to produce a relative angular deformation $\theta_1 - \theta_2$ of its two ends = the rotational spring constant × the angular deformation.

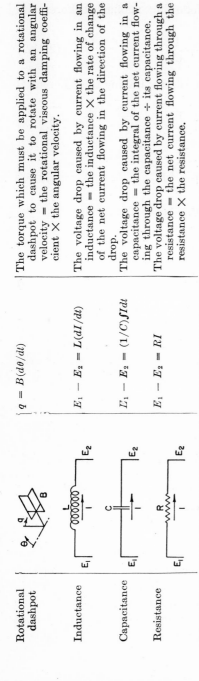

Rotational dashpot	$q = B(d\theta/dt)$	The torque which must be applied to a rotational dashpot to cause it to rotate with an angular velocity = the rotational viscous damping coefficient × the angular velocity.
Inductance	$E_1 - E_2 = L(dI/dt)$	The voltage drop caused by current flowing in an inductance = the inductance × the rate of change of the net current flowing in the direction of the drop.
Capacitance	$E_1 - E_2 = (1/C)\int I\,dt$	The voltage drop caused by current flowing in a capacitance = the integral of the net current flowing through the capacitance ÷ its capacitance.
Resistance	$E_1 - E_2 = RI$	The voltage drop caused by current flowing through a resistance = the net current flowing through the resistance × the resistance.

English gravitational units

t = time in seconds
X = distance in ft
M = mass in slugs
K = spring constant in lb/ft
D = damping coefficient in lb/ft per sec
F = force in pounds

q = torque in lb ft
J = inertia in slug ft^2
θ = angle in radians
G = torsional spring constant in lb ft/rad
B = rotational damping coefficient in lb ft/rad per sec

Electrical units

E = volts
I = amperes
L = henries
C = farads
R = ohms

* From Ahrendt and Taplin, *Automatic Feedback Control*, McGraw-Hill Book Co., Inc., New York, 1951.

This equation is solved in the following manner. Differentiate (2.21-1); then

$$\dot{E}_1 = R\dot{I} + \frac{1}{C} I \tag{2.21-2}$$

Since E_1 is a constant, its derivative is zero; leaving the differential equation to be solved,

$$0 = R\dot{I} + \frac{1}{C} I \tag{2.21-3}$$

or in operational form,

$$0 = \left(Rp + \frac{1}{C}\right) I \tag{2.21-4}$$

The root of the characteristic equation is

$$p = -\frac{1}{RC} \tag{2.21-5}$$

and the solution is

$$I = c_1 \epsilon^{-t/RC} \tag{2.21-6}$$

where c_1 is a constant depending on the initial conditions. For this case, when the switch is closed with no charge across the capacitor, the capacitor acts initially as a short circuit, so that the full voltage E_1 is applied across the resistor. Since the voltage drop across the resistor is

$$E_1 = IR \tag{2.21-7}$$

the initial current is

$$I = \frac{E_1}{R} \tag{2.21-8}$$

Therefore the constant in (2.21-6) is determined, and the answer is

$$I = \frac{E_1}{R} \epsilon^{-t/RC} \tag{2.21-9}$$

The preceding example shows how the operation of electric circuits can be expressed by differential equations. However, it is not this type of application in which we are generally interested. For control work, we want output-to-input relationships. Often current-to-voltage relationships are used as intervening steps; but in the final result the output and input are usually in the same units, such as voltage out to voltage in, force out to force in, position out to position in, etc.

Thus a transfer concept arises. What, for example, is the relationship of the voltage E_o across the capacitor, to the input voltage E_1? This could be found by solving for E_o and dividing that relation by E_1. Thus

$$E_o = \frac{1}{C} \int I \, dt \tag{2.21-10}$$

or in operator form,

$$E_o = \frac{I}{Cp} \tag{2.21-11}$$

Substituting (2.21-9) in (2.21-10),

$$E_o = \frac{1}{C} \int \frac{E_1}{R} \epsilon^{-t/RC} \, dt \tag{2.21-12}$$

Integrating between arbitrary times of t_1 and t_2, with C and R as constants,

$$E_o = \frac{E_1}{RC} \times RC\epsilon^{-t/RC} \Big|_{t_2}^{t_1} \tag{2.21-13}$$

$$= E_1(\epsilon^{-t_1/RC} - \epsilon^{-t_2/RC}) \tag{2.21-14}$$

If t_1 is taken as the time the switch is closed, and t_2 is any time t thereafter, the result is

$$\frac{E_o}{E_1} = 1 - \epsilon^{-t/RC} \tag{2.21-15}$$

A plot of (2.21-15) is given in Fig. 2.21-2. At $t = RC$, the value of E_o is 63% of its final value. This time is called the time constant of the circuit.

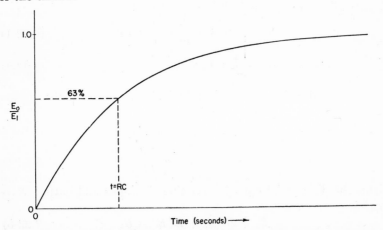

Fig. 2.21-2.   Transient response for the R-C circuit shown in Fig. 2.21-1.

It should also be noted that if (2.21-10) is substituted in (2.21-1) the result is

$$E_1 = RI + E_o \qquad (2.21\text{-}16)$$

Now if the operational form in (2.21-11) is substituted in (2.21-16) for I, and the relation of E_o/E_1 is solved, it is

$$\frac{E_o}{E_1} = \frac{1}{1 + RCp} \qquad (2.21\text{-}17)$$

Thus two output-to-input relations have been solved. Equation (2.21-15) is a time relation and (2.21-17) is an operational relation. In subsequent discussion it will be shown that the operational form (2.21-17) is much easier to handle and interpret. Then RC will be replaced by the symbol T, which denotes the time constant associated with this transfer relation, and the operator p will be replaced by the more versatile Laplace transform operator s.

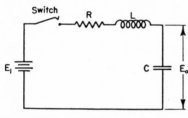

FIG. 2.22-1.   Resistance-inductance-capacitance circuit.

2.22 ELECTRIC CIRCUIT WITH RESISTANCE, CAPACITANCE, AND INDUCTANCE. Figure 2.22-1 is an electric circuit with resistance, capacitance, and inductance. In order to find the transfer relation between the voltage across the capacitor and that applied to the input, the following equations are needed.

$$E_1 = RI + L\frac{dI}{dt} + \frac{1}{C}\int I\,dt \qquad (2.22\text{-}1)$$

$$E_o = \frac{1}{C}\int I\,dt \qquad (2.22\text{-}2)$$

Using operational notation and dividing (2.22-2) by (2.22-1) yields

$$\frac{E_o}{E_1} = \frac{1/Cp}{R + Lp + 1/Cp} \qquad (2.22\text{-}3)$$

$$= \frac{1}{1 + RCp + LCp^2} \qquad (2.22\text{-}4)$$

Thus the differential equation relating the input and output voltages is

$$E_o + RC\dot{E}_o + LC\ddot{E}_o = E_1 \qquad (2.22\text{-}5)$$

The roots of the characteristic equation are

$$p = \frac{-RC \pm \sqrt{R^2C^2 - 4LC}}{2LC} \qquad (2.22\text{-}6)$$

where the roots may be real and unequal, real and equal, or complex conjugates, depending on the value of the radical.

The solution of (2.22-5) is

$$E_o = E_1 + c_1\epsilon^{[-RC+\sqrt{R^2C^2-4LC}]t/2LC} + c_2\epsilon^{[-RC-\sqrt{R^2C^2-4LC}]t/2LC}$$
$$(2.22\text{-}7)$$

where the coefficients c_1 and c_2 are determined by the initial conditions. If the switch was suddenly closed and the voltage across the capacitor was initially zero, then at $t = 0$, both E_o and $\dot{E}_o = 0$. These two initial conditions can be used to evaluate c_1 and c_2 by equating (2.22-7) and the derivative of (2.22-7) to zero at $t = 0$. Thus (2.22-7) at $t = 0$ becomes

$$0 = E_1 + c_1 + c_2 \qquad (2.22\text{-}8)$$

The derivative of (2.22-7) is

$$\dot{E}_o = c_1\left(\frac{-RC + \sqrt{R^2C^2 - 4LC}}{2LC}\right)\epsilon^{[-RC+\sqrt{R^2C^2-4LC}]t/2LC}$$
$$+ c_2\left(\frac{-RC - \sqrt{R^2C^2 - 4LC}}{2LC}\right)\epsilon^{[-RC-\sqrt{R^2C^2-4LC}]t/2LC} \qquad (2.22\text{-}9)$$

At $t = 0$, eq. (2.22-9) reduces to

$$0 = c_1\left(\frac{-RC + \sqrt{R^2C^2 - 4LC}}{2LC}\right) + c_2\left(\frac{-RC - \sqrt{R^2C^2 - 4LC}}{2LC}\right)$$
$$(2.22\text{-}10)$$

Simultaneous solution of (2.22-8) and (2.22-10) yields

$$c_1 = E_1\left(\frac{-RC - \sqrt{R^2C^2 - 4LC}}{2\sqrt{R^2C^2 - 4LC}}\right) \qquad (2.22\text{-}11)$$

$$c_2 = E_1\left(\frac{+RC - \sqrt{R^2C^2 - 4LC}}{2\sqrt{R^2C^2 - 4LC}}\right) \qquad (2.22\text{-}12)$$

Finally, the time relation between E_o and E_1 is

$$\frac{E_o}{E_1} = 1 + \frac{-RC - \sqrt{R^2C^2 - 4LC}}{2\sqrt{R^2C^2 - 4LC}}\ \epsilon^{[-RC+\sqrt{R^2C^2-4LC}]t/2LC}$$

$$+ \frac{RC - \sqrt{R^2C^2 - 4LC}}{2\sqrt{R^2C^2 - 4LC}}\ \epsilon^{[-RC-\sqrt{R^2C^2-4LC}]t/2LC} \qquad (2.22\text{-}13)$$

Equation (2.22-13) may be used for all the possibilities that the roots as given in (2.22-6) might have. However, in the case where the radical is zero, so that equal roots result, (2.22-13) becomes indeterminate. In that case, (2.22-13) still can be used, but it is necessary to express the exponential terms as power series, keeping the radical term until it cancels out, or becomes negligible.

It is apparent from the examples that obtaining the general form of the differential equation is not too difficult. However, when initial conditions are taken into account, the equations become quite involved. A much simpler method, namely the Laplace transform, exists and is described in Chapter 3. In the Laplace transform method, the initial conditions are included in writing the system equations. The results are cataloged and listed in a table of Laplace transform equations. Thus the solution to the case covered in this section is given by Laplace transform eq. 00.101 or 00.120 in the Appendix, the proper equation depending on whether the roots are real or complex.

In order to standardize the solutions further, equations of the form of (2.22-4) are nondimensionalized. Since the roots of (2.22-4) may be either real and unequal, real and equal, or complex conjugates, the equation may be expressed in the following three different ways.

1. When the roots are real and unequal,

$$\frac{E_o}{E_1} = \frac{1}{(1 + T_1 p)(1 + T_2 p)} \qquad (2.22\text{-}14)$$

where T_1 and T_2 are the negative reciprocals of the two roots.

2. When the roots are real and equal,

$$\frac{E_o}{E_1} = \frac{1}{(1 + Tp)^2} \qquad (2.22\text{-}15)$$

where T is the negative reciprocal of the repeated root.

3. When the roots are complex conjugates,

$$\frac{E_o}{E_1} = \frac{1}{1 + 2\zeta p/\omega_1 + p^2/\omega_1{}^2} \tag{2.22-16}$$

where ω_1 is the natural frequency of the system in radians per second, and ζ is the "damping ratio."

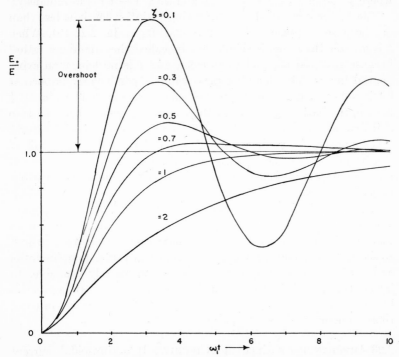

FIG. 2.22-2. Typical transient responses for various values of the damping ratio, ζ.

Cases 1 and 2 are similar to that covered in Section 2.21. Case 3 represents the nondimensionalized form for quadratic factors with complex roots. Values for ω_1 and ζ are found by equating like coefficients in (2.22-4) and (2.22-16). Thus

$$\omega_1 = \frac{1}{\sqrt{LC}} \tag{2.22-17}$$

$$\zeta = \frac{R}{2}\sqrt{\frac{C}{L}} \tag{2.22-18}$$

Substituting these values in (2.22-13) yields

$$\frac{E_o}{E_1} = 1 + \frac{1}{\sqrt{1 - \zeta^2}}\, \epsilon^{-\zeta \omega_1 t} \sin\,(\omega_1 \sqrt{1 - \zeta^2}\, t - \psi) \qquad (2.22\text{-}19)$$

where $\psi = \tan^{-1} (\sqrt{1 - \zeta^2}/-\zeta)$, and $\omega_1 \sqrt{1 - \zeta^2}t$ is in radians.

The factor ζ is called the "damping ratio" when it is less than one because it appears as an exponential factor in (2.22-19). When ζ is greater than one, it should not be called the "damping ratio" because real and unequal roots exist, and ζ is no longer an exponential factor. The damping ratio value is particularly important for it indicates how the output voltage reaches its final value. If ζ is zero, the output oscillates at the natural frequency between zero and two. If ζ is very low, the oscillation eventually dies out, but it takes many cycles to do so. As ζ becomes larger, the magnitude of the overshoot becomes less; until when $\zeta = 1$, the roots are real and the system is well damped. Figure 2.22-2 shows the various transient results.

If the transition from the specific form of (2.22-4) to the appropriate general form of (2.22-14), (2.22-15), or (2.22-16) had been made earlier, considerable time could have been saved. Then insight to the system response in terms of its time constants, damping ratio, and natural frequency would have been immediately available. In latter sections, whenever the quadratic term appears, the roots will be found and the behavior obtained by relating the nature of those roots to nondimensional equations.

2.23 IMPEDANCE OF ELECTRIC CIRCUITS. If a sinusoidal current flows through an inductance, the voltage across the inductance is also sinusoidal. This can be shown by letting the instantaneous current

$$i = I \cos \omega t \qquad (2.23\text{-}1)$$

where I is the maximum value of the current, ω is the frequency in radians per second. Then the instantaneous voltage is

$$e = L \frac{di}{dt} \qquad (2.23\text{-}2)$$

$$= -L\omega I \sin \omega t \qquad (2.23\text{-}3)$$

Thus the voltage leads the current by 90° and is ωL times the amplitude of the current. Since in complex number notation,

$$j = \sqrt{-1} = 1\angle 90° \qquad (2.23\text{-}4)$$

the voltage-current relation can be expressed as

$$E = j\omega L I \qquad (2.23\text{-}5)$$

where E is the maximum voltage and I is the maximum current.
The factor $j\omega L$ is known as the impedance of an inductance.

Similarly, if a sinusoidal current flows through a capacitor, the
voltage-current relation is

$$E = \frac{I}{j\omega C} \qquad (2.23\text{-}6)$$

It should be mentioned that in arriving at (2.23-5) and (2.23-6),
we have actually performed a transformation. Thus these equations,
although conventional in electrical literature, are valid only as long
as they are interpreted to denote a relationship such as that which
exists between (2.23-2) and (2.23-5).

For resistances, the voltage-current relation is

$$E = IR \qquad (2.23\text{-}7)$$

The impedance of a circuit for a sinusoidal frequency is

$$Z = \frac{E}{I} \qquad (2.23\text{-}8)$$

Applying this to the circuit of Fig. 2.21-1 yields the result

$$Z = R + \frac{1}{j\omega C} \qquad (2.23\text{-}9)$$

Similarly, for the circuit of Fig. 2.22-1, the impedance is

$$Z = R + j\omega L + \frac{1}{j\omega C} \qquad (2.23\text{-}10)$$

2.24 FREQUENCY RESPONSE OF CIRCUITS. The relations of the preceding section may be used to obtain the frequency response of an
electric circuit. The frequency response is, by definition, the steady-

state vector ratio of the output to the input for sinusoidal inputs of various frequencies. It is found by methods similar to those in the preceding section. Thus for the circuit shown in Fig. 2.21-1, the input voltage and current are related by

$$E_1 = \left(R + \frac{1}{j\omega C} \right) I \qquad (2.24\text{-}1)$$

and the output voltage and the current are related by

$$E_o = \frac{1}{j\omega C} I \qquad (2.24\text{-}2)$$

Eliminating the current I in the above equations, the frequency response equation is

$$\frac{E_o}{E_1} = \frac{1}{1 + RCj\omega} \qquad (2.24\text{-}3)$$

Comparison of (2.24-3) with (2.21-17) reveals an interesting similarity, namely, that if $j\omega$ is substituted for p in (2.21-17), eq. (2.24-3) is obtained. This similarity is not just coincidence. It always occurs. This follows from the example in Section 2.23 by the relation between the sinusoidal current flowing through an inductance and the voltage across the inductance. The two are related by the derivative action noted in (2.23-2). Since p is the symbol denoting d/dt and since $j\omega$ denotes the effect of the derivative of a sinusoidal wave, $j\omega$ may be substituted for p in an equation to obtain the steady-state relation between two variables for sinusoidal signals. Accordingly, the frequency response equation for Fig. 2.22-1 is

$$\frac{E_o}{E_1} = \frac{1}{1 + RCj\omega - LC\omega^2} \qquad (2.24\text{-}4)$$

2.25 FREQUENCY RESPONSE POLAR PLOTS. When various values of ω are substituted into a frequency response equation, a polar plot (called a frequency response plot) is obtained. As an example, consider (2.24-3), and let $RC = 10$. Then (2.24-3) becomes

$$\frac{E_o}{E_1} = \frac{1}{1 + 10j\omega} \qquad (2.25\text{-}1)$$

If $\omega = 0$, then $E_o/E_1 = 1$. If $\omega = 0.01$, then

$$\frac{E_o}{E_1} = \frac{1}{1 + 0.1j} \tag{2.25-2}$$

$$= \frac{1}{1.005\angle 5.7°} \tag{2.25-3}$$

$$= 0.995\angle - 5.7° \tag{2.25-4}$$

Likewise, other values of ω may be substituted, so that the result is as given in Table 2.25-1. A locus of these frequency response points is shown in Fig. 2.25-1.

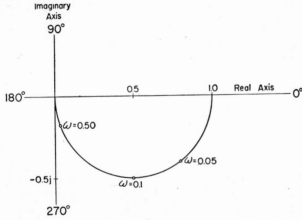

Fig. 2.25-1. Frequency response plot of $E_o/E_1 = 1/(1 + 10j\omega)$.

TABLE 2.25-1

AMPLITUDE AND PHASE VALUES FOR $E_o/E_1 = 1/(1 + 10j\omega)$

ω	Amplitude	Phase
0	1.000	0°
0.01	0.995	−5.7°
0.02	0.981	−11.3°
0.03	0.958	−16.7°
0.05	0.894	−26.6°
0.07	0.819	−35.0°
0.10	0.707	−45.0°
0.15	0.555	−56.3°
0.20	0.447	−63.4°
0.30	0.316	−71.6°
0.50	0.196	−78.7°
1.00	0.099	−84.3°

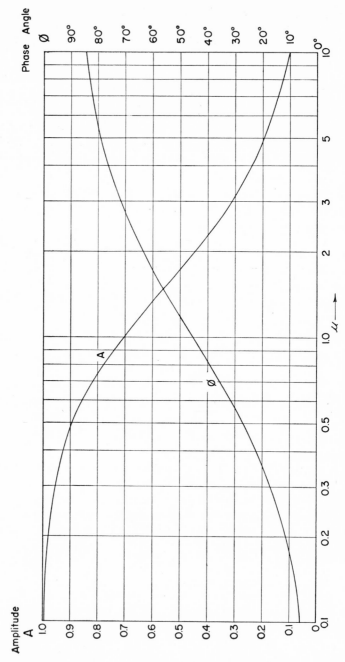

Fig. 2.26-1.   Amplitude and phase plot for $A\angle\phi = 1/(1 + ju)$, where $u = T\omega$.

Frequency response plots are very important. In later sections it will be shown that systems are designed using them. Another main feature is that the frequency response points can be obtained by mathematical calculation as was done above, or they may be obtained by experimental procedure. That is, a sinusoidal voltage may be applied to the network, and the relative amplitude and phase shift recorded. This procedure, repeated for a number of frequencies, yields a frequency locus which may be used for stability and performance studies.

Circuits such as Figs. 2.21-1 and 2.22-1 are called high-frequency filters. This is because the amplitude of the output decreases as the applied frequency is increased. They are often used in control circuits to reduce the amplitude of high frequencies (which appear due to unwanted noise disturbances).

2.26 DIMENSIONLESS FREQUENCY OPERATOR. The voltage ratio in (2.25-1) does not have any units, since a voltage is divided by another voltage. It is frequency-dependent, however, as was shown in Section 2.25. By introducing a dimensionless frequency unit u, the expression may be made more general. Thus if

$$u = RC\omega \qquad (2.26\text{-}1)$$

then (2.24-3) becomes

$$\frac{E_o}{E_1} = \frac{1}{1 + ju} = A\angle\phi \qquad (2.26\text{-}2)$$

This expression may be plotted as a function of u, with the result that a universal chart is obtained which is applicable to any expression of the form (2.24-3). As equations of this form frequently occur in mechanical as well as electric systems, such a chart is very useful. Figure 2.26-1 is a plot of the amplitude and phase for this function.

The use of Fig. 2.26-1 for calculating the frequency locus of (2.25-1) is discussed below. By equating like coefficients of (2.25-1) and (2.26-2), it is seen that

$$u = 10\omega \qquad (2.26\text{-}3)$$

and

$$\omega = 0.1u$$

The points may now be read directly. That is, when $\omega = 0.5$, $u = 5$. Looking on the chart where $u = 5$, it is seen that the amplitude is

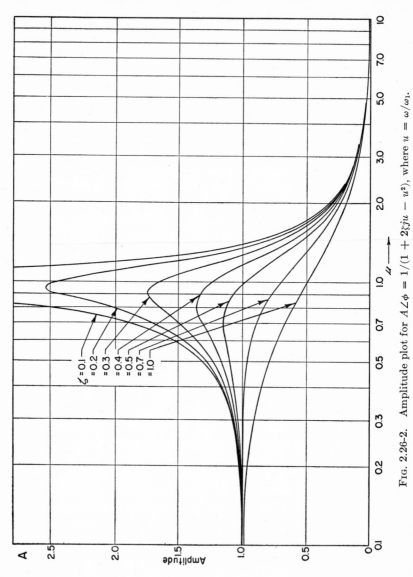

FIG. 2.26-2.   Amplitude plot for $A\angle\phi = 1/(1 + 2\zeta j u - u^2)$, where $u = \omega/\omega_1$.

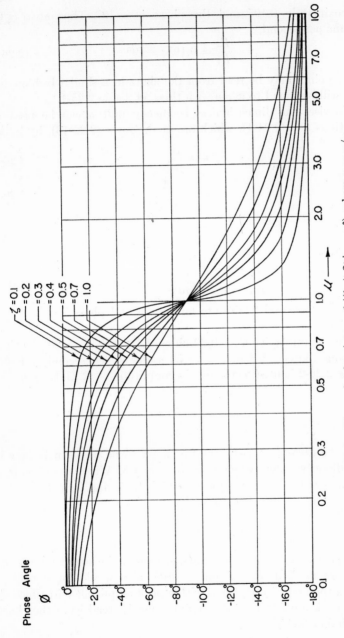

FIG. 2.26-3.   Phase plot for $A \angle \phi = 1/(1 + 2\zeta j u - u^2)$, where $u = \omega/\omega_1$.

$$\frac{\Theta_0(\omega)}{\Theta_n(\omega)} = \frac{1}{1 - \frac{\omega^2}{\omega_e^2} + j \frac{2\zeta \omega}{\omega_e}} = M$$

approximately 0.195 and the phase is $-79°$. Thus at $\omega = 0.5$ radians per second,

$$\frac{E_o}{E_1} = 0.195\angle -79° \qquad (2.26\text{-}4)$$

Other points may be read from the chart in a similar fashion, and they will be found to agree with those of Table 2.25-1.

Likewise, the dimensionless frequency unit u can be used for equations like (2.24-4), which are of the form (2.22-16), by letting

$$u = \frac{\omega}{\omega_1} \qquad (2.26\text{-}5)$$

$$\omega_1 = \frac{1}{\sqrt{LC}} \qquad (2.26\text{-}6)$$

$$\zeta = \frac{R}{2}\sqrt{\frac{C}{L}} \qquad (2.26\text{-}7)$$

Thus (2.24-4) becomes

$$\frac{E_o}{E_1} = \frac{1}{1 + 2\zeta ju - u^2} = A\angle\phi \qquad (2.26\text{-}8)$$

Figures 2.26-2 and 2.26-3 are amplitude and phase charts of this function.

As an example, let $R = 1000$ ohms, $L = 20$ h, $C = 20$ μf. Then, equating like coefficients, $\omega_1 = 50$ radians per second, $\zeta = 0.5$. Figure 2.26-2 is used to obtain the amplitude of (2.24-4) by letting

$$u = \frac{\omega}{50} \qquad (2.26\text{-}9)$$

and $\omega = 50u$

As in the case of (2.25-1), the frequency locus points may now be read directly. Thus when $\omega = 75$, $u = 1.5$. When $u = 1.5$, from Fig. 2.26-2 the amplitude for $\zeta = 0.5$ is 0.51, and from Fig. 2.26-3 the phase is $-130°$. Therefore, when $\omega = 75$,

$$\frac{E_o}{E_1} = 0.51\angle -130° \qquad (2.26\text{-}10)$$

This means that if a 75 radians-per-second sinusoidal input voltage were applied, the output voltage also would be sinusoidal, lagging the input by $130°$ and with a peak amplitude 0.51 times the input peak amplitude. Other points may be read from the charts in a similar fashion.

The dimensionless frequency operator u is a very useful tool in control analysis. It enables one to simplify his equations, since specific physical constants can be replaced by the more informative constants ζ, ω_1, and T. Thus as one solves a complicated problem, he can "pin-point" trouble caused by too high or too low a ζ, ω_1, or T; and knowing the cause of a problem, the designer can quickly locate and often easily remedy it.

2.30 Mechanical systems

Figure 2.30-1 shows a mass which is acted upon by forces f_1, f_2, and f_3. These forces may be resolved into components along the

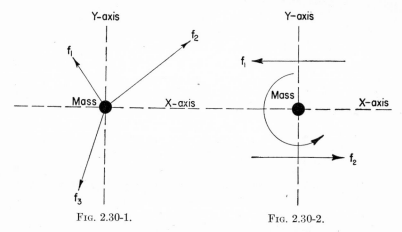

FIG. 2.30-1.   FIG. 2.30-2.

X-axis and the Y-axis. The motion of the mass in the X-Y plane will follow Newton's law, namely, the net force equals the mass times the acceleration. Thus the basic equations governing translational motion are

$$\Sigma \text{ forces in the } X \text{ direction} = M\ddot{X} \qquad (2.30\text{-}1)$$

$$\Sigma \text{ forces in the } Y \text{ direction} = M\ddot{Y} \qquad (2.30\text{-}2)$$

where the force is in pounds, M is the mass in slugs, $\ddot{X}$ and $\ddot{Y}$ are the accelerations in feet per sec².

However, the mass may have motion even though the net forces in the X and Y directions are zero. This is shown in Fig. 2.30-2, where the force in the Y direction is zero, and in the X direction there are two equal and oppositely directed noncolinear forces.

These forces cause a rotation of the mass, giving the basic rotational motion relation,

$$\Sigma \text{ torques} = J\ddot{\theta} \qquad (2.30\text{-}3)$$

where torque is in foot-pounds, J is the inertia in slug-feet^2, $\ddot{\theta}$ is the angular acceleration in radians per sec^2.

Like electric systems, many mechanical systems can be expressed by linear differential equations. The form of the equations for mechanical systems and the manner in which they are obtained are similar to electric systems. Often electrical analogues are obtained of mechanical systems, and likewise, mechanical analogues may be formed for electric systems. This is discussed further in the chapter on automatic computers.

Translational systems for which linear differential equations may be written are those containing masses, which generate a net force proportional to the mass times the acceleration, damping devices like dashpots, in which the force is proportional to the velocity; and springs, whose force is proportional to the distance of elongation or compression. Rotational systems are identical to translational systems, except that torque replaces force, inertia replaces mass, and angular motion replaces linear motion. The examples given will illustrate these points.

2.31 ROTATIONAL SYSTEM EXAMPLES. An example of a rotational system is shown in Fig. 2.31-1. It consists of an applied torque Q

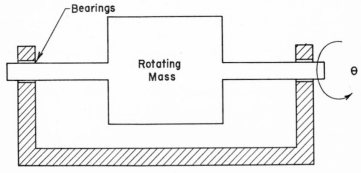

Fig. 2.31-1.

acting on a mass with inertia J, and bearings which have a viscous damping coëfficient B. Equating the opposing torques, we have the expression describing the system,

$$J\ddot{\theta} = -B\dot{\theta} + Q \qquad (2.31\text{-}1)$$

Using operational notation, the relation between the turning rate $\dot{\theta}$ and the torque is

$$\frac{\dot{\theta}}{Q} = \frac{1}{B + Jp} = \frac{1}{B} \times \frac{1}{1 + Jp/B} \qquad (2.31\text{-}2)$$

Comparison of (2.31-2) with the electric system example (2.21-17) reveals that they are of the same form. Therefore it is reasonable to conclude that the analysis and discussion of the electrical example can be applied to this mechanical example.

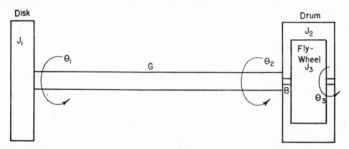

Fig. 2.31-2.

Thus if a unit step torque Q_i is applied to the mechanical system, the rotation speed $\dot{\theta}$ is

$$\theta = \frac{Q_i}{B}\left(1 - \epsilon^{-Bt/J}\right) \qquad (2.31\text{-}3)$$

This corresponds to (2.21-15). Similarly, if a sinusoidal torque of maximum amplitude Q_i were applied, the rotation speed would vary sinusoidally, and its amplitude and phase with respect to the applied torque would be described by

$$\frac{\dot{\theta}}{Q_i} = \frac{1}{B} \times \frac{1}{1 + Jj\omega/B} \qquad (2.31\text{-}4)$$

where J and B are constants depending on the system, ω is the sinusoidal frequency in radians per second, $j = \sqrt{-1}$. This corresponds to the form in (2.25-1), and the discussions there are equally applicable here. Thus the chart in Fig. 2.26-1 may be used for this mechanical system.

A more complicated rotational system is shown in Fig. 2.31-2. It consists of a shaft with a disk on one end and a drum on the other. Inside the drum is a flywheel. The system has the following constants.

J_1 = inertia of the disk

J_2 = inertia of the drum

J_3 = inertia of the flywheel

B = viscous damping coefficient between the flywheel and the drum

G = torsional spring constant of the shaft

When a torque Q is applied to the disk, the equations describing the system are

$$Q = J_1\ddot\theta_1 + G\theta_1 - G\theta_2 - 0\theta_3 \qquad (2.31\text{-}5)$$

$$0 = -G\theta_1 + J_2\ddot\theta_2 + B\dot\theta_2 + G\theta_2 - B\dot\theta_3 \qquad (2.31\text{-}6)$$

$$0 = 0\theta_1 - B\dot\theta_2 + J_3\ddot\theta_3 + B\dot\theta_3 \qquad (2.31\text{-}7)$$

In Chapter 3 it will be shown how simultaneous differential equations like the above are handled.

2.32 TRANSLATIONAL SYSTEM EXAMPLE. An example of a translational system is shown in Fig. 2.32-1. Here a mass is suspended between a spring and a dashpot. If it is subjected to a force $F(t)$, the system equation is

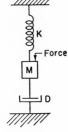

$$M\ddot X + D\dot X + KX = F(t) \qquad (2.32\text{-}1)$$

This equation may be written in operational form as

$$(Mp^2 + Dp + K)X = F(t) \qquad (2.32\text{-}2)$$

It will be noticed that the form of the equation is similar to (2.22-5), the quadratic case discussed in the electric system section. Thus the equations of mechanical systems also can be expressed in

FIG. 2.32-1.

dimensionless form. If the roots are complex, the proper form is

$$K\left(\frac{p^2}{\omega_1{}^2} + \frac{2\zeta p}{\omega_1} + 1\right) X = F(t) \qquad (2.32\text{-}3)$$

where, by equating like coefficients,

$$\omega_1 = \sqrt{\frac{K}{M}}, \qquad \zeta = \frac{D}{2\sqrt{KM}}$$

Therefore nondimensional solutions are applicable to mechanical as well as electric systems. Indeed, if one thinks in terms of nondimensional solutions, he can catalog many of the more common problems, and the extensive Laplace transform equations in the appendix serve as a table of answers. This is discussed further in Chapter 3.

2.40 Electromechanical systems

Electric motors are an excellent example of an electro-mechanical system. A voltage is applied to a motor, and mechanical motion results. Sometimes the inverse is done. Then the motor becomes a generator. Electric power may be used with hydraulic systems to control the flow, and consequently mechanical force. Conversely, hydraulic power may actuate electric monitoring instruments.

The number of occurrences of combined electric and mechanical systems is, of course, limitless. Hence it is essential to be able to relate such systems mathematically. Let us examine the example provided by the electric motor. Essentially, the mechanical part of the motor is the same as the first example in Section 2.31. It consists of a rotating mass composed of the armature and the motor load with viscous friction damping. For linear analysis, dead spots and coulomb friction are neglected. The torque applied to the system comes from the electric input.

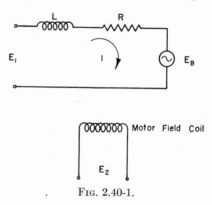

Fig. 2.40-1.

Figure 2.40-1 shows the electric diagram of a d-c motor, where E_1 is the voltage applied to the armature, E_2 is a fixed voltage applied to the motor field coil, E_B is the back emf developed by the armature motion, L is the inductance of the armature winding, R is the resistance of the armature winding, I is the current which flows through the armature winding.

When a voltage is applied to the armature, the relation in operational notation is

$$E_1 = (R + Lp)I + E_B \qquad (2.40\text{-}1)$$

The back emf generated by the motor is proportional to its speed of rotation and to the flux. For this case, the flux may be assumed to be generated largely by the motor field coil, and hence may be approximated by a constant. The speed of rotation is not a constant. Therefore

$$E_B = K\dot\theta \qquad (2.40\text{-}2)$$

where K is the back emf in volts per radian per second.

The output power can be expressed as

$$\text{horsepower} = \frac{E_B I}{746} \qquad (2.40\text{-}3)$$

$$= \frac{K\dot\theta I}{746} \qquad (2.40\text{-}4)$$

Since one horsepower is 550 foot-pounds per second,

$$\text{horsepower} = \frac{\dot\theta Q}{550} \qquad (2.40\text{-}5)$$

Equating (2.40-4) and (2.40-5) and solving for torque yields

$$Q = \tfrac{550}{746} KI \quad \text{ft-lb} \qquad (2.40\text{-}6)$$

Equation (2.40-6) can now be substituted in (2.31-1), so that

$$0.737KI = J\ddot\theta + B\dot\theta \qquad (2.40\text{-}7)$$

Combining (2.40-1), (2.40-2), and (2.40-7) yields as the final result,

$$\frac{\theta}{E_1} = \frac{0.737K}{(Jp^2 + Bp)(R + Lp) + 0.737K^2 p} \qquad (2.40\text{-}8)$$

where θ is the armature rotation in radians.

PROBLEMS

2-1. Solve the following differential equations.

(a) $\ddot\theta + 3\dot\theta + 2\theta = 5$

(b) $\ddot\theta + 3\dot\theta + 2\theta = t$

(c) $\dddot\theta + 6\ddot\theta + 12\dot\theta + 8\theta = 0$

(d) $\dddot\theta + 4\ddot\theta + 6\dot\theta + 4\theta = 4$

(e) $\dddot\theta + 2\ddot\theta + \dot\theta + 2\theta = 4$

2-2. Show that

$$\epsilon^{j3t} = \cos 3t + j \sin 3t$$

$$\epsilon^{-j\omega t} = \cos \omega t - j \sin \omega t$$

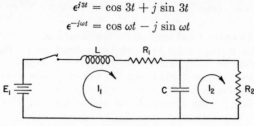

PROB. 2-3.

2-3. The circuit shown in the figure may be described by two simultaneous differential equations when the switch is closed, or by one differential equation when the switch is open. Write the differential equations for both cases. Do not solve the equations.

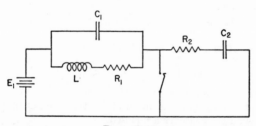

PROB. 2-4.

2-4. How many simultaneous differential equations are required to describe the operation of the circuit shown when the switch is open? When the switch is closed? What are these equations? Do not solve the equations.

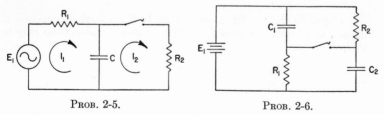

PROB. 2-5.   PROB. 2-6.

2-5. How many simultaneous differential equations are required to describe the operation of the circuit shown when the switch is open? When the switch is closed? What are these equations? Do not solve the equations.

2-6. How many simultaneous differential equations are required to describe the operation of the circuit shown when the switch is open? When the switch is closed? What are these equations? What is the steady-state charge across each capacitor when the switch is open? When the switch is closed?

2-7. Find the operational relation for the following.

(a) The voltage ratio between the voltage across R_2 and E_1 for the circuit shown in Problem 2-3 when the switch is closed.

(b) The voltage ratio between the voltage across R_1 and E_1 for the circuit shown in Problem 2-3 when the switch is closed.

(c) I_1/E_1 for the circuit shown in Problem 2-3 when the switch is closed.

(d) I_1/E_1 for the circuit shown in Problem 2-5 when the switch is closed; when the switch is open.

(e) The voltage ratio between the voltage across R_2 and E_1 for the circuit shown in Problem 2-5 when the switch is closed.

(f) The voltage ratio between the voltage across R_2 and E_1 for the circuit shown in Problem 2-6 when the switch is closed; when the switch is open.

2-8. Find ζ and ω_1 when the circuit shown in Fig. 2.22-1 has the following values.

(a) $R = 1000$ ohms, $L = 20$ h, $C = 20$ μf
(b) $R = 200$ ohms, $L = 20$ h, $C = 20$ μf
(c) $R = 200$ ohms, $L = 10$ h, $C = 16$ μf

2-9. Evaluate eq. 2.22-19 for each of the cases in Problem 2-8.

2-10. Find the impedance Z for each of the circuits in Problems 2-3 through 2-6 when the switches are closed.

2-11. Find ζ and ω_1 for the following.

$$\text{(a)} \quad \frac{1}{1 + 0.1p + 0.01p^2}. \qquad \text{(b)} \quad \frac{1}{10 + 2p + 0.1p^2}$$

2-12. Calculate the amplitude and phase of the following functions at a sufficient number of points so that the frequency-response locus may be determined.

$$\text{(a)} \quad \frac{1}{1 + 0.1j\omega - 0.01\omega^2} \qquad \text{(c)} \quad \frac{5}{j\omega}$$

$$\text{(b)} \quad \frac{1}{1 + 0.2j\omega} \qquad \text{(d)} \quad \frac{5}{j\omega(1 + 0.2j\omega)(1 + 0.1j\omega - 0.01\omega^2)}$$

2-13. What value does the dimensionless frequency operator u have when ω equals 1, 2, 3, 5, and 10 in the example in Problem 2-12a? For the example in Problem 2-12b?

2-14. Two masses, M_1 and M_2, are suspended vertically by weightless springs in a tube as shown. A force F is applied to M_2.

(a) Write the equations of motion.

(b) What are the operational relations X_1/F, X_2/F, X_1/X_2?

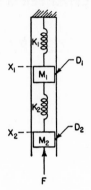

PROB. 2-14.

2-15. Draw a figure for a rotational system which may be represented by the differential equation

$$J\ddot{\theta} + B\dot{\theta} + G\theta = Q$$

2-16. Draw a figure for a translational system which may be represented by the differential equation

$$M\ddot{X} + KX = F$$

2-17. Draw a schematic of an electric circuit that is described by an equation of the same type as that in Problem 2-15. Repeat this for the equation in Problem 2-16. Repeat this for the equations describing the example in Fig. 2.31-2.

CHAPTER 3

THE LAPLACE TRANSFORM

3.00 Introduction[3,15,47,16]

The Laplace transform ($\mathcal{L}$-transform) is a mathematical tool which greatly facilitates the solution of constant-coefficient linear differential equations. Although the method was developed over 150 years ago by P. S. Laplace, only in recent years has it achieved widespread usage. The Laplace transform method enables differential equations to be transformed into relatively simple algebraic equations which can be manipulated until the desired form is obtained. Then they may be transformed back into complete solutions of the original differential equations. Initial conditions or boundary values may be readily included. Furthermore, as most problems fall into similar patterns, their solutions may be catalogued and filed for later use.

Essentially, the Laplace transform eliminates time, t, as the independent variable in differential equations and substitutes in its place the operator s. This operator, although it is a complex quantity (that is, it contains a real and an imaginary part), may be handled algebraically much the same as the operator p in Chapter 2. In fact, if all initial conditions are zero, the operators s and p are almost identical. The major difference between the classical method used in Chapter 2 and the Laplace transform is that the Laplace transform enables definite rules to be established, so that exact values of initial conditions may be included as the equations are written. Hence when a transformation back to the time domain is made, the complete solution is obtained.

The transformation from the time domain to the operational form is accomplished by integrating the differential equation between the time limits of zero and infinity. At $t = 0^+$, the functions have their initial conditions, but before $t = 0$, all variables are assumed zero. The particular integral that is used is fortunately relatively simple.

Further, since in the Laplace transform method the problems fall into repeating patterns, generally the desired problem can be found in an already prepared table of Laplace transforms. Thus it is seldom that the transformation integral is needed.

In general, the user should become familiar with a few of the relatively simple basic derivations, and he should be challenged to obtain a fuller understanding of the mathematical principles on which the Laplace transformation is based.

As an example of how the Laplace transformation is used, consider (2.10-1), one of the examples in Chapter 2. This differential equation is

$$x + 3\dot{x} + 2\ddot{x} = 1 \qquad (3.00\text{-}1)$$

and the solution given by (2.10-9) is

$$x = c_1 \epsilon^{-t/2} + c_2 \epsilon^{-t} + 1 \qquad (3.00\text{-}2)$$

Suppose that the differential equation had initial values of

$$x = 0.5 \qquad (3.00\text{-}3)$$

$$\dot{x} = 1.0 \qquad (3.00\text{-}4)$$

Then the exact solution found by evaluating both (3.00-2) and its derivative at $t = 0$ would be

$$x = \epsilon^{-t/2} - 1.5\epsilon^{-t} + 1 \qquad (3.00\text{-}5)$$

The steps in finding the solution of (3.00-5) by the Laplace transformation will be given and the necessary principles pointed out. In later sections these principles will be discussed in detail. The Laplace transform of (3.00-1) is

$$X + 3sX - 3x_0 + 2s^2 X - 2x_0 s - 2\dot{x}_0 = \frac{1}{s} \qquad (3.00\text{-}6)$$

where X denotes the Laplace transform of x, x_0 is the initial value of x, $\dot{x}_0$ is the initial value of $\dot{x}$. Solving (3.00-6) for X yields

$$X = \frac{1 + (3x_0 + 2\dot{x}_0)s + 2x_0 s^2}{s(1 + 3s + 2s^2)} \qquad (3.00\text{-}7)$$

Factoring the denominator of (3.00-7) and inserting numerical values for x_0 and $\dot{x}_0$, the result is

$$X = \frac{1 + 3.5s + s^2}{s(1 + s)(1 + 2s)} \qquad (3.00\text{-}8)$$

The answer to (3.00-8) is given in the Appendix by Laplace transform eq. (02.120) as

$$x = \epsilon^{-t/2} - 1.5\epsilon^{-t} + 1 \qquad (3.00\text{-}9)$$

Before proceeding with fundamental Laplace transform derivations, several typical points should be noted about this particular problem. These are:

1. The Laplace transforms of x and its derivatives are the same as the operational notation in Chapter 2 if all the initial values are zero. If the initial values are not zero, additional terms are added in the *numerator* of the final function.

2. The Laplace transform of x is denoted by X, but the Laplace transform of 1 is $1/s$.

3. A definite manner of numbering equations such as (3.00-8) is followed in this book so that the time solution can be located quickly.

4. Specific rules have been established for handling initial values.

5. Different symbols (such as x for a function of time and X for a function of s) should be used. In general, lower case letters are used to denote functions of time, and capital letters functions of s. However, little confusion should occur, as it is usually evident from inspection of the equation whether the equation is a function of s or of t.

3.10 The Laplace transformation integral

The Laplace transformation integral is by definition

$$F(s) = \int_0^\infty \epsilon^{-st} f(t) dt \qquad (3.10\text{-}1)$$

or in abbreviated form

$$F(s) = \mathcal{L}f(t) \qquad (3.10\text{-}2)$$

where s is the Laplace operator, $f(t)$ is a known function of time for values of time greater than zero, $F(s)$ is a function of the Laplace operator s, $\mathcal{L}$ denotes the transformation process.

The transformation back to the time domain may be accomplished by evaluating

$$f(t) = \frac{1}{2\pi j} \oint F(s)\epsilon^{st} \, ds \qquad (3.10\text{-}3)$$

where $\oint$ denotes integration about a closed contour.

	Time function type	$f_{(t)}$ for $t > 0$	Sketch of $f(t)$	Corresponding $F(s)$
a	unit step (displacement)	1	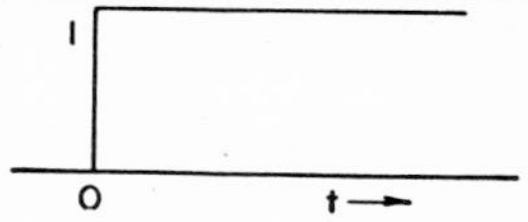	$1/s$
b	exponential decaying term	$\dfrac{1}{T}\epsilon^{-t/T}$	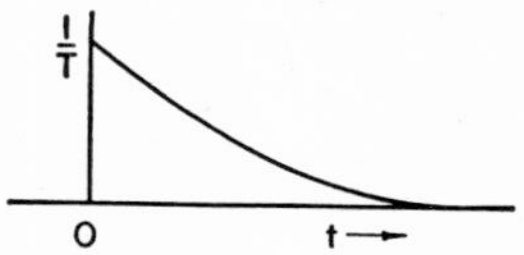	$1/(1 + Ts)$
c	sinusoidal wave	$\omega_1 \sin \omega_1 t$	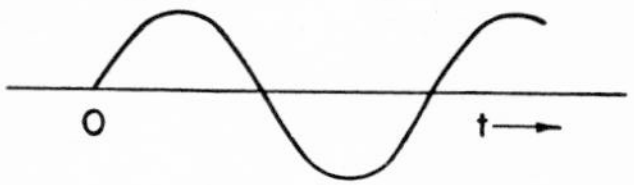	$\dfrac{1}{1 + s^2/\omega_1^2}$
d	damped sinusoidal wave	$\dfrac{\omega_1}{A} \epsilon^{-\zeta \omega_1 t} \sin \omega_1 At$ where $A = \sqrt{1 - \zeta^2}$		$\dfrac{1}{1 + 2\zeta(s/\omega_1) + (s^2/\omega_1^2)}$
e	slope step (rate)	t	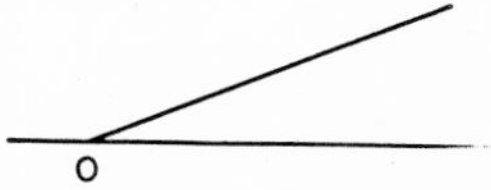	$1/s^2$
f	delayed unit step (displacement)	$f(t) = 0$ for $t < a$ $f(t) = 1$ for $t > a$	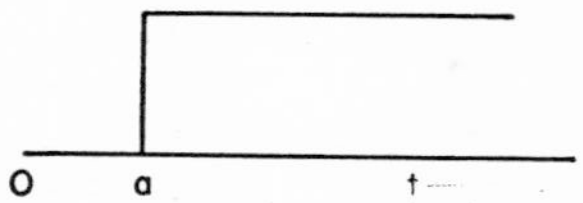	$(1/s)\epsilon^{-as}$
g	delayed slope input (rate)	$f(t) = 0$ for $t < a$ $f(t) = t - a$ for $t > a$	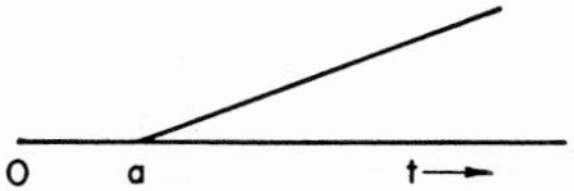	$(1/s^2)\epsilon^{-as}$

FIG. 3.10-1. Typical Laplace transformations.

or symbolically

$$f(t) = \mathcal{L}^{-1}F(s) \tag{3.10-4}$$

where $\mathcal{L}^{-1}$ denotes the inverse transformation process.

As contour integration involves mathematics beyond that assumed in this book, and since each $F(s)$ is uniquely related to an $f(t)$, the transform pairs can be obtained using (3.10-1) rather than (3.10-3). Transform pair tables such as appendix 6 may be prepared so that knowing one the other may be obtained. Fig. 3.10-1 shows typical examples.

When a function of time is multiplied by a constant, the transform is multiplied by the same constant. Thus

$$\mathcal{L}kf(t) = kF(s) \tag{3.10-5}$$

Similarly, two time functions may be added as follows

$$\mathcal{L}[f_1(t) + f_2(t)] = F_1(s) + F_2(s) \tag{3.10-6}$$

3.11 LAPLACE TRANSFORM OF A UNIT STEP. A unit step, such as shown in Fig. 3.10-1a, may be represented by

$$f(t) = 1 \tag{3.11-1}$$

Its transform is

$$F(s) = 1/s \tag{3.11-2}$$

This can be shown by substituting (3.11-1) in (3.10-1). Then

$$F(s) = \int_0^\infty \epsilon^{-st}\, dt = - \left.\frac{\epsilon^{-st}}{s}\right|_0^\infty = \frac{1}{s} \tag{3.11-3}$$

3.12 LAPLACE TRANSFORM OF AN EXPONENTIAL DECAYING TERM.

If

$$f(t) = \frac{1}{T}\,\epsilon^{-t/T} \tag{3.12-1}$$

then

$$F(s) = \frac{1}{1 + Ts} \tag{3.12-2}$$

as shown in Fig. 3.10-1b. The derivation is obtained by substituting (3.12-1) in (3.10-1); then

$$F(s) = \int_0^\infty \frac{1}{T}\,\epsilon^{-(1/T+s)t}\, dt = \frac{1}{1 + Ts} \tag{3.12-3}$$

3.13 LAPLACE TRANSFORM OF A SINUSOIDAL WAVE. If

$$f(t) = \omega_1 \sin \omega_1 t \tag{3.13-1}$$

where ω_1 is a constant, then

$$F(s) = \frac{1}{1 + s^2/\omega_1^2} \tag{3.13-2}$$

The derivation follows. Change $\sin \omega_1 t$ to its corresponding exponential form. Then

$$f(t) = \omega_1 \sin \omega_1 t = \frac{\omega_1}{2j} \left(\epsilon^{j\omega_1 t} - \epsilon^{-j\omega_1 t} \right) \tag{3.13-3}$$

Substituting (3.13-3) in (3.10-1) yields

$$F(s) = \frac{\omega_1}{2j} \int_0^\infty \left[\epsilon^{-(s-j\omega_1)t} - \epsilon^{-(s+j\omega_1)t} \right] dt \tag{3.13-4}$$

$$= \frac{\omega_1}{2j} \left[\frac{1}{s - j\omega_1} - \frac{1}{s + j\omega_1} \right] = \frac{1}{1 + s^2/\omega_1^2} \tag{3.13-5}$$

3.14 LAPLACE TRANSFORM OF A DELAYED FUNCTION. If $f(t)$ is a step function starting at a time a seconds as shown in Fig. 3.10-1f rather than at $t = 0$, its Laplace transform is obtained by separating the transformation integral into two parts. The first part integrates between $t = 0$ and $t = a$, and the second part integrates from $t = a$ to $t = \infty$. Thus

$$F(s) = \int_0^\infty f(t) \epsilon^{-st} \, dt \tag{3.14-1}$$

$$= \int_0^a 0 \epsilon^{-st} \, dt + \int_a^\infty 1 \epsilon^{-st} \, dt \tag{3.14-2}$$

$$= 0 - \left. \frac{\epsilon^{-st}}{s} \right|_a^\infty = \frac{\epsilon^{-as}}{s} \tag{3.14-3}$$

Similarly, for any function which is delayed a seconds, the transform relation is expressed as

$$f(t - a) = \epsilon^{-as} F(s) \tag{3.14-4}$$

where $F(s)$ is the transform of the time function without delay, and $f(t - a)$ indicates that the function is zero until $t = a$. That is,

$$F(s) = \mathcal{L}f(t) \tag{3.14-5}$$

3.15 LAPLACE TRANSFORM OF A DERIVATIVE. The transform of the first derivative of $f(t)$ is

$$\mathcal{L}\dot{f}(t) = sF(s) - f(0^+) \tag{3.15-1}$$

where $f(0^+)$ is the value of $f(t)$ at $t = 0^+$

$$F(s) = \mathcal{L}f(t) \tag{3.15-2}$$

This can be shown by an integration by parts. Substitute $u = f(t)$ and $dv = \epsilon^{-st}\,dt$ in

$$\int u\,dv = uv - \int v\,du \tag{3.15-3}$$

and solve for the Laplace transform of $f(t)$ rather than $\dot{f}(t)$. Thus

$$F(s) = \mathcal{L}f(t) = \int_0^\infty f(t)\epsilon^{-st}\,dt = \left. \frac{-1}{s} f(t)\epsilon^{-st} \right|_0^\infty$$

$$+ \frac{1}{s}\int_0^\infty \frac{df(t)}{dt}\epsilon^{-st}\,dt \tag{3.15-4}$$

$$= \frac{f(0^+)}{s} + \frac{1}{s}\int_0^\infty \dot{f}(t)\epsilon^{-st}\,dt \tag{3.15-5}$$

Multiplying by s yields the final result

$$\mathcal{L}\dot{f}(t) = \int_0^\infty \dot{f}(t)\epsilon^{-st}\,dt = sF(s) - f(0^+) \tag{3.15-6}$$

In the same manner it can be shown that

$$\mathcal{L}\ddot{f}(t) = s^2 F(s) - sf(0^+) - \dot{f}(0^+) \tag{3.15-7}$$

$$\mathcal{L}\dddot{f}(t) = s^3 F(s) - s^2 f(0^+) - s\dot{f}(0^+) - \ddot{f}(0^+) \tag{3.15-8}$$

Higher derivatives follow a similar pattern.

3.16 LAPLACE TRANSFORM OF AN INTEGRAL. Integration of (3.15-3) by parts where $u = \epsilon^{-st}$ and $dv = f(t)dt$ provides a method of obtaining the Laplace transform of the integral of a function of time. Thus

$$\mathcal{L}f^{(-1)}(t) = \frac{F(s)}{s} + \frac{f^{(-1)}(0^+)}{s} \tag{3.16-1}$$

$$\mathcal{L}f^{(-2)}(t) = \frac{F(s)}{s^2} + \frac{f^{(-1)}(0^+)}{s^2} + \frac{f^{(-2)}(0^+)}{s} \tag{3.16-2}$$

where $f^{(-1)}(t)$ is the first integral of $f(t)$ with respect to time, $f^{(-2)}(t)$ is the second integral of $f(t)$ with respect to time, $f^{(-1)}(0^+)$ is the value which $f^{(-1)}(t)$ has at $t = 0^+$, $f^{(-2)}(0^+)$ is the value which $f^{(-2)}(t)$ has at $t = 0^+$.

3.20 Inverse Laplace transform of functions

The inverse transform of a function of s can be found by the use of (3.10-3). However, it is generally found by the association of transform pairs obtained by (3.10-1). Thus, if

$$F(s) = \frac{1}{1 + Ts} \tag{3.20-1}$$

then, from (3.12-2) and (3.12-1),

$$f(t) = \frac{1}{T} \epsilon^{-t/T} \tag{3.20-2}$$

Generally, the functions of s are not this simple, so that a method of breaking up complex expressions into simpler ones and utilizing (3.10-6) is needed. For example, an expression such as

$$F(s) = \frac{1}{(1 + 0.5s)(1 + 4s)} \tag{3.20-3}$$

may be broken into

$$F(s) = \frac{-1}{7(1 + 0.5s)} + \frac{8}{7(1 + 4s)} \tag{3.20-4}$$

and solved in the same manner as (3.20-1) with the result

$$f(t) = -\tfrac{2}{7}\epsilon^{-2t} + \tfrac{2}{7}\epsilon^{-0.25t} \tag{3.20-5}$$

3.21 PARTIAL FRACTION EXPANSIONS WHEN DENOMINATOR ROOTS ARE UNEQUAL. A rather simple method exists for finding the partial fraction expansion of a proper fraction whose denominator roots are all different. The procedure follows. If

$$F(s) = \frac{A(s)}{B(s)} \tag{3.21-1}$$

where $A(s)$ and $B(s)$ are polynomials in s, then

$$F(s) = \frac{A(s)}{K_0(s - a)(s - b)(s - c) \ldots} \tag{3.21-2}$$

where K_0 is the coefficient of the highest power of s in $B(s)$. This can be expressed as

$$F(s) = \frac{K_1}{s - a} + \frac{K_2}{s - b} + \frac{K_3}{s - c} + \ldots \tag{3.21-3}$$

where a, b, c, etc., are roots of s in $B(s) = 0$, and K_1, K_2, K_3, etc. are constants to be determined. Each constant is found by multiplying (3.21-2) and (3.21-3) by the corresponding root factor and setting s equal to the root. Thus in order to find K_1, multiplying by $(s - a)$ yields

$$K_1 + \frac{K_2(s - a)}{(s - b)} + \frac{K_3(s - a)}{(s - c)} + \ldots = (s - a)F(s) \quad (3.21\text{-}4)$$

$$= \frac{A(s)}{K_0(s - b)(s - c) \ldots} \quad (3.21\text{-}5)$$

Next, let $s = a$; then (3.21-5) becomes

$$K_1 = \frac{A(a)}{K_0(a - b)(a - c) \ldots} = (s - a)F(s) \Big|_{s=a} \quad (3.21\text{-}6)$$

Similarly, $K_2 = \dfrac{A(b)}{K_0(b - a)(b - c) \ldots} = (s - b)F(s) \Big|_{s=b}$ (3.21-7)

$$K_3 = \frac{A(c)}{K_0(c - a)(c - b) \ldots} = (s - c)F(s) \Big|_{s=c} \quad (3.21\text{-}8)$$

etc.

As an example, consider

$$F(s) = \frac{14s^2 + 55s + 51}{2s^3 + 12s^2 + 22s + 12} \quad (3.21\text{-}9)$$

The denominator roots are $s = -1$, -2, and -3. Therefore (3.21-9) may be expressed as

$$F(s) = \frac{14s^2 + 55s + 51}{2(s + 1)(s + 2)(s + 3)} \quad (3.21\text{-}10)$$

or in partial fraction form,

$$F(s) = \frac{K_1}{s + 1} + \frac{K_2}{s + 2} + \frac{K_3}{s + 3} \quad (3.21\text{-}11)$$

Thus $K_0 = 2$, $a = -1$, $b = -2$, and $c = -3$. From (3.21-6)

$$K_1 = \frac{(14 - 55 + 51)}{2(1)(2)} = 2.5 \quad (3.21\text{-}12)$$

Similarly, $K_2 = 1.5$ and $K_3 = 3$. If any of the constants K_1, K_2, K_3, etc. are zero, it indicates that the fraction $F(s)$ is not "reduced." That is, the numerator and denominator contain equal roots. When this happens, the numerator as well as the denominator should be factored and the like terms cancelled out.

This same procedure may be used for complex roots. However, in this case the quantities K_n are also complex, and they occur in conjugate pairs. The time solution is obtained by expressing each term in the form of (3.20-1).

Appendix 2 gives methods for finding roots of equations.

3.22 PARTIAL FRACTION EXPANSION WHEN SOME DENOMINATOR ROOTS ARE EQUAL. Often the denominator of $F(s)$ contains two or more identical roots such as

$$F(s) = \frac{1}{s(s+2)^3(s+3)} \qquad (3.22\text{-}1)$$

In cases like this, the proper partial fraction expansion is

$$F(s) = \frac{C_1}{s+2} + \frac{C_2}{(s+2)^2} + \frac{C_3}{(s+2)^3} + \frac{K_1}{s+3} + \frac{K_2}{s} \qquad (3.22\text{-}2)$$

where the constants K_1 and K_2 may be determined by the method in Section 3.21, and the constants C_1, C_2, and C_3 are determined in the following manner.

The constant C_3 is determined as are the constants in Section 3.21. That is,

$$C_3 = (s+2)^3 F(s) \Big|_{s=-2} = \frac{1}{s(s+3)} \Big|_{s=-2} = -\frac{1}{2} \qquad (3.22\text{-}3)$$

However, C_2 is found from the relation

$$C_2 = \frac{d}{ds}(s+2)^3 F(s) \Big|_{s=-2} = \frac{d}{ds}\left[\frac{1}{s(s+3)}\right]\Big|_{s=-2} = \frac{1}{4} \qquad (3.22\text{-}4)$$

This may be shown by multiplying $F(s)$ by $(s+2)^3$ and differentiating. Thus

$$(s+2)^3 F(s) = C_1(s+2)^2 + C_2(s+2) + C_3$$
$$+ K_1\frac{(s+2)^3}{(s+3)} + K_2\frac{(s+2)^3}{s} \qquad (3.22\text{-}5)$$

$$\frac{d}{ds}\left[(s+2)^3 F(s)\right] = 2C_1(s+2) + C_2$$
$$+ \frac{K_1(s+2)^2(2s+7)}{(s+3)^2} + \frac{K_2(s+2)^2(2s-2)}{s^2} \quad (3.22\text{-}6)$$

If $s = -2$ in (3.22-6), then (3.22-4) is obtained. Similarly,

$$C_1 = \frac{1}{2!}\frac{d^2}{ds^2}(s+2)^3 F(s)\Big|_{s=-2}$$
$$= \frac{1}{2}\frac{d^2}{ds^2}\left[\frac{1}{s(s+3)}\right]\Big|_{s=-2} = -\frac{3}{8} \quad (3.22\text{-}7)$$

The final complete expansion is

$$F(s) = \frac{-3}{8(s+2)} + \frac{1}{4(s+2)^2} - \frac{1}{2(s+2)^3}$$
$$+ \frac{1}{3(s+3)} + \frac{1}{24s} \quad (3.22\text{-}8)$$

General rules may be formulated for multiple denominator root cases, namely, if

$$F(s) = \frac{A(s)}{B(s)} = \frac{A(s)}{(s-a)^n(s-b)}$$

then $\quad F(s) = \frac{C_1}{(s-a)} + \frac{C_2}{(s-a)^2} + \ldots + \frac{C_n}{(s-a)^n} + \frac{K_1}{(s-b)}$
$$(3.22\text{-}9)$$

where a is a multiple occuring root and b is a single root. The values for the C coefficients are

$$C_n = (s-a)^n F(s)\Big|_{s=a} \quad (3.22\text{-}10)$$

$$C_{n-1} = \frac{1}{1!}\frac{d}{ds}\left[(s-a)^n F(s)\right]\Big|_{s=a} \quad (3.22\text{-}11)$$

$$C_{n-2} = \frac{1}{2!}\frac{d^2}{ds^2}\left[(s-a)^n F(s)\right]\Big|_{s=a} \quad \text{etc.} \quad (3.22\text{-}12)$$

3.23 INVERSE TRANSFORMATION EXAMPLE. When a $F(s)$ is expressed in partial fraction form such as

$$F(s) = \frac{K_1}{s} + \frac{K_2}{s-r_2} + \frac{K_3}{s-r_3} + \ldots \quad (3.23\text{-}1)$$

the inverse Laplace transformation is

$$f(t) = K_1 + K_2 \epsilon^{r_2 t} + K_3 \epsilon^{r_3 t} + \ldots \qquad (3.23\text{-}2)$$

where r_2, r_3, etc. are the denominator roots of $F(s)$. The roots may have any value and may be either real, imaginary, or complex.

Imaginary and complex roots are handled in the same manner as real roots, but the algebra is more involved. As an example, consider

$$F(s) = \cfrac{1}{s\left(1 + 2\zeta \cfrac{s}{\omega_1} + \cfrac{s^2}{\omega_1^2}\right)}$$

$$= \frac{\omega_1^2}{s(s + \zeta\omega_1 + j\omega_1 \sqrt{1 - \zeta^2})(s + \zeta\omega_1 - j\omega_1 \sqrt{1 - \zeta^2})} \qquad (3.23\text{-}3)$$

Expressed in partial fraction form, this becomes

$$F(s) = \frac{K_1}{s} + \frac{K_2}{s + \zeta\omega_1 + j\omega_1 \sqrt{1 - \zeta^2}} + \frac{K_3}{s + \zeta\omega_1 - j\omega_1 \sqrt{1 - \zeta^2}} \qquad (3.23\text{-}4)$$

K_1, K_2, and K_3 are found as follows

$$K_1 = sF(s)\Big|_{s=0} = 1 \qquad (3.23\text{-}5)$$

$$K_2 = (s + \zeta\omega_1 + j\omega_1 \sqrt{1 - \zeta^2})F(s)\Big|_{s = -\omega_1(\zeta + j\sqrt{1-\zeta^2})}$$

$$= \frac{1}{2j \sqrt{1 - \zeta^2} \, (\zeta + j \sqrt{1 - \zeta^2})} \qquad (3.23\text{-}6)$$

$$= \frac{1}{2 \sqrt{1 - \zeta^2}} \epsilon^{j(\psi + \pi/2)} \qquad (3.23\text{-}7)$$

$$K_3 = \frac{1}{2 \sqrt{1 - \zeta^2}} \epsilon^{-j(\psi + \pi/2)} \qquad (3.23\text{-}8)$$

where $\psi = \tan^{-1} (\sqrt{1 - \zeta^2}/-\zeta)$.

Substituting into (3.23-2),

$$f(t) = 1 + \frac{1}{2 \sqrt{1 - \zeta^2}} \epsilon^{-\zeta\omega_1 t - j(\omega_1 \sqrt{1 - \zeta^2} t - \psi - \pi/2)}$$

$$+ \frac{1}{2 \sqrt{1 - \zeta^2}} \epsilon^{-\zeta\omega_1 t + j(\omega_1 \sqrt{1 - \zeta^2} t - \psi - \pi/2)} \qquad (3.23\text{-}9)$$

Since
$$\epsilon^{-j(x-\pi/2)} + \epsilon^{j(x-\pi/2)} = 2 \sin x \qquad (3.23\text{-}10)$$

The final answer is

$$f(t) = 1 + \frac{1}{\sqrt{1 - \zeta^2}} \epsilon^{-\zeta \omega_1 t} \sin (\omega_1 \sqrt{1 - \zeta^2} \, t - \psi) \qquad (3.23\text{-}11)$$

which is the same as pair 00.101 in Appendix 6. It should be noted that K_2 and K_3 are complex conjugates. Hence, in deriving a transform pair having complex roots, only one need be found.

3.30 Laplace transform pairs coding system

In order to identify polynomial fractions in s so that they may be quickly identified with their proper inverse Laplace transforms, a flexible numbering system is used in this book. Each polynomial fraction in s is assigned a five-digit number. The first two denote the characteristic of the numerator, and the last three, the denominator. A decimal point separates the first two and last three digits. The particular significance of each digit is as follows.

First digit indicates the power of s which can be factored out of the numerator.

Second digit indicates the order of s in the numerator.

Third digit indicates the power of s which can be factored out of the denominator.

Fourth digit indicates the number of real roots in the denominator distinct from zero.

Fifth digit indicates the number of pairs of complex roots in the denominator.

As an example, the equation

$$F(s) = \frac{1 + 2s + 10s^2}{s(1 + s)(1 + 2s)(1 + s + s^2)} \qquad (3.30\text{-}1)$$

is given the number 02.121 because s cannot be factored out of the numerator, the order of s in the numerator is 2, one s can be factored out of the denominator, there are 2 real roots ($s = -1$ and $s = -0.5$) in the denominator, and there is one pair of complex roots due to the factor $(1 + s + s^2)$. Many more examples can be found in the table of Laplace transforms in the appendix. It will be noted that there are several cases in the Appendix where two or more equations have the same number. However, the user should have no difficulty in identifying the one which fits his particular problem.

Although many pairs are given in the Appendix, occasionally the user will not find the particular one he needs. In this case, he can derive the solution by breaking up the fraction into partial fractions, using the techniques of Sections 3.21 and 3.22.

Full advantage should be taken of the information obtainable in a table of Laplace transform pairs. For example, the table can be used to find the derivative or integral of a function. Thus if

$$X = \frac{1}{s(1 + s + s^2)} \tag{3.30-2}$$

then using transform pair 00.101,

$$x = 1 + 1.16\epsilon^{-0.5t} \sin (49.7t° - 120°) \tag{3.30-3}$$

The derivative of x can be found by applying (3.15-6) to (3.30-2) with the result

$$\mathcal{L}\dot{x} = \frac{1}{1 + s + s^2} \tag{3.30-4}$$

Using transform pair 00.001,

$$\dot{x} = 1.16\epsilon^{-0.5t} \sin 49.7t° \tag{3.30-5}$$

It should be noted that the derivative of $\sin 49.7t°$ is $(49.7/57.3)$ $\cos 49.7t°$ and not $49.7 \cos 49.7t°$, as the proper unit for angles is the radian.

Some difficulty may have been encountered in arriving at the initial value of x which is needed to obtain (3.30-4). This value is zero. It may be obtained by letting $t = 0$ in (3.30-3), but a simpler method utilizing a Laplace transform theorem exists and is discussed in Section 3.40. After a little practice the simplicity and time-saving features of the Laplace transform become increasingly apparent.

3.40 Initial and final value theorems

A Laplace transform theorem may be used to find the initial value of a function. The theorem is

$$\lim_{t \to 0} f(t) = \lim_{s \to \infty} sF(s) \tag{3.40-1}$$

This theorem may be proved by using the relation for the Laplace transform of a derivative developed in Section 3.15. The limit as s approaches infinity is taken of each side of (3.15-6). Thus

$$\lim_{s \to \infty} \left[\int_0^\infty \dot{f}(t) \epsilon^{-st} \, dt \right] = \lim_{s \to \infty} [sF(s) - f(0^+)] \qquad (3.40\text{-}2)$$

Since s is a constant in the above integral, the left side of (3.40-2) becomes zero, with the result

$$0 = \lim_{s \to \infty} [sF(s) - f(0^+)] \qquad (3.40\text{-}3)$$

As s is not contained in $f(0)^+$, the final result is

$$f(0^+) = \lim_{t \to 0} f(t) = \lim_{s \to \infty} sF(s) \qquad (3.40\text{-}4)$$

This theorem is very useful in control analysis problems. Some of its applications are discussed in greater detail in Sections 12.30, 12.40, and 12.50, and in Section 12.31 a general initial value equation is developed.

The final value of a function may also be found by the Laplace transformation to be

$$\lim_{t \to \infty} f(t) = \lim_{s \to 0} sF(s) \qquad (3.40\text{-}5)$$

The proof is similar to the initial value theorem. Let s approach zero instead of infinity in (3.40-2). Then the left side is

$$\lim_{s \to 0} \left[\int_0^\infty \dot{f}(t) \epsilon^{-st} \, dt \right] = \int_0^\infty \dot{f}(t) \, dt = \lim_{t \to \infty} \int_0^t \dot{f}(t) \, dt$$
$$= \lim_{t \to \infty} [f(t) - f(0^+)] \qquad (3.40\text{-}6)$$

and the right side is

$$\lim_{s \to 0} [sF(s) - f(0^+)] \qquad (3.40\text{-}7)$$

Since $f(0^+)$ contains neither s nor t, it cancels out when (3.40-6) and (3.40-7) are equated. Thus

$$\lim_{t \to \infty} f(t) = \lim_{s \to 0} sF(s) \qquad (3.40\text{-}8)$$

However, the final value theorem does not apply unless all the denominator roots of $F(s)$, except $s = 0$, have negative real parts.

3.50 Examples of the Laplace transform method

Several typical problems to which the Laplace transform method may be applied are shown in Fig. 3.50-1. The differential equation describing the circuit when the switch is closed in Fig. 3.50-1a is

$$e_1 = Ri + \frac{1}{C} \int_0^t i \, dt + e_2(0^+) \qquad (3.50\text{-}1)$$

The operational notation is

$$E_1 = \left(R + \frac{1}{Cs}\right)I + \frac{e_2(0^+)}{s} \qquad (3.50\text{-}2)$$

where E_1 and I are the Laplace transforms of e_1 and i. If e_1 is 10 volts,

$$E_1(s) = 10/s \qquad (3.50\text{-}3)$$

The above may be solved for the Laplace transforms of I, E_2, and E_3 with the result

$$I = \frac{C[10 - e_2(0^+)]}{1 + RCs} \qquad (3.50\text{-}4)$$

$$E_3 = IR = \frac{RC[10 - e_2(0^+)]}{1 + RCs} \qquad (3.50\text{-}5)$$

$$E_2 = E_1 - E_3 = \frac{10 + RCse_2(0^+)}{s(1 + RCs)} \qquad (3.50\text{-}6)$$

Substituting the numerical values shown in Fig. 3.50-1a, the equations become

$$I = \frac{9 \times 10^{-6}}{1 + s} \qquad (3.50\text{-}7)$$

$$E_3 = \frac{9}{1 + s} \qquad (3.50\text{-}8)$$

$$E_2 = \frac{10(1 + 0.1s)}{s(1 + s)} \qquad (3.50\text{-}9)$$

The inverse Laplace transformations of I and E_3, are given in Appendix 6 by eq. 00.010, and the solution to E_2 by 01.110. The final answers are

$$i = 9 \times 10^{-6}\epsilon^{-t} \quad \text{amp} \qquad (3.50\text{-}10)$$

$$e_3 = 9\epsilon^{-t} \quad \text{v} \qquad (3.50\text{-}11)$$

$$e_2 = 10 - 9\epsilon^{-t} \quad \text{v} \qquad (3.50\text{-}12)$$

The initial value theorem may be applied to (3.50-7), (3.50-8), and (3.50-9) with the result

$$i(0^+) = \lim_{s \to \infty} \frac{9 \times 10^{-6}s}{1+s} = 9 \times 10^{-6} \quad \text{amp} \qquad (3.50\text{-}13)$$

$$e_3(0^+) = \lim_{s \to \infty} \frac{9s}{1+s} = 9 \quad \text{v} \qquad (3.50\text{-}14)$$

$$e_2(0^+) = \lim_{s \to \infty} \frac{10+s}{1+s} = 1 \quad \text{v} \qquad (3.50\text{-}15)$$

In a relatively simple problem such as this, the results may be evident from an inspection of the circuit. However, in more compli-

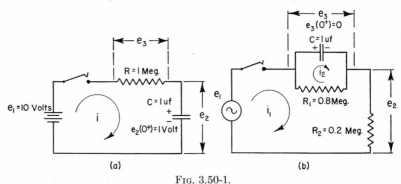

(a)   (b)

Fig. 3.50-1.

cated problems the initial value theorem can save considerable time. Similarly, the final value theorem can be applied to the equations with the results that i and e_3 become zero, while e_2 becomes 10 volts. This particular circuit is used often in control systems as a high-frequency filter.

The circuit in Fig. 3.50-1b contains two loop currents, and hence requires two differential equations to describe its operation after the switch is closed (but only one equation, with proper initial conditions, when the switch is open.)   These are

$$e_1 = R_1 i_1 + R_2 i_1 - R_1 i_2 \qquad (3.50\text{-}16)$$

$$0 = -R_1 i_1 + R_1 i_2 + \frac{1}{C} \int_0^t i_2 \, dt \qquad (3.50\text{-}17)$$

Transformed, these equations become

$$E_1 = (R_1 + R_2)I_1 - R_1 I_2 \qquad (3.50\text{-}18)$$

$$0 = -R_1 I_1 + \left(R_1 + \frac{1}{Cs}\right)I_2 \qquad (3.50\text{-}19)$$

The transformed equations may be solved as if they were algebraic ones to yield

$$E_2 = \frac{R_2(1 + R_1Cs)}{R_1 + R_2 + R_1R_2Cs} E_1 \qquad (3.50\text{-}20)$$

$$E_3 = \frac{R_1}{R_1 + R_2 + R_1R_2Cs} E_1 \qquad (3.50\text{-}21)$$

$$I_1 = \frac{1 + R_1Cs}{R_1 + R_2 + R_1R_2Cs} E_1 \qquad (3.50\text{-}22)$$

$$I_2 = \frac{R_1Cs}{R_1 + R_2 + R_1R_2Cs} E_1 \qquad (3.50\text{-}23)$$

When the numerical values shown in Fig. 3.50-1b are substituted into the above equations, they may be solved for any particular e_1 input function. Thus if e_1 is a unit step input,

$$E_1 = 1/s \qquad (3.50\text{-}24)$$

$$E_2 = \frac{0.2(1 + 0.8s)}{s(1 + 0.16s)} \qquad (3.50\text{-}25)$$

$$E_3 = \frac{0.8}{s(1 + 0.16s)} \qquad (3.50\text{-}26)$$

$$I_1 = \frac{1 + 0.8s}{s(1 + 0.16s)} \times 10^{-6} \qquad (3.50\text{-}27)$$

$$I_2 = \frac{0.8 \times 10^{-6}}{1 + 0.16s} \qquad (3.50\text{-}28)$$

The inverse Laplace transforms may be found in the Appendix to be

$$e_2 = 0.2 + 0.8\epsilon^{-6.25t} \quad \text{v} \qquad (3.50\text{-}29)$$

$$e_3 = 0.8 - 0.8\epsilon^{-6.25t} \quad \text{v} \qquad (3.50\text{-}30)$$

$$i_1 = 1 + 4\epsilon^{-6.25t} \quad \mu\text{a} \qquad (3.50\text{-}31)$$

$$i_2 = 5\epsilon^{-6.25t} \quad \mu\text{a} \qquad (3.50\text{-}32)$$

This circuit is called a "lead circuit" because if e_1 is a sinusoidal frequency, e_2 is also sinusoidal and has a positive (or leading) phase shift. This circuit is often used in control circuits and is discussed extensively in later sections.

The algebraic method used to solve the above example also may be applied to the rotational example in Section 2.31 which was described by eqs. (2.31-5), (2.31-6), and (2.31-7).

PROBLEMS

3-1. Write the Laplace transform of the following equations, including the initial conditions.

(a) $\ddot{\theta} + 3\dot{\theta} + 2\theta = 5$, (initial conditions: $\dot{\theta} = 2$, $\theta = -1$)

(b) $\ddot{\theta} + 3\dot{\theta} + 2\theta = t$, (initial conditions: $\dot{\theta} = 2$, $\theta = -1$)

(c) $\dddot{\theta} + 6\ddot{\theta} + 12\dot{\theta} + 8\theta = 0$, (initial conditions: $\ddot{\theta} = \dot{\theta} = 5$, $\theta = 2$)

(d) $\dddot{\theta} + 4\ddot{\theta} + 6\dot{\theta} + 4\theta = 4$, (initial conditions: $\ddot{\theta} = \dot{\theta} = -1$, $\theta = 10$)

(e) $\dddot{\theta} + 2\ddot{\theta} + \dot{\theta} + 2\theta = 4$, (initial conditions: $\ddot{\theta} = \dot{\theta} = \theta = 3$)

3-2. What is the number of the Laplace transform pair which gives the solution to θ for each equation in Problem 3-1?

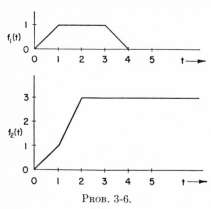

PROB. 3-6.

3-3. Find $\theta(t)$ for each equation in Problem 3-1.

3-4. Find the Laplace transform of $\dot{\theta}(t)$ for each equation in Problem 3-1. What is the initial value of $\dot{\theta}(t)$? What is the final value?

3-5. Repeat Problem 3-4 for $\ddot{\theta}(t)$ instead of $\dot{\theta}(t)$.

3-6. Find the Laplace transform of the functions shown in the figure.

3-7. Circuits like those in Problems 2-3 through 2-6 may be readily solved with the aid of the Laplace transformation. Referring to the circuits shown in the problem section of Chapter 2, solve the following.

(a) With reference to the figure shown in Problem 2-3, find:

(1) The Laplace transform equations describing the operation of the circuit when the switch is closed; when the switch is open.

(2) Assume that E_1 is a voltage of unity magnitude, and that no charge exists on the capacitor when the switch is open. Find $I_1(t)$ and $I_2(t)$ when the switch is closed, assuming $R_1 = R_2 = 1000$ ohms, $L = 20$ h, and $C = 20$ μf.

(3) Assume that E_1 is a voltage of unity magnitude and that the switch is closed until C has charged to its steady-state value. What is the charge on C? Find $I_2(t)$ when the switch is opened.

(b) With reference to the figure shown in Problem 2-4, find:

(1) The Laplace transform equations describing the operation of the circuit when the switch is closed; when the switch is open.

(2) Assume that E_1 is a voltage of unity magnitude, and that the circuit elements have the following values.

$$R_1 = 200 \text{ ohms} \qquad C_1 = 16 \text{ } \mu f$$
$$R_2 = 1000 \text{ ohms} \qquad C_2 = 1 \text{ } \mu f$$
$$L = 10 \text{ h}$$

If the switch is closed until steady-state conditions are reached and then opened, what is the voltage across the switch? What is the current through the inductor?

(c) With reference to the figure shown in Problem 2-5, find:

(1) The Laplace transform equations describing the operation of the circuit when the switch is closed; when the switch is open.

(2) Assume that E_1 is a voltage of unity magnitude, and that $R_1 = R_2 = 100,000$ ohms and $C = 1\,\mu f$. If the switch is closed until steady-state conditions are reached, and then opened, what is the voltage across the switch?

(3) Assume that $E_1 = \sin \omega_1 t$ and that the resistors and capacitor have the values given above. What is the relation of the steady-state voltage across C to the voltage E_1 when the switch is closed? When the switch is open?

(d) With reference to the figure shown in Problem 2-6, find:

(1) The Laplace transform equations describing the operation of the circuit when the switch is closed; when the switch is open.

(2) Assume that E_1 is a voltage of unity magnitude, and that $R_1 = R_2 = 100,000$ ohms and $C_1 = C_2 = 2\,\mu f$. If the switch is closed until steady-state conditions are reached and then opened, what is the voltage across the switch? What is the initial value of the first derivative with respect to time of the voltage across the switch?

3-8. Find the partial fraction expansions for the following.

(a) $F(s) = \dfrac{20}{(s+2)(s+4)}$

(b) $F(s) = \dfrac{1}{s(1+2s)(1+5s)}$

(c) $F(s) = \dfrac{300}{s^2(s+3)(s^2+10s+100)}$

(d) $F(s) = \dfrac{6(s+4)}{s(s+5)(s+1)(s+2)}$

(e) $F(s) = \dfrac{1}{s^2(1+0.1s)(1+0.5s)(1+4s)}$

(f) $F(s) = \dfrac{1+0.185s}{s(1+0.344s)(1+0.034s)(1+0.032s+0.0072s^2)}$

3-9. Find the inverse Laplace transforms for each example in Problem 3-8.

3-10. Differentiate eq. (3.30-3) by conventional methods.

3-11. Derive the following Laplace transform pairs.

(a) 00.001 where $\zeta \neq 0$ (d) 00.220 where $T_1 = T_2$

(b) 00.201 where $\zeta \neq 0$ (e) 01.110

(c) 00.220 where $T_1 \neq T_2$ (f) 01.320 where $T_1 \neq T_2$

3-12. Derive the output-to-input relation for any of the circuits in Appendix 3. (Assume all initial conditions are zero.)

CHAPTER 4

BLOCK DIAGRAM NOTATION

4.00 Introduction

The first step in the analysis of an automatic control system is to express the system as a block diagram describing the scheme of operation. A series of boxes, each representing a major component, is connected together by arrows showing the directions of signal flow. Each box is then described by a mathematical relation called a transfer function, which describes the output-to-input ratio of that element as accurately as possible. Linear differential equations are generally adequate for this purpose, and their use has enabled the development of a definite set of analysis techniques called linear design theory.

In cases where linear equations are not applicable, a number of tools exist (such as automatic computers, numerical integration, or even pure intuition), but none of these possesses the simplicity and ease of linear analysis. Hence it is often wise to make even rough approximations in order to keep an analysis linear. This is particularly true in a first analysis, after which a more detailed study is undertaken when more is known about the general characteristics and requirements of the system. An example of this type of approximation which is often used is the small-angle approximation for trigonometric functions, namely,

$$\sin \theta = \theta \tag{4.00-1}$$

$$\tan \theta = \theta \tag{4.00-2}$$

$$\cos \theta = 1 \tag{4.00-3}$$

where θ is a small angle measured in radians (0.5 radian or less).

The equations associated with each block are transformed into the Laplace form as functions of s, so that they may be combined with those of other blocks to obtain desired expressions upon which system performance can be judged. It was noted in Section 3.00 that the initial condition terms in a transform expression always appear in the numerator. In Chapters 2 and 3 it was shown that it is the denominator roots which determine system stability. Hence in a linear system no initial value can affect the stability. Without the initial condition terms in a transfer equation, the steady-state rela-

tion for sinusoidal inputs between two variables, so important in control analysis, may be calculated directly by substituting $j\omega$ for s, as was shown in Section 2.25. For these reasons, plus the fact that the initial conditions

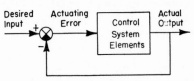

Fig. 4.00-1. Basic control system block diagram.

are generally zero, the initial condition terms are not included on block diagrams.

In the process of arriving at a suitable block diagram, as much of the mechanical and electrical details are omitted as possible. Thus an amplifier which serves only to increase the signal level may be

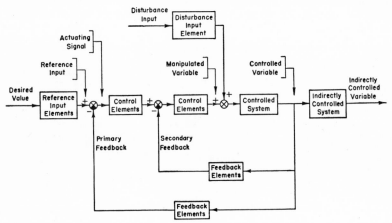

Fig. 4.00-2. A more complex block diagram of control system elements.

designated simply by the letter K, leaving the actual tube type, power supply levels, etc., to the electrical schematic. However, if the amplifier contains a filter to eliminate high frequencies, the filter characteristics should be included. It will be found that most control systems have voltage levels, and angular and linear displacement measurements intermixed throughout the system. Here again care should be taken to eliminate as many nonessential blocks as possible.

Very simple control systems can be represented by the basic block diagram in Fig. 4.00-1. A desired input and an actual output are compared. If any difference between the two exists, an error signal occurs and is applied to the control system elements, causing the output to reduce the error. Fig. 4.00-2 represents a more typical block diagram containing more than one feedback path and having unwanted disturbances injected into the system. Analysis procedures for both diagrams are identical. In this book, generally, the subscript i on a variable indicates the input, o indicates the output, and e indicates the error. In some multiple loop and other cases this cannot be followed, but the purpose of the variable should be evident from the block diagram.

4.10 Block diagram elements

Block diagrams consist of arrows showing the direction of signal flow, differential and summing symbols as shown in Fig. 4.10-1,

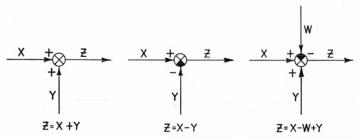

$$Z = X + Y \qquad Z = X - Y \qquad Z = X - W + Y$$

Fig. 4.10-1   Junction point symbols.

indicating the manner in which signals are combined, and boxes. The junction points are left open and a plus sign is used when the signal is added. When the signal is subtracted the junction point is filled in and a minus sign used as shown. Each box represents the transfer relation existing between the input and output of that box. When this relation is expressed as a linear differential equation and its Laplace transform obtained (neglecting initial conditions), it is found that a rational fraction in the Laplace operator s results.

Since the object of a block diagram is to achieve as much information as possible in a compact form, the transform relation associated with each box should combine brevity and clarity in such a manner that the nature of the relation is immediately evident. In Chapters

2 and 3 it was pointed out that dynamic systems could be described by similar mathematical equations. Just as these equations were coded to obtain an extensive Laplace transform table, so can they be coded and abbreviated for block diagram use. It will be found

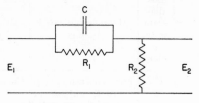

(a) Electrical Circuit

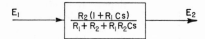

(b) Box Diagram Showing Actual Transfer Function

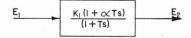

(c) Box Diagram Showing Generalized Transfer Relation

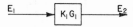

(d) Box Diagram Indicating Both a Constant and a Frequency Dependent Factor Exists

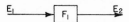

(e) Box Diagram Showing That Some Function Exists Between E_1 and E_2

Fig. 4.10-2.   Different box diagram forms.

that all output-to-input relations have one or more of the following features.

1. Numerator and denominator roots that can be put in the form of T, ζ, and ω_1 as in the Laplace transform tables. (These terms will be represented by the letter G, such that when $s = 0$, $G = 1$.)

2. Constants that can be factored out of the equation after it is in the T, ζ, and ω_1 form. (These terms will be represented by the letter K.)

Table 4.10-1

Typical Box Output-to-Input Laplace Transform Transfer Relations,
Their Box Representation, and Meaning

No.	$F(s)$	Box diagram representation	Meaning indicated by box	Meaning indicated by actual $F(s)$
1	$\dfrac{4(1 + 1.25s)}{s(1 + 0.25s)}$	$\dfrac{KG}{s}$	For constant step input, output in steady state changes at constant rate $K \times$ (input). G denotes frequency-dependent terms also in the relation.	Constant rate to constant input factor $= 4$. The frequency-dependent portion (other than s) is a "lead" type similar to the circuit in Fig. 3.50-1b.
2	$\dfrac{1}{1 + Ts}$	G	For constant step input, output equals input in steady state, but with sinusoidal input, the output amplitude and phase differ from input.	Fig. 2.21-1 shows typical function inside the box. Fig. 2.21-2 shows transient response of output to a step input. Fig. 2.26-1 charts amplitude and phase of this.
3	10	K	The output $= K \times$ (input) for any type of input.	The box may be an amplifier with a gain of 10.
4	$\dfrac{K}{s(1 + T_1 s)(1 + T_2 s)}$	$\dfrac{KG}{s}$	Same as No. 1.	Constant rate to constant input $= K$. Frequency-dependent factor G is a double filter form. Box contains motor-like function; see eq. (2.40-8).
5	$\dfrac{1}{1 + 2\zeta s/\omega_1 + s^2/\omega_1{}^2}$	G	Same as No. 2.	See Figs. 2.22-1, 2.22-2, 2.26-2, and 2.26-3 for typical characteristics.
6	$\dfrac{5s}{1 + 5s}$	sKG	For constant rate input, output $= K \times$ (input rate). A frequency-dependent factor is also present.	$K = 5$. G is of the same form as in No. 2.

3. Factors of s that can be factored out of the numerator or denominator, and thus indicate that the basic function of the box is an order of integration or differentiation.

These relations are illustrated by the examples in Table 4.10-1 and by Fig. 4.10-2, which shows the steps in a box representation evolution. It may be seen from the examples that combinations of K, G, and s give much basic information in a compact form. When several boxes are combined, the same basic information about the combination is obtained by combining the simple basic information associated with each box. Numerical subscripts are generally given to the K and G terms of each box, so that the particular effect of each box in a control system may be shown.

Another representation for the transfer characteristic of each box is simply the letter F with a numerical subscript such as shown in Fig. 4.10-2e. Although this notation does not give any informative data about the box characteristics such as the K, G, and s notation did, it does provide a single symbol which can be used in over-all block diagram equations.

4.20 Single-loop block diagrams

Figure 4.20-1 presents a simple control system in three common forms that are used in analysis. The junction points on these diagrams indicate that θ_e (the error signal), θ_i (the input signal), and θ_o (the output signal) are related by the equation

$$\theta_e = \theta_i - \theta_o \qquad (4.20\text{-}1)$$

Each box indicates the relation between the variable designated by the arrow going out of the box and the variable designated by the arrow going into the box. Thus

$$\frac{X}{\theta_e} = F_1 = K_1 = 20 \qquad (4.20\text{-}2)$$

$$\frac{Y}{X} = F_2 = K_2G_2 = \frac{1 + 0.2s}{10(1 + 0.02s)} \qquad (4.20\text{-}3)$$

$$\frac{Z}{Y} = F_3 = G_3 = \frac{1}{1 + 0.01s} \qquad (4.20\text{-}4)$$

$$\frac{\theta_o}{Z} = F_4 = \frac{K_4G_4}{s} = \frac{5}{s(1 + 0.2s)(1 + 0.05s)} \qquad (4.20\text{-}5)$$

where $K_2 = 0.1$ and $K_4 = 5$. Note that $G_n = 1$ when $s = 0$ for all cases.

The above five equations may be combined algebraically to obtain any desired block diagram relation. Two of the major equations associated with any control system block diagram are θ_o/θ_i and θ_o/θ_e. Here θ_o/θ_i is called the "closed-loop equation." It is the

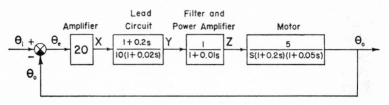

(a) Block Diagram Showing Actual System Constants.

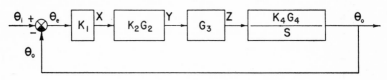

(b) Block Diagram Using K, G and s symbols.

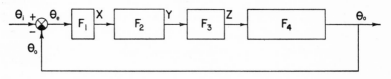

(c) Block Diagram Using F symbols.

Fig. 4.20-1.   Block diagram forms for a motor positioning control system.

expression for the entire system function complete with feedback. The denominator roots of the closed-loop equation determine stability. The θ_o/θ_e relation is called the "open-loop equation." It gets its name from the fact that if no output feedback existed, the system would be an open-loop type. Systems designed for open-loop operation have the disadvantage of not being so inherently accurate as closed-loop systems, since there is no error-detecting device which actuates the system when the output and input are unequal. This book is primarily concerned with the design of closed-loop systems. The open-loop equation is very important, however, as it is uniquely related to the closed-loop equation; and it will be shown later that it is easier to manipulate and analyze the open-loop equation.

The open-loop equation for the system in Fig. 4.20-1 is obtained by multiplying together eqs. (4.20-2) through (4.20-5). Thus

$$\frac{\theta_o}{\theta_e} = \frac{X}{\theta_e} \cdot \frac{Y}{X} \cdot \frac{Z}{Y} \cdot \frac{\theta_o}{Z} = F_1 F_2 F_3 F_4 \tag{4.20-6}$$

$$= \frac{K_1 K_2 K_4 G_2 G_3 G_4}{s} \tag{4.20-7}$$

Because the open-loop equation is so important in analysis work, special symbols are assigned to it. In this book we will use the subscript o in both the F and K, G and s notations to denote the open-loop transfer function relation which applies to the entire control system under consideration. Section 4.30 gives the notation used for subsidiary loops. Thus (4.20-6) and (4.20-7) become

$$\frac{\theta_o}{\theta_e} = F_o = \frac{K_o G_o}{s} \tag{4.20-8}$$

where

$$F_o = F_1 F_2 F_3 F_4 \tag{4.20-9}$$

$$K_o = K_1 K_2 K_4 \tag{4.20-10}$$

$$G_o = G_2 G_3 G_4 \tag{4.20-11}$$

The s factor in (4.20-8) is important as it indicates immediately that this system is Type 1 (see Section 4.53); K_o also has a special meaning as it is the "velocity constant" of the system (see Section 4.53). The F_o symbol is useful because of its brevity.

The closed-loop equation may be found by dividing both sides of (4.20-1) by θ_o.

Then

$$\frac{\theta_e}{\theta_o} = \frac{\theta_i}{\theta_o} - 1 \tag{4.20-12}$$

Rearranging (4.20-12) and using (4.20-8),

$$\frac{\theta_o}{\theta_i} = \frac{F_o}{1 + F_o} \tag{4.20-13}$$

When numerical values for the system of Fig. 4.20-1 are substituted into (4.20-13), it becomes

$$\frac{\theta_o}{\theta_i} = \frac{1}{1 + 0.1s + 0.008s^2 + 0.00017s^3 + 0.000001s^4} \tag{4.20-14}$$

This equation accurately describes the transfer relation between the input and output of the system. In order to find the output for any given input, factor the denominator of (4.20-14) and multiply by the Laplace transform of the input to obtain the Laplace transform of the output. The output as a function of time is found by taking its inverse transform.

As an example, if the input is a unit step function, then

$$\theta_i = 1/s \tag{4.20-15}$$

and after factoring, the transform of the output is

$$\theta_o = \frac{1}{s(1 + 0.0103s)(1 + 0.0166s)(1 + 0.0731s + 0.00585s^2)} \tag{4.20-16}$$

This equation is of the same form as transform pair 00.121 in Appendix 6, where $T_1 = 0.0103$ sec, $T_2 = 0.0166$ sec, $\zeta = 0.48$, $\omega_1 = 13.07$ radians per sec. Substitution of these values in the transform pair gives the time solution of the output. This relation is discussed further in Section 4.40.

It is usually important to know not only the output response, but also the response of the other variables in the system. The magnitude of signal levels, including their velocities and accelerations, may be found by solving for the Laplace transform of the desired quantity. In this way tolerances may be assigned to control parameters. Two other methods for determining these relationships are the use of automatic computing equipment and numerical integration, which are covered in Chapters 13 and 12, respectively.

It can be seen that for a system with fixed values on all elements, such as the one in this example, an output response can be determined. Suppose, however, that the output response was not satisfactory. What procedure could be followed to improve the system? A "brute force" method would be to change one of the elements (such as the gain), find the new θ_o/θ_i relation, factor it, and find the new output response. It is evident that this method would be time-consuming.

A simpler method exists and is described in detail in later chapters. It utilizes transfer function plots of the system for sinusoidal inputs (see Section 2.25). From the shape and frequency distribution on these plots, the nature of the θ_o/θ_i denominator roots and transient response can be judged.

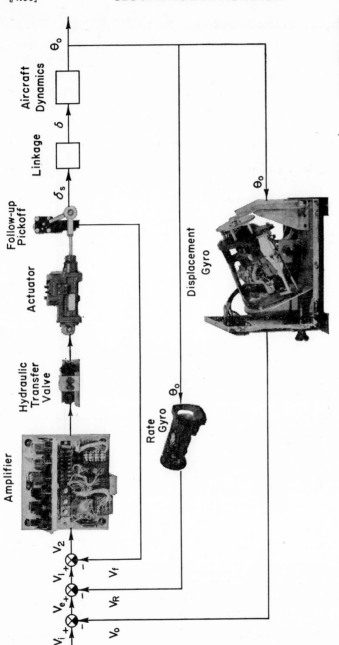

Fig. 4.30-1. Components of an aircraft automatic pilot. (From "A Comparison of Predicted and Experimentally Determined Longitudinal Dynamic Responses of a Stabilized Airplane," by Smaus, Gore, and Waugh, *NACA TN2578*, December, 1951.)

4.30 Multiple-loop block diagrams

The automatic pilot for an airplane is one example of a multiple-loop control system. The autopilot functions to keep an airplane traveling in a desired direction, θ_i. Its principal components are shown in Fig. 4.30-1, and its block diagram in Fig. 4.30-2. If the

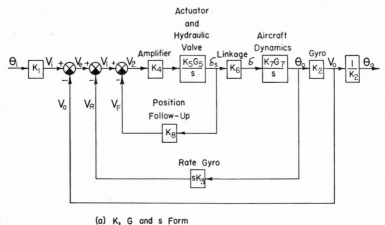

(a) K, G and s Form

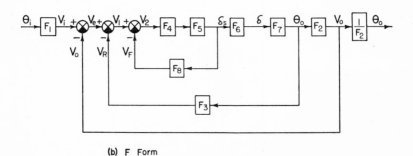

(b) F Form

Fig. 4.30-2.   Block diagram of a typical aircraft automatic pilot.

plane deviates from the desired course, the deviation is detected by a gyro whose output voltage V_o is proportional to the magnitude of the deviation. This, compared with a voltage, V_i, representing the desired path, forms the system error signal V_e. It has been found that feeding back a signal V_R proportional to the rate of heading change, improves the system operation. The selection and use of signals such as this are discussed in later sections. For the present, it may be said that if a system "knows" how fast it is approaching a desired value, it also "knows" when to start slowing down. This added information helps the system, and hence improves performance.

The rate and error signals combine to form V_1, which is compared with another feedback signal, V_f, representing the actual position of the aircraft control surface δ. The control surface feedback signal is necessary for stability and accuracy purposes. It makes the over-all system a Type 1 rather than a Type 2 (defined in Section 4.50) system, and it also establishes a definite relation between the steady-state control surface deflection and V_1. This does not mean that a Type 1 system is generally better than a Type 2, but rather that in this particular application its merits are greater. The difference between V_1 and V_f, denoted by V_2, is amplified and applied to a hydraulic valve. This valve acts as a flow regulator for highly pressurized hydraulic fluid whose flow is proportional to the input signal. The pressure magnitude is such that it can move the control surface easily in either direction, depending on the polarity of V_2. Between the hydraulic actuator position and control surface there is a linkage having a mechanical advantage denoted by K_6. Thus if V_2 is a constant voltage, a constant hydraulic flow results, causing the control surface to move at a constant rate. Operationally, this may be expressed as

$$\frac{\delta}{V_2} = \frac{K_4 K_5 K_6}{s(1 + Ts)} \tag{4.30-1}$$

or

$$\frac{\delta}{V_2} = \frac{K_4 K_5 K_6 G_5}{s} \tag{4.30-2}$$

where $K_4 K_5 K_6$ is in radians per second per volt, T represents the hydraulic valve lag in seconds, G_5 denotes $1/(1 + Ts)$ (note that $G = 1$, when $s = 0$), and the subscripts denote which box the symbol is associated with.

The relation between the aircraft heading and the control surface deflection may be expressed, within limits, by a linear differential equation of the form

$$b\ddot{\theta}_o + a\dot{\theta}_o + \theta_o = e\delta + c \int \delta \, dt \tag{4.30-3}$$

where the coefficients a, b, c and e are constants for a given speed and atmosphere condition. This equation is found by the simultaneous solution of force and moment equations which describe the dynamic characteristics of the airplane. Typical force equations consist of two parts. One sums all the forces in the direction of flight (engine thrust minus the drag of each major airplane part), and the other sums all the normal forces (the downward force of gravity and the upward or downward force of the air acting on such airplane elements as the wings, fuselage, etc.). Also, equations are written for the moments due to these forces with respect to the airplane's center of gravity. Extensive wind-tunnel testing is generally performed to verify the force and moment equations.

In operational form (4.30-3) becomes

$$\frac{\theta_o}{\delta} = \frac{c + es}{s(1 + as + bs^2)} \tag{4.30-4}$$

or in abbreviated form,

$$\frac{\theta_o}{\delta} = \frac{K_7 G_7}{s} \tag{4.30-5}$$

where $K_7 = c, \qquad G_7 = \frac{1 + es/c}{1 + as + bs^2}$

The autopilot block diagram has one major loop and two minor loops. Each of these has an open-loop relation associated with it. Because open-loop relations are very important in control analysis, special symbols are assigned to them. As noted in Section 4.20, the symbol F_o is reserved for the over-all system open-loop equation. Hence

$$F_o = \frac{V_o}{V_e} = \frac{F_2 F_4 F_5 F_6 F_7}{1 + F_4 F_5 F_8 + F_3 F_4 F_5 F_6 F_7} \tag{4.30-6}$$

For the inner loops, we again use the subscript o to indicate that it is an open-loop relation, and in addition we add an arbitrary number to indicate that it is associated with an inner loop. Thus

$$F_{o1} = \frac{V_R}{V_1} = \frac{F_3 F_4 F_5 F_6 F_7}{1 + F_4 F_5 F_8} \tag{4.30-7}$$

$$F_{o2} = \frac{V_f}{V_2} = F_4 F_5 F_8 \tag{4.30-8}$$

Using the K, G, and s notation, the system open-loop function is

$$\frac{V_o}{V_e} = \frac{K_o G_o}{s} = \frac{K_2 K_4 K_5 K_6 K_7 G_5 G_7}{s(K_3 K_4 K_5 K_6 K_7 G_5 G_7 + K_4 K_5 K_8 G_5 + s)} \tag{4.30-9}$$

where
$$K_o = \frac{K_2 K_6 K_7}{K_3 K_6 K_7 + K_8},$$

$$G_o = \frac{K_4 K_5 G_5 G_7 (K_3 K_6 K_7 + K_8)}{K_4 K_5 G_5 (K_3 K_6 K_7 G_7 + K_8) + s}$$

(Note that $G_o = 1$ when $s = 0$).

Similarly,
$$\frac{V_R}{V_1} = K_{o1} G_{o1} = \frac{K_3 K_4 K_5 K_6 K_7 G_5 G_7}{K_4 K_5 K_8 G_5 + s} \qquad (4.30\text{-}10)$$

$$\frac{V_f}{V_2} = \frac{K_{o2} G_{o2}}{s} = \frac{K_4 K_5 K_8 G_5}{s} \qquad (4.30\text{-}11)$$

where
$$K_{o1} = \frac{K_3 K_6 K_7}{K_8} \qquad G_{o1} = \frac{K_4 K_5 K_8 G_5 G_7}{K_4 K_5 K_8 G_5 + s}$$

$$K_{o2} = K_4 K_5 K_8, \qquad G_{o2} = G_5$$

(Note that G_{o1} and G_{o2} both equal one when $s = 0$)

There is a simple method for obtaining the above relations in addition to the block-by-block-equation method used in the preceding section. It may be stated as follows.

Any input variable is related to any output variable by a summing equation containing as many terms as there are signal paths between the two variables, excluding those paths through which the output can affect the input. Each term describes the effect of that path, and contains a factor for each box the path passes through. Each path starts at the output variable and travels to the input variable. If a box is a forward function (that is, the arrow denoting signal flow on the block diagram is in the opposite direction as the path is moving), the transfer equation associated with that box appears as a denominator term. If the box is a feedback function (the path moves with the signal flow as denoted by the arrows), the transfer equation is a numerator factor.

In equation form, this is

$$\frac{\text{input variable}}{\text{output variable}} = \sum_{\text{paths}} \frac{\text{feedback terms}}{\text{forward terms}} \qquad (4.30\text{-}12)$$

As an example, there are three paths between V_e and V_o, so that the relation has three terms and is

$$\frac{V_e}{V_o} = \frac{1}{F_2 F_4 F_5 F_6 F_7} + \frac{F_3}{F_2} + \frac{F_8}{F_2 F_6 F_7} \qquad (4.30\text{-}13)$$

Similarly, between V_i and V_o there are four paths, and the relation is

$$\frac{V_i}{V_o} = 1 + \frac{1}{F_2 F_4 F_5 F_6 F_7} + \frac{F_3}{F_2} + \frac{F_8}{F_2 F_6 F_7} \qquad (4.30\text{-}14)$$

In general, the relations should be derived by both the short-cut method and the block-by-block substitution method, so that one may be sure of the accuracy.

In analyzing a multiple-loop system, the designer usually starts with the innermost loop and selects values so that it is stable. He then proceeds to the next loop, doing the same until the system is completed. Although the inner loops are generally adjusted so that they are stable, this is not necessary and sometimes not desirable. It is possible to have an unstable inner loop and still have a stable over-all system. Systems of this type contain "nonminimum phase" functions. They occur intentionally by design and unintentionally when the controlled dynamics are of a nature that they contain such terms. Chapter 6 discusses these functions in fuller detail, explaining the necessary requirements for over-all stability.

4.40 Approximate system transient response

It is desirable to be able to look at a stable equation such as (4.20-14) and to state the approximate system speed of response. One method is to drop all the s terms except the first. Then a first-order approximation is

$$\frac{\theta_o}{\theta_i} = \frac{1}{1 + 0.1s} \qquad (4.40\text{-}1)$$

The response of (4.40-1) to a step θ_i input is shown in Figure 4.40-1. It reaches 63% of its final value in 0.1 second, and this value, which is the same as the denominator first-power s coefficient, is generally referred to as the time constant of a first-order equation.

Higher order equations do not have such a simple relation, as they may oscillate considerably before settling out. Therefore an arbitrary definition of system time constant arises. One definition is the time required to reach 63% of the final value. The importance of the time constant is that it provides a handy reference for judging system performance. Although overshoot is not limited by a 63% time constant definition, the definition still serves its basic purpose and may be used.

Another approximation often used is obtained by dropping all the s terms higher than the second order. Thus (4.20-14) becomes

$$\frac{\theta_o}{\theta_i} = \frac{1}{1 + 0.1s + 0.008s^2} \qquad (4.40\text{-}2)$$

and the response of this second-order approximation to a step input also is shown in Figure 4.40-1, along with the response of the complete equation.

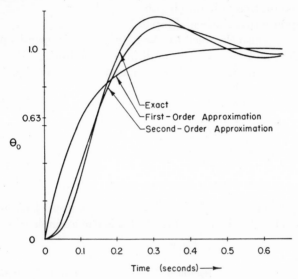

Fig. 4.40-1.   System response to unit step input.

First- and second-order approximations, when used with caution, are very valuable in that they provide a quick idea of the system operation.

4.50 Types of control systems

In the design of a control system, the final criterion is how adequately the output follows the input. This is equivalent to stating the magnitude of the allowable error for various inputs. The desired performance for all control systems is not the same. In each, various factors such as cost, size, weight, and purpose must be thoroughly considered. Only seldom is it desirable for the output to follow the input instantaneously. As a simple example, nobody would care to step into an elevator that instantly moved from floor to floor. Similarly, an airplane autopilot should not respond too fast to input commands. Also, in every control system there are extraneous inputs (such as gear backlash, stray voltage pick-up, and suddenly applied forces like the firing torque of a gun or a gust of wind) whose effect must be minimized. Therefore it is conventional to judge system performance by the following characteristics.

1. Response to a unit step input
2. Response to a unit rate input
3. Response to a sinusoidal input

Systems are also classified by the nature of their open-loop transfer function, and most systems fall into the following three types.

Type 0 systems are those in which a constant error signal causes a constant output in the steady state.

Type 1 systems are those in which a constant error signal causes a constant output rate in the steady state.

Type 2 systems are those in which a constant error signal causes a constant output acceleration in the steady state.

It will be shown that the type of a system is determined by the number of integrations in the open-loop function.

4.51 TYPE 0 SYSTEMS. The inner loop of the autopilot discussed in Section 4.30 and redrawn in Fig. 4.51-1 is one example of a Type 0

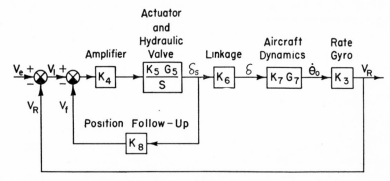

FIG. 4.51-1.　Example of a Type 0 control system.

system, since the voltage V_R is a constant times V_1 in the steady state, as indicated by (4.30-10).

Type 0 systems have their open-loop functions denoted by K_oG_o, as shown in Fig. 4.51-2a, and their output-to-input relation is

$$\frac{\theta_o}{\theta_i} = \frac{K_oG_o}{1 + K_oG_o} \qquad (4.51\text{-}1)$$

In the steady state the output for a unit step input is

$$\theta_o = \frac{K_o}{1 + K_o} \qquad (4.51\text{-}2)$$

Thus the output never is equal to the input in the steady state, and only when the gain K_o is large does the error θ_e become small.

It is conventional to call the steady state magnitude of θ_o for a constant θ_e signal of unity amplitude the "position constant" and

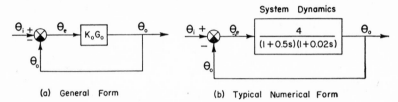

(a) General Form   (b) Typical Numerical Form

Fig. 4.51-2.   Block diagrams of a Type 0 control system.

denote it by the letter K_p. By definition,

$$K_p = \lim_{s \to 0} F_o \qquad (4.51\text{-}3)$$

where F_o is the open-loop transfer function. Although (4.51-3) applies to any system, it has particular significance for Type 0 systems. Since there is no s factor in this type system,

$$F_o = K_oG_o \qquad (4.51\text{-}4)$$

and therefore

$$K_p = K_o \qquad (4.51\text{-}5)$$

in these systems, where K_p is usually positive, but it may be either positive or negative. Thus whenever the open-loop function is K_oG_o, it indicates that the system is Type 0 with K_p equal to K_o.

For the typical example shown in Figure 4.51-2b, the following relations exist.

$$K_p = K_o = 4 \qquad (4.51\text{-}6)$$

$$G_o = \frac{1}{(1 + 0.5s)(1 + 0.02s)} \qquad (4.51\text{-}7)$$

$$\frac{\theta_o}{\theta_e} = \frac{4}{(1 + 0.5s)(1 + 0.02s)} \qquad (4.51\text{-}8)$$

$$\frac{\theta_o}{\theta_i} = \frac{0.8}{1 + 0.104s + 0.002s^2} = \frac{0.8}{(1 + 0.0255s)(1 + 0.0785s)}$$

$$(4.51\text{-}9)$$

$$\frac{\theta_e}{\theta_i} = \frac{0.2(1 + 0.52s + 0.01s^2)}{(1 + 0.0255s)(1 + 0.0785s)} \qquad (4.51\text{-}10)$$

These may be used to show typical Type 0 system operation. If θ_i is a unit step input, the Laplace transform of the error signal is

$$\theta_e = \frac{0.2(1 + 0.52s + 0.01s^2)}{s(1 + 0.0255s)(1 + 0.0785s)} \qquad (4.51\text{-}11)$$

Using the Laplace final value theorem,

$$\theta_e = 0.2 = \frac{1}{1 + K_p} \qquad (4.51\text{-}12)$$

which agrees with (4.51-2). If the input is a unit rate,

$$\theta_e = \frac{0.2(1 + 0.52s + 0.01s^2)}{s^2(1 + 0.0255s)(1 + 0.0785s)} \qquad (4.51\text{-}13)$$

and again applying the final value theorem,

$$\theta_e = \infty \qquad (4.51\text{-}14)$$

This result is due to the $0.2t$ factor in the time solution (see Laplace transform eq. 02.220), which follows logically, since a rate input is the integral of a unit input. Hence when a step input causes a fixed error, a rate input causes an error increasing at a fixed rate.

Because θ_e may be appreciable, it can be said then that a Type 0 control system is desirable only for limited input signals, unless the gain is very high.

4.52 DYNAMIC GAIN. Unit step and rate inputs are valuable in determining the static characteristics, but generally the dynamic characteristics are more important. These may be judged by the steady-state response to sinusoidal inputs of various frequencies. In Section 2.24 it was shown that this could be found by substituting $j\omega$ for the operator, which was p in that case and is s in the present cases.

We can demonstrate that this is true by considering (4.51-10) and letting $\theta_i(t) = \sin \omega_1 t$. Thus

$$\theta_i(s) = \frac{1}{\omega_1(1 + s^2/\omega_1^2)}, \tag{4.52-1}$$

$$\theta_e = \frac{0.2(1 + 0.52s + 0.01s^2)}{\omega_1(1 + s^2/\omega_1^2)(1 + 0.0255s)(1 + 0.0785s)} \tag{4.52-2}$$

The solution is given by Laplace transform eq. 02.021, and in the steady state

$$\theta_e = 0.2 \left\{ \frac{(1 - 0.01\omega_1^2)^2 + (0.52\omega_1)^2}{[1 + (0.0255\omega_1)^2][1 + (0.0785\omega_1)^2]} \right\}^{1/2} \sin (\omega_1 t + \psi) \tag{4.52-3}$$

where

$$\psi = \tan^{-1} \frac{0.52\omega_1}{1 - 0.01\omega_1^2} - \tan^{-1} 0.0255\omega_1 - \tan^{-1} 0.0785\omega_1$$

The amplitude is the same as would have been obtained by substituting $j\omega$ for s directly in (4.51-10). A sketch of the amplitude vs. frequency for (4.52-3) is shown in Fig. 4.52-1. This plot indicates the amplitude at which the error signal would oscillate for a sinusoidal input of unit magnitude. At very high frequencies the error amplitude is unity; hence the system does not respond at all to these signals. At lower frequencies

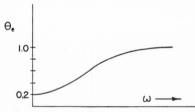

Fig. 4.52-1. Steady-state maximum error amplitude for sinusoidal inputs as a function of frequency.

the error amplitude is lower, indicating better action of the control system.

Plots such as this are valuable in determining the dynamic response of any type of system. The error amplitude is not always less than one, even in this case. Sometimes it will be found that the error amplitude reaches values of 2 or 3 for some frequencies. High values will indicate a high overshoot or oscillatory condition. In later chapters methods are developed which serve as an aid in determining the probable overshoot.

4.53 TYPE 1 SYSTEMS. In Type 1 systems there is no steady-state error when a step input is applied. This is because the system contains an integrating element in the open-loop portion. Figure 4.53-1 shows a typical integrating circuit. A constant voltage v_1 causes the motor to turn at a constant rate, so that the voltage v_2 increases at a constant rate. Assuming the motor has a negligible lag,

$$v_2 = \int v_1 \, dt \qquad (4.53\text{-}1)$$

or in operational form,

$$V_2 = \frac{V_1}{s} \qquad (4.53\text{-}2)$$

If such an element were inserted after the error signal in a Type 0 system, a constant error voltage would cause an increasing voltage,

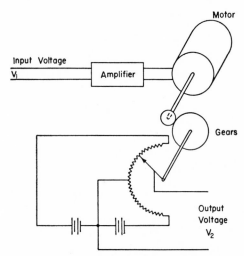

Fig. 4.53-1. An example of a simple integrating element.

which would in turn cause the output to change until the error became zero. With an integrator, the system is classified Type 1.

Type 1 systems are those in which the output-to-error relation is such that a constant error signal causes a constant output rate. Thus

$$F_o = \frac{K_o G_o}{s} \qquad (4.53\text{-}3)$$

for all Type 1 systems. The magnitude of the steady state output rate $\dot{\theta}_o$ for a constant unit error signal is called the "velocity constant" and given the symbol K_v. By definition,

$$K_v = \lim_{s \to 0} sF_o \tag{4.53-4}$$

As in the case of (4.51-3), (4.53-4) applies to any system type. It has particular significance for Type 1 systems, however. The value of K_v may be either positive or negative. This is illustrated by the two systems shown in Fig. 4.53-2. When K_v is negative and the system is stable, it indicates that there are an odd number of

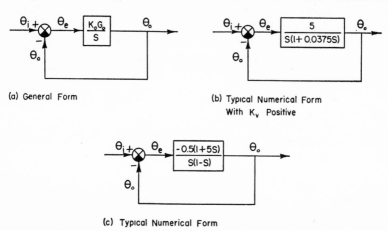

(a) General Form

(b) Typical Numerical Form
With K_v Positive

(c) Typical Numerical Form
With K_v Negative

FIG. 4.53-2. Block diagrams of a Type 1 control system.

denominator roots of F_o with positive real parts. These functions (called non minimum-phase terms) are discussed in Chapter 6. Such systems generally tend to overshoot or lead the input.

The position constant K_p for Type 1 systems is

$$K_p = \lim_{s \to 0} F_o = \lim_{s \to 0} \frac{K_o G_o}{s} = \infty \tag{4.53-5}$$

This means that there is no steady-state error in a Type 1 system for a "position" or unit step input, and this may be demonstrated by considering the error-to-input relation for Fig. 4.53-2b,

$$\frac{\theta_e}{\theta_i} = \frac{s(1 + 0.0375s)}{5(1 + 0.15s)(1 + 0.05s)} \tag{4.53-6}$$

Letting θ_i be a unit step input and applying the final value theorem,

$$\theta_e = 0 \qquad (4.53\text{-}7)$$

If θ_i is a unit rate input, however, θ_e in the steady state is

$$\theta_e = \frac{1}{K_v} = 0.2 \qquad (4.53\text{-}8)$$

Thus a Type 1 control system has a zero steady-state error for a unit step input and a constant error of $1/K_v$ for a unit rate input. The error for sinusoidal inputs is determined in the same manner as in the example in Section 4.52. A high K_v value usually indicates a system with a low response time. A rule of thumb which is roughly accurate is

$$T_N = 1/K_v \quad \text{sec} \qquad (4.53\text{-}9)$$

where T_N is the speed of response for a unit step input.

4.54 TYPE 2 SYSTEMS. It would seem that the addition of another integrator in a Type 1 system would result in zero steady-state error for rate inputs. Such is the case and these systems are called Type 2. Similarly, it might appear that the more integrators that are present in a system, the better its accuracy. This, however, is not generally true. Additional integrators help systems to have low static errors, but often they do this at the expense of having large transient overshoots. Also, such systems are usually hard to adjust and difficult to stabilize.

Therefore most control systems are either Type 0, 1, or 2, of which Type 2 are those with two integrating elements in the open-loop function. The open-loop equation for all Type 2 systems is of the form

$$F_o = \frac{K_o G_o}{s^2} \qquad (4.54\text{-}1)$$

which indicates that a constant error voltage causes a constant output acceleration. The ratio of the steady state $\ddot{\theta}$ magnitude to a constant error signal is called the acceleration constant and given the symbol K_a. By definition.

$$K_a = \lim_{s \to 0} s^2 F_o \qquad (4.54\text{-}2)$$

and may be positive or negative. As in the cases of (4.51-3) and (4.53-4), (4.54-2) applies to any system type. For Type 2 systems $K_a = K_o$.

Table 4.54-1 summarizes the values for K_p, K_v, and K_a for different systems. The larger the constants are, the smaller the system error will be for unit position, rate or velocity inputs. Thus a Type

TABLE 4.54-1

SUMMARY OF K_p, K_v, AND K_a VALUES FOR DIFFERENT SYSTEMS

System types	F_o equation form*	K_p	K_v	K_a
$-n$	$s^n K_o G_o$	0	0	0
0	$K_o G_o$	K_o	0	0
1	$(K_o G_o)/s$	∞	K_o	0
2	$(K_o G_o)/s^2$	∞	∞	K_o
$2 + n$	$(K_o G_o)/s^{2+n}$	∞	∞	∞

* n is a positive integer.

2 system has no steady-state error for a position or rate input, and a constant error for an acceleration input. Any system of higher order than a Type 2 has zero steady-state error, while any system of lower order than a Type 0 has an infinite steady-state error for any of the three inputs.

Type 2 systems have an inherent stability problem, discussed in later chapters, which may be seen by considering a simple example. If

$$\frac{\theta_o}{\theta_e} = F_o = \frac{1}{s^2(1 + s)} \tag{4.54-3}$$

the output to input relation is

$$\frac{\theta_o}{\theta_i} = \frac{1}{1 + s^2 + s^3} \tag{4.54-4}$$

This is unstable since the denominator does not contain an s to the first power term. Therefore, for stability, it is necessary for F_o to have an s to the first power term in the numerator.

Figure 4.54-1b shows a typical Type 2 relation. Using the constants shown,

$$\frac{\theta_o}{\theta_i} = \frac{1 + 1.6s}{1 + 1.6s + 0.65s^2 + 0.05s^3} = \frac{1 + 1.6s}{(1 + 0.1s)(1 + 0.5s)(1 + s)} \tag{4.54-5}$$

$$\frac{\theta_e}{\theta_i} = \frac{s^2(1 + 0.077s)}{1.54(1 + 0.1s)(1 + 0.5s)(1 + s)} \tag{4.54-6}$$

Application of the final value theorem shows that the steady-state error is zero for a unit step or rate input, but for a unit acceleration input

$$\theta_e(s) = \frac{(1 + 0.077s)}{1.54s(1 + 0.1s)(1 + 0.5s)(1 + s)} \qquad (4.54\text{-}7)$$

and in the steady state

$$\theta_e(t) = \lim_{s \to 0} s\theta_e(s) = \frac{1}{1.54} \qquad (4.54\text{-}8)$$

which is typical of Type 2 systems.

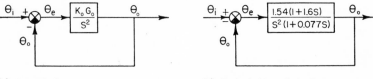

(a) General Form   (b) Typical Numerical Form With K_a Positive

Fig. 4.54-1.   Block diagrams of a Type 2 control system.

4.60 Components

Some of the major types of control system components are the following.

1. Sensing elements, which are usually employed to detect the error between a desired and an actual signal.

2. Amplifiers, which increase the signal voltage levels.

3. Power elements, such as electric motors or hydraulic valves, which control the output motion.

4. Compensating functions, which improve stability, speed of response, and/or accuracy (these are discussed in detail in Chapter 9).

Figure 4.60-1 shows seventeen different types of sensing elements. Some additional elements are shown in Fig. 4.60-2, which also shows methods of connecting the sensing elements to an amplifier and a power element.

Suggested applications for the sensing circuits of Fig. 4.60-2 include the following uses.

(b) For stabilized motor, prime mover, drive or machine speeds under variable loads; for stabilized peripheral speeds of driven members; for rate of flow control; for wire drawing.

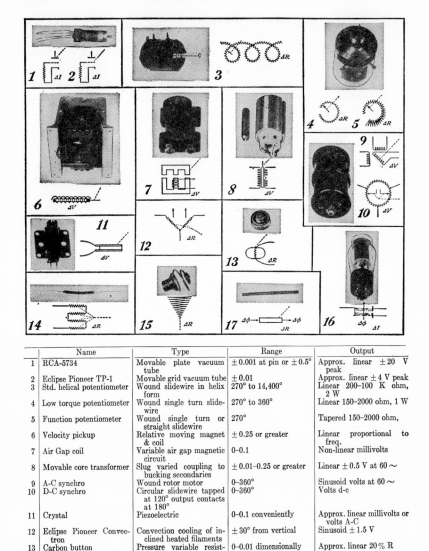

	Name	Type	Range	Output
1	RCA-5734	Movable plate vacuum tube	± 0.001 at pin or ± 0.5°	Approx. linear ± 20 V peak
2	Eclipse Pioneer TP-1	Movable grid vacuum tube	± 0.01	Approx. linear ± 4 V peak
3	Std. helical potentiometer	Wound slidewire in helix form	270° to 14,400°	Linear 200–100 K ohm, 2 W
4	Low torque potentiometer	Wound single turn slidewire	270° to 360°	Linear 150–2000 ohm, 1 W
5	Function potentiometer	Wound single turn or straight slidewire	270°	Tapered 150–2000 ohm,
6	Velocity pickup	Relative moving magnet & coil	± 0.25 or greater	Linear proportional to freq.
7	Air Gap coil	Variable air gap magnetic circuit	0–0.1	Non-linear millivolts
8	Movable core transformer	Slug varied coupling to bucking secondaries	± 0.01–0.25 or greater	Linear ± 0.5 V at 60 ∼
9	A-C synchro	Wound rotor motor	0–360°	Sinusoid volts at 60 ∼
10	D-C synchro	Circular slidewire tapped at 120° output contacts at 180°	0–360°	Volts d-c
11	Crystal	Piezoelectric	0–0.1 conveniently	Approx. linear millivolts or volts A-C
12	Eclipse Pioneer Convectron	Convection cooling of inclined heated filaments	± 30° from vertical	Sinusoid ± 1.5 V
13	Carbon button	Pressure variable resistance	0–0.01 dimensionally	Approx. linear 20 % R
14	Resistance strain gage	Strained resistance wire	0–1 % of 50–2000 ohm	Linear microamps and millivolts
15	Resistance spring motion transducer	Pre-stressed, plated wound wire	0.01 to 10 in. or greater	Linear medium R or volts
16	Magnetically deflected beam tubes	Vacuum tube	Various field strengths	Approx. linear milliamps
17	Variable reluctance transducer	Stress-variable reluctance metal in magnetic circuit	Various (determined by arrangement)	Approx. linear, usually; millivolts

FIG. 4.60-1. Seventeen types of sensing elements. (From "Transducers, Sensing Elements for Servos," by J. R. Stovall, *Electrical Manufacturing*, April, 1950.)

(c) For conductivity of solutions—valve or pump flow control to maintain solution conductivity for paper processing; for temperature regulation of plating solutions and baths by regulating generator current flow; for maintaining dielectric constant of solutions by control of heating and/or pressure process; for maintaining given solution density by controlling discharge pump or valves; for maintaining insulation thickness and uniformity through equipment speed control; for fuel or power control for glass furnaces.

(d) For furnace temperature control by monitoring color; for photographic printing and timing light control; for lighting intensity circuit control; for automatic stopping, starting of machinery and processes.

(e) For precise frequency control of a-c generators; for engine rpm control.

(f) For follow-up servo system control for radar, gunfire, turret and automatic pilot controls; for remote hydro-plant control—starting, stopping, load and temperature controls; for remote indication and control of switch gear, circuit breakers and load for sectionalizing and service restoration of electric utilities.

In general, these sensing circuits may be used for automatic level control of liquids, solids, powders and gases in tanks, (e.g., enamel tanks and wire drawing tanks); for air conditioning equipment; for industrial x-ray machines; for control of current and timing for spot, seam, butt, flash welding; for geodetic exploration equipment, for moisture control of automatic drying machine (for textiles and paper); for balancing gas mixing valves for proper combustion control; for remote positioning system; for radar antenna slewing, motor servo.

The power element in Fig. 4.60-2 is a "clutch-servo." The prime mover and the gears it engages run continuously, and provide a source of kinetic energy which is readily available. This energy is transferable to the unit's output shaft by excitation of either clutch coil. When current flows in either clutch coil, it magnetizes a powdered iron mixture which effectively locks the output gear with the prime motor-driven gear. The output motion direction depends on which clutch coil is energized. The operation is analogous to a powerful vacuum tube amplifier where a few milliamperes control over a hundred watts.

The output torque is proportional to the current flowing in the

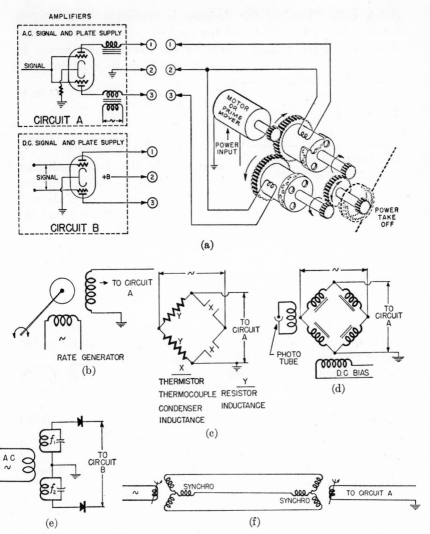

Fig. 4.60-2. Sensing elements and control circuit arrangements. (a) basic components of the servo, a mechanism that transforms a signal into an instantaneous force proportional to the signal. (b), (c), (d), (e), and (f) may be used to activate the basic clutch circuits A and B, generating high torque to position and control contiguous or remote devices. See p. 90 for suggested applications. (Courtesy Lear, Inc.)

clutch coils. Therefore the designer is interested in a relation between the coil current and the applied voltage. Figure 4.60-3 shows the electrical diagram relating the voltage and current. In operational form, the relation is

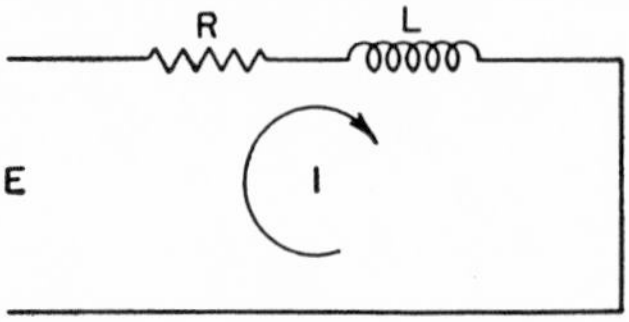

$$\frac{I}{E} = \frac{1}{R + Ls} \qquad (4.60\text{-}1)$$

or

$$\frac{I}{E} = \frac{1}{R[1 + (L/R)s]} \qquad (4.60\text{-}2)$$

Fig. 4.60-3. Electrical diagram for a clutch-servo.

where R is the total resistance in the circuit including the coil resistance and the source resistance, L is the inductance of the coil. Equation (4.60-2) is particularly informative, as it says that the time constant (coefficient of s) decreases as R increases. Thus a high-impedance source, such as a pentode tube, yields a lower response time. Typical time constant values are the following.

0.140 sec with no source impedance

0.065 sec when a triode tube is used

0.025 sec when a pentode tube is used

Other electric motor types that are commonly used are the d-c motor described in Section 2.40 and the 2-phase electric motor. Figure 4.60-4 shows an electrical diagram for a 2-phase motor. Both the reference voltage and the signal voltage are of the same carrier frequency (for example, 60 c), but their phase is 90° apart. The reference voltage has a constant magnitude, usually about 115 volts, and the signal voltage has a magnitude that varies from zero to the same as the reference voltage. The motor speed is proportional to the magnitude of the signal voltage. Reversal of the shaft rotational direction is accomplished by merely reversing the phase of the signal voltage. The rate generator shown in Fig. 4.60-2 is actually a 2-phase motor being used as a voltage generator.

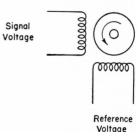

Signal Voltage

Reference Voltage

Fig. 4.60-4. Electrical diagram for a two-phase motor.

Another important power source is a hydraulic valve. The operation of most values is very similar to the clutch servo, except that hydraulic fluid flow is controlled. The current flow in two coils (generally called solenoids) controls the position of a spool, which in turn controls the amount and direction of fluid flow. As in the case of the clutch servo, the speed of response is largely proportional to L/R, where L is the inductance of the solenoids and R is the resistance in the circuit. Sometimes, however, the mass of the spool is such that it must also be taken into account.

PROBLEMS

4-1. For values of θ less than 0.5 radian, calculate and plot the following:

$$\theta, \quad \sin\theta, \quad \tan\theta$$

4-2. Express the following functions in K, G, and s notation, and state the value of K, and G.

(a) $F(s) = \dfrac{5}{s(1 + 0.1s)}$

(b) $F(s) = \dfrac{1}{s(s + 4)(s + 2)}$

(c) $F(s) = \dfrac{4s(2 + s)}{(1 + 2s)(1 + s)(1 + 5s)}$

(d) $F(s) = \dfrac{10}{s^2(1 + 0.1s + 0.01s)}$

(e) $F(s) = \dfrac{s^2}{(1 + 0.1s)(1 + 0.01s)^2}$

4-3. Find θ_o/θ_e for the following functions, express the result in the K, G, and s notation, and state the value of K and G.

(a) $\dfrac{\theta_o}{\theta_i} = \dfrac{1}{1 + 0.1s + 0.01s^2}$

(b) $\dfrac{\theta_o}{\theta_i} = \dfrac{2}{6 + 11s + 6s^2 + s^3}$

(c) $\dfrac{\theta_o}{\theta_i} = \dfrac{4 + 6s}{4 + 6s + 4s^2 + s^3}$

(d) $\dfrac{\theta_o}{\theta_i} = \dfrac{82 + 98s + 59s^2}{82 + 98s + 59s^2 + 10s^3 + s^4}$

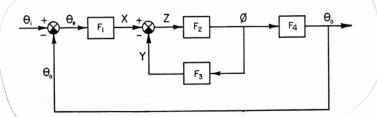

PROB. 4-4.

4-4. Find θ_o/θ_i and F_o for the block diagram shown.

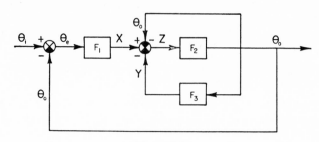

PROB. 4-5.

4-5. Find θ_o/θ_i and F_o for the block diagram shown.

4-6. Write the operational equation for the following differential equations (neglect initial conditions), and express each in a block diagram.

    (a) $\theta + 2\dot{\theta} + \ddot{\theta} = \phi + \dot{\phi}$

    (b) $\theta + 3\dot{\theta} + \ddot{\theta} = \phi$

    (c) $\theta + 2\dot{\theta} = 5\phi + 2\dot{\phi} + 3\ddot{\phi}$

4-7. If $\theta_i(t)$ is a unit step input, find $\theta_o(t)$ for each of the control systems given in Problem 4-3.

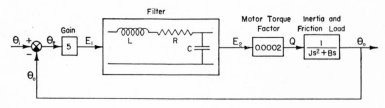

PROB. 4-8.

4-8. The system shown has the following constants.

$$R = 1000 \text{ ohms} \qquad J = 0.20 \times 10^{-6} \text{ slug-ft}^2$$
$$L = 20 \text{ h} \qquad\qquad B = 40 \times 10^{-6} \text{ ft-lb/radian/sec}$$
$$C = 20 \text{ }\mu\text{f} \qquad\qquad E_1 = 5 \text{ v/radian}$$

(a) Derive the following transfer relations.

$$E_2/E_1, \qquad \theta_o/\theta_e, \qquad \theta_o/\theta_i$$

(b) Plot the frequency response for F_o.

(c) Find $\theta_o(t)$ when $\theta_i(t)$ is a unit step input.

(d) Repeat (a), (b), and (c) for $R = 200$ ohms.

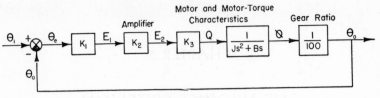

PROB. 4-9.

4-9. The system shown has the following characteristics.

K_1, part of the error sensing device, denotes the effect of a synchro arrangement yielding 1 volt at E_1 per degree error.

K_2 denotes the gain of the amplifier.

K_3, part of the motor, relates the torque developed by the motor to the applied voltage. The motor torque is proportional to the applied voltage, and is 0.02 ft-lb when 10 v are applied.

J, the motor inertia, is 5×10^{-6} slug-ft^2.

B, the output friction coefficient is 250×10^{-6} ft-lb/radian/sec.

The moment of inertia of the gears and output load is negligible.

A 100-to-1 reduction gear connects the load to the motor.

(a) Express K_1 in volts per radian.

(b) Express K_3 in ft-lb/volt.

(c) Find θ_o/θ_i.

(d) If the damping ratio of the control system is $\zeta = 0.35$, what is K_2? What is the natural frequency of the system? What is the steady-state error for an input of $\theta_i(t) = 50°/\text{sec}$?

4-10. State the type of system that each of the examples in Problem 4-3 represents. What are K_v, K_p, and K_a for each system?

CHAPTER 5

THE NYQUIST CRITERION

5.00 Introduction

The Nyquist criterion provides a simple graphical method for determining the stability of a linear system. Its derivation is given in Appendix 5. Fortunately, the results can be stated simply so that, unless one desires to do so, it is not necessary to go through the derivation in order to apply the criterion. The basis for the Nyquist criterion involves the mathematics of complex variables, conformal mapping, and residues. As such, the criterion provides an excellent example of how mathematics can be utilized to provide simple practical relations.

The Nyquist criterion relates the nature of the transfer function response plot for sinusoidal input frequencies to the location of roots of the "characteristic equation." Both were discussed briefly in Chapter 2. Transfer function plots were introduced in Sections 2.24 and 2.25, and the importance of the roots of the characteristic equation were covered in Section 2.10. To study system stability, a characteristic equation of the whole system must be obtained. Then, as pointed out in Section 2.10, stability exists if, and only if, there are no roots of the characteristic equation with positive real parts. These roots could be obtained by factoring the characteristic equation. However, in most cases that is not the easy way, since finding the roots of high-order equations is a long, tedious task. Further, even though one has the roots of the characteristic equation, he does not always know the nature of the transient solution. That is, the system may be stable, but still have a slowly decaying oscillation. This is not desirable, for a properly designed system should assume its desired value without hunting or appreciable overshoot.

The Nyquist criterion provides a method which simultaneously determines stability, indicates the approximate nature of the transient response, and enables one to judge how improvements may be made. Further, as the Nyquist criterion uses the frequency response characteristic, it lends itself to experimental procedures very nicely. Often the designer has a component in a control system which, though difficult to analyze mathematically, may have a transfer frequency response that can be obtained rather easily by laboratory procedures. Thus the over-all design can proceed, using the experimental results for this component.

5.10 The characteristic equation

The characteristic equation is the denominator of the output-to-input relation equated to zero after all fractions have been cleared. In Chapter 4 the general output-to-input relation was shown to be

$$\frac{\theta_o}{\theta_i} = \frac{F_o}{1 + F_o} \tag{5.10-1}$$

Thus the characteristic equation is

$$1 + F_o = 0 \tag{5.10-2}$$

As an example, consider the system in Fig. 5.10-1, where

$$F_o = \frac{4}{s(1 + 0.04s)} \tag{5.10-3}$$

For this case,

$$\frac{\theta_o}{\theta_i} = \frac{1}{1 + 0.25s + 0.01s^2} \tag{5.10-4}$$

If (5.10-4) is expressed in differential equation notation, it is

$$\theta_o + 0.25\dot{\theta}_o + 0.01\ddot{\theta}_o = \theta_i \tag{5.10-5}$$

Thus it is seen that the characteristic equation for this system is

$$1 + 0.25s + 0.01s^2 = 0 \tag{5.10-6}$$

which is the same as that which would have been obtained by substituting directly into (5.10-2) and clearing fractions. The roots of the characteristic equation are

$$s = -5 \quad \text{and} \quad -20 \tag{5.10-7}$$

If a unit step θ_i is applied to the system, the output, using Laplace transform eq. 00.120, is

$$\theta_o = 1 - 1.33\epsilon^{-5t} + 0.33\epsilon^{-20t} \tag{5.10-8}$$

Since the exponential terms decay to zero in the steady state, θ_o becomes 1, and this system is stable.

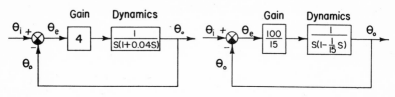

FIG. 5.10-1.   FIG. 5.10-2.

As a second example, consider the system in Fig. 5.10-2, where

$$F_o = \frac{100}{15} \times \frac{1}{s(1 - \frac{1}{15}s)} \tag{5.10-9}$$

Here the characteristic equation is

$$1 + 0.15s - 0.01s^2 = 0 \tag{5.10-10}$$

and the roots are

$$s = -5 \quad \text{and} \quad +20 \tag{5.10-11}$$

If a unit step θ_i is applied to this system, the output is

$$\theta_o = 1 - 0.8\epsilon^{-5t} - 0.2\epsilon^{20t} \tag{5.10-12}$$

Because of the positive exponent in the last term, this system is unstable. Stability exists if, and only if, there are no roots of the characteristic equation with positive real parts. Some examples of the roots which a stable system may have are

$$s = -5, -2, 0 \tag{5.10-13}$$

$$s = -5, -2 + j8, -2 - j8, -10 \tag{5.10-14}$$

$$s = -5, j8, -j8 \tag{5.10-15}$$

$$s = -2 + j8, -2 - j8 \tag{5.10-16}$$

where $j = \sqrt{-1}$.

The zero root in (5.10-13) denotes that the output in this system will increase at a fixed rate for a unit step input. This type of system is called a velocity servo, since the input controls the turning rate. The roots with imaginary parts in the last three examples indicate that an oscillation exists in the system of 8 radians per second. In cases (5.10-14) and (5.10-16) the oscillation is damped; that is, it dies out. However, in (5.10-15) the oscillation persists, and the system it denotes will have a steady-state oscillation at 8 radians per second. Such a system, called "neutrally stable," seldom occurs, as discussed in Section 2.10.

Examples of roots which an unstable system might have are

$$s = +5, \ -2, \ 0 \tag{5.10-17}$$

$$s = -5, \ +2 + j8, \ +2 - j8, \ -10 \tag{5.10-18}$$

$$s = +5, \ j8, \ -j8 \tag{5.10-19}$$

$$s = +2 + j8, \ +2 - j8 \tag{5.10-20}$$

$$s = +5, \ -2 + j8, \ -2 - j8 \tag{5.10-21}$$

The $+5$ term in (5.10-17), (5.10-19), and (5.10-21) gives rise to a diverging output due to an ϵ^{5t} term. In (5.10-18) and (5.10-20) an 8-radians-per-second oscillation of ever-increasing amplitude occurs.

5.20 The s-plane

It has been found convenient to plot the location of the roots of a system. For this a "root-plane" or "s-plane" is used, where one axis is the real part and the other axis is the imaginary part. Thus the roots of (5.10-18) may be plotted as shown in Fig. 5.20-1. By our definition of stability, any system is unstable if any root of its characteristic equation has a positive real part. This could be restated as follows. Any system is unstable if any of the roots of its characteristic equation lies in the right half of the s-plane. The advantage of this is that the Nyquist criterion is based on a definite relation between the s-plane and the transfer function plane.

It should be noted that the location of a root of the characteristic equation on the real axis of the s-plane causes an exponentially decreasing or increasing term in the system response, depending on its sign. Similarly, location off the real axis occurs only in conjugate pairs and causes an oscillation in the system response. Any complex root causes either an increasing or decreasing oscillation, depending on the sign of the real part. Because the imaginary axis denotes oscillation, it is thought of as the frequency axis, and s is generally written as

$$s = \sigma + j\omega \qquad (5.20\text{-}1)$$

where σ is the real part, ω is the imaginary part, and the units have been so chosen that ω is in radians per second. Because frequency in radians per second arises naturally, it is the conventional frequency unit that is used. Thus throughout this book frequency will

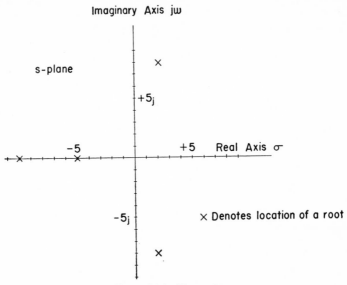

Fig. 5.20-1. The s-plane.

always refer to radians per second unless otherwise stated. The number of radians is 2π times the frequency in oscillations, or cycles, per second.

5.30 The transfer function plane

The transfer function plane is a locus of the vector ratio between any two variables for steady-state* sinusoidal inputs. Examples were given in Sections 2.25 and 2.26. When the input is a fixed sinusoidal frequency, the output is also sinusoidal at the same fre-

---

* Strictly speaking, there is no steady-state relation when the transfer function contains positive denominator roots. However, this technicality does not affect the validity of the Nyquist criterion.

quency, and the amplitude and phase of the output compared with the input determine one point on the transfer function plot (see Section 1.30). As the frequency is varied from zero to infinity, the series of points plotted with real part *vs.* imaginary part form a locus known as the system transfer function. It was shown in Section 2.25 that the same locus could be obtained by substituting $j\omega$ in the operational transfer function expression for s. Thus for the case

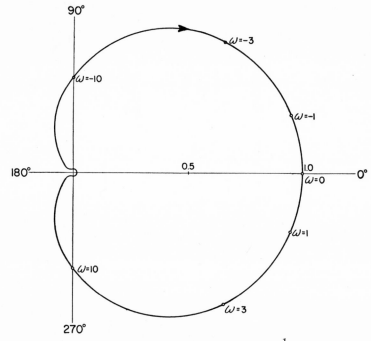

FIG. 5.30-1. Transfer function plot of $\dfrac{1}{1 + 0.25j\omega - 0.01\omega^2}$.

where the transfer function expression is (5.10-4), the mathematical expression which yields the transfer function locus is

$$\frac{\theta_o}{\theta_i} = \frac{1}{1 + 0.25j\omega - 0.01\omega^2} \tag{5.30-1}$$

The transfer function plot of (5.30-1) is shown in Fig. 5.30-1 for both positive and negative frequency values. Both positive and negative frequencies have important physical as well as mathematical meanings. The polarity of a frequency depends on the assumed positive polarity of the angular rotation. If a certain relation exists between two elements in a linear system for a positive rotation of one of them, the mirror image of that relation exists if the rotation polarity is reversed. This is often observed in laboratory experiments when using a mechanically driven synchro, whose rotation direction may be reversed, as a source of signal frequency inputs. The same relation exists in a mathematical analysis, and one important application is that it enables mathematical principles

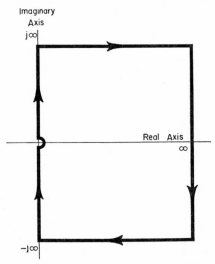

Fig. 5.30-2. s-plane plot including all points in the right half plane.

to be applied to control problems; namely, a closed contour in the transfer function plane has a definite relation (discussed in Section 5.40) to a closed contour in the s-plane. We choose a contour in the s-plane which includes all points in the right half plane, and thus we arrive at the Nyquist criterion for stability.

The particular closed contour in the s-plane which is used for the Nyquist criterion is shown in Fig. 5.30-2. It includes all points in the right half s-plane, and it passes through all points on the imaginary axis except the point at the origin. The point at the origin, and only that point, is eliminated by the small semicircle shown in Fig. 5.30-2. The nature of the s-plane locus at infinity and at the origin are important in that they enable general mathematical relations to be defined for the shape of the transfer function plot at

$\omega = 0$ and ∞, and the imaginary axis part of the locus is important as it corresponds to sinusoidal frequencies. The transfer function points for negative values of ω are the mirror images of the positive values, as can be seen in Fig. 5.30-1. Therefore it is customary to plot only the points for positive values, bearing in mind that this result is only one-half of the complete polar plot.

5.40 Relation between the s-plane and the transfer function plane

The relation between the s-plane and the transfer function plane which always exists is as follows.

Given any polynomial in s divided by another polynomial in s such as

$$F(s) = \frac{(s + a_1)(s + a_2)(s + a_3) \; \cdots}{(s + b_1)(s + b_2)(s + b_3) \; \cdots} \tag{5.40-1}$$

where a_n and b_n are roots of $F(s)$, and may be real, imaginary, complex, or zero. Then (where $s = j\omega$), the transfer function plot $F(j\omega)$ encircles the origin in a manner determined by the relation,

$$N = P - Z \tag{5.40-2}$$

where N is the number of encirclements of the origin (counterclockwise is positive for increasing ω), P is the number of denominator roots of $F(s)$ with positive real parts, Z is the number of numerator roots of $F(s)$ with positive real parts.

It should be noted that P and Z represent points inside the s-plane contour shown in Fig. 5.30-2. Also the existence of this relation depends on the manner in which the locus closes in the s-plane. It is closed so that it includes all points in the right half plane. Since all the roots which may cause an instability are located there, it becomes evident why this relation is so valuable. A different s-plane contour than that in Fig. 5.30-2 could be used with values of s along this new contour being substituted for s in (5.40-1), and (5.40-2) would still apply except that P and Z would then refer to points inside the new contour. The particular contour shown in Fig. 5.30-2 is used because it includes all roots of $F(s)$ which affect system stability.

As an example, consider

$$F(s) = \frac{1}{1 - 0.04s} \tag{5.40-3}$$

This has $Z = 0$ and $P = 1$ due to the positive root at $s = 25$. When $s = j\omega$, eq. (5.40-3) becomes

$$F(j\omega) = \frac{1}{1 - 0.04j\omega} \qquad (5.40\text{-}4)$$

A plot of (5.40-3) for s, increasing from $-j\infty$ to $+j\infty$ and circling back to $-j\infty$ as in Fig. 5.30-2, is shown in Fig. 5.40-1. The main question lies in the nature of the locus of $F(s)$ when s goes from $+j\infty$

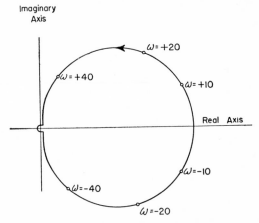

Fɪɢ. 5.40-1.   Transfer function plot (also called frequency response or polar plot) of $F(s) = 1/(1 - 0.04s)$.

to $-j\infty$. As shown in Fig. 5.30-2, s assumes a value of $+\infty$ (Note: not $+j\infty$). Thus at this point,

$$F(\infty) = \frac{1}{1 - 0.04(\infty + j0)} = 0^{+}\angle 180° \qquad (5.40\text{-}5)$$

so that the locus has a very small amplitude as it crosses the negative axis, hence encircling the origin once. Thus

$$N = 1 \qquad (5.40\text{-}6)$$

and (5.40-2) is satisfied.

As a second example, consider

$$F(s) = \frac{1}{1 + 0.04s} \qquad (5.40\text{-}7)$$

where $Z = 0$ and $P = 0$. The locus for this is shown in Fig. 5.40-2. At $s = \infty$, the value of (5.40-7) is

$$F(\infty) = \frac{1}{1 + 0.04(\infty + j0)} = 0^+\angle 0° \qquad (5.40\text{-}8)$$

This example does not encircle the origin, so that

$$N = 0 \qquad (5.40\text{-}9)$$

and again (5.40-2) is satisfied.

It should be noted that (5.40-2) applies to any function of the type (5.40-1). Thus (5.40-3) and (5.40-7) may be combined in any

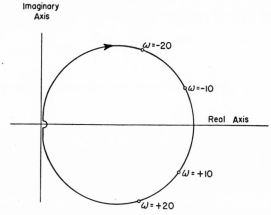

Fig. 5.40-2.   Frequency response plot of $F(s) = 1/(1 + 0.04s)$.

way (add, subtract, multiply, divide), and to the resulting combination (5.40-2) still applies. If (5.40-3) and (5.40-7) are added, the result is

$$F(s) = \frac{1}{(1 + 0.04s)} + \frac{1}{(1 - 0.04s)} \qquad (5.40\text{-}10)$$

$$= \frac{2}{(1 + 0.04s)(1 - 0.04s)} \qquad (5.40\text{-}11)$$

It can be shown that for this result,

$$N = 1 \qquad (5.40\text{-}12)$$

$$P = 1 \qquad (5.40\text{-}13)$$

$$Z = 0 \qquad (5.40\text{-}14)$$

Similarly, the closed path in the s-plane need not be that shown in Fig. 5.30-2. If another path is used, (5.40-2) applies, but with the modification that P and Z must be points inside the closed path.

5.50 The Nyquist criterion

The Nyquist criterion is an application of (5.40-2). It eliminates the technicality of whether or not a locus encircles the origin by using the open-loop transfer function F_o. Our definition of stability is that, after clearing fractions, there must not be any roots with positive real parts of

$$1 + F_o = 0 \qquad (5.50\text{-}1)$$

This is equivalent to saying that if

$$F(s) = 1 + F_o \qquad (5.50\text{-}2)$$

the necessary and sufficient criterion for stability is that Z of (5.50-2) must equal zero, or

$$N = P \qquad (5.50\text{-}3)$$

Since P for $1 + F_o$ is the same as P for F_o, the latter is generally referred to. Similarly, since N is the number of encirclements of the origin of $1 + F_o$, it is the same as the number of encirclements of the -1 point of F_o.

The Nyquist criterion stated in summary form is as follows:

1. Given the open-loop transfer function F_o as a function of s.

2. Let $s = j\omega$, and plot F_o for values of ω from $-\infty$ to 0 to $+\infty$. (In practice, as the negative frequencies are the mirror images of the positive frequencies, they are generally omitted.)

3. Then N will always equal $P - Z$, but if the system is stable, Z must equal zero, and N must equal P, where N is the number of encirclements of the -1 point of the $F_o(j\omega)$ plot, (N is positive when going counterclockwise for increasing frequencies), P is the number of denominator roots of $F_o(s)$ with positive real parts, Z is the number of roots of $1 + F_o(s) = 0$ with positive real parts.

4. There may be some doubt about how the locus is closed between $\omega = 0^+$ and $\omega = 0^-$ when the amplitude is infinite. The locus should be closed then by circling clockwise from $\omega = 0^-$ to $\omega = 0^+$ $180n°$, where n is the order of s, which can be factored out of the denominator. This is illustrated by the many examples in

Chapter 6, and can be demonstrated by substituting values along the contour of Fig. 5.30-2 in the particular $F_o(s)$ under consideration.

The value of P may be found by factoring the denominator of F_o, or Routh's criterion, discussed in Section 6.30, may be used.

Chapter 6 discusses in detail most of the general shapes that a stable open-loop transfer function can have. Figures 5.10-1 and

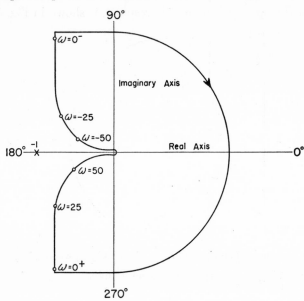

Fig. 5.50-1. Polar plot of $F_o = 4/s(1 + 0.04s)$, where $s = j\omega$.

5.10-2 will be used as basic examples of the criterion. The open-loop expression for Fig. 5.10-1 is

$$\frac{\theta_o}{\theta_e} = \frac{4}{s(1 + 0.04s)} \qquad (5.50\text{-}4)$$

Inspection of (5.50-4) shows that

$$P = 0 \qquad (5.50\text{-}5)$$

A plot of the open-loop frequency response is shown in Fig. 5.50-1. From this it is seen that, using -1 as the encirclement point,

$$N = 0 \qquad (5.50\text{-}6)$$

Thus $\qquad\qquad\qquad\qquad N = P \qquad\qquad\qquad\qquad (5.50\text{-}7)$

and the system is stable.

The open-loop expression for Fig. 5.10-2 is

$$\frac{\theta_o}{\theta_e} = \frac{100}{s(15 - s)} \qquad (5.50\text{-}8)$$

Inspection of (5.50-8) shows that

$$P = 1 \qquad (5.50\text{-}9)$$

A plot of the open-loop frequency response is shown in Fig. 5.50-2,

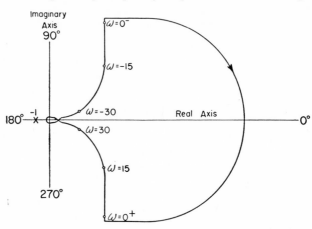

FIG. 5.50-2.   Polar plot of $F_o = 100/s(15 - s)$, where $s = j\omega$.

and again using -1 as the encirclement point,

$$N = 0 \qquad (5.50\text{-}10)$$

Since N does not equal P, this system is unstable. Further, since

$$Z = P - N = 1 \qquad (5.50\text{-}11)$$

the system has one unstable root. The charts in Figs. 2.26-1, 2.26-2, and 2.26-3 are extremely useful as an aid in plotting these functions. The reader, as an exercise, should determine the path of the locus around the origin for the function shown in Fig. 5.50-2. This will show the advantage of using the -1 point rather than the origin in determining stability.

From this brief discussion, it is evident that the Nyquist criterion provides a method of determining system stability which is useful. In later chapters it will be shown that:

1. The nearness of the locus to the -1 point is a criterion of how oscillatory a system is.

2. The axis at which the $\omega = 0^+$ point goes out reveals the system type, and is an indication of the type of signals the system will accurately handle.

3. The frequencies around unity amplitude are an indication of the system speed of response.

4. Unstable open-loop systems such as Fig. 5.10-2 can be stabilized.

5.60 Application of the Nyquist criterion to related problems

A modification of the Nyquist criterion is very useful in determining the effect of a variable coefficient upon equation roots. The method is outlined below. Any polynomial in s, such as

$$a_0 + a_1 s + a_2 s^2 + a_3 s^3 + \ldots = 0 \qquad (5.60\text{-}1)$$

can be written in the form

$$b_0 + b_1 s + b_2 s^2 + b_3 s^3 + \ldots + c_0 + c_1 s + c_2 s^2 + c_3 s^3 + \ldots = 0$$
$$(5.60\text{-}2)$$

where b_n and c_n may have any value as long as

$$b_0 + c_0 = a_0$$
$$b_1 + c_1 = a_1, \quad \text{etc.}$$

This can now be rewritten as

$$1 + \frac{b_0 + b_1 s + b_2 s^2 + \ldots}{c_0 + c_1 s + c_2 s^2 + \ldots} = 0 \qquad (5.60\text{-}3)$$

Thus (5.60-3) is in the form of $1 + F_o = 0$, where

$$F_o = \frac{b_0 + b_1 s + b_2 s^2 + \ldots}{c_0 + c_1 s + c_2 s^2 + \ldots} \qquad (5.60\text{-}4)$$

and discussions about F_o are equally applicable to (5.60-4).

An application of (5.60-4) will now be discussed. If it were desired to know the effect of X in

$$1 + 1.5s + Xs^2 + 2s^3 = 0 \qquad (5.60\text{-}5)$$

on the nature of the equation roots, (5.60-4) could be applied by expressing (5.60-5) as

$$F_o = \frac{Xs^2}{1 + 1.5s + 2s^3} \qquad (5.60\text{-}6)$$

$$= \frac{Xs^2}{(1 + 2s)(1 - 0.5s + s^2)} \qquad (5.60\text{-}7)$$

Applying the normal Nyquist technique to (5.60-7), we obtain

$$P = 2 \tag{5.60-8}$$

and the equation to be plotted,

$$F_o(j\omega) = \frac{-X\omega^2}{(1 + 2j\omega)(1 - 0.5j\omega - \omega^2)} \tag{5.60-9}$$

This is plotted in Fig. 5.60-1. It may be seen that if X is a positive small number or any negative number, the -1 point lies outside the

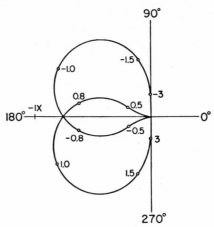

Fig. 5.60-1.   Polar plot of $F_o = \dfrac{-\omega^2}{(1 + 2j\omega)(1 - 0.5j\omega - \omega^2)}$.

contour, and hence

$$N = 0 \tag{5.60-10}$$

so that (5.60-5) has two roots with positive real parts. If X is a positive number greater than 1.33, the -1 point is inside the contour, and

$$N = +2 \tag{5.60-11}$$

so that (5.60-5) has no roots with positive real parts.

   Similarly, the same technique could be applied to an equation such as

$$5 + (4 + 3X)s + 2Xs^2 + s^3 = 0 \tag{5.60-12}$$

by expressing it in the form

$$F_o = \frac{X(3s + 2s^2)}{5 + 4s + s^3} \tag{5.60-13}$$

PROBLEMS

5-1. What is the characteristic equation of each system given in Problem 4-3? Do any of these characteristic equations have any roots with positive real parts?

5-2. Why does a root of the characteristic equation with a positive real part denote instability?

5-3. Plot the location of the following roots on the s-plane.

$$s = -2, 4, -1 + j3, -1 - j3, 7, -6, 3 + j6, 3 - j6.$$

Which of these roots have positive real parts?

5-4. Determine by both the N, P, and Z criterion and by plotting the transfer function locus which of the following functions encircle the *origin* when the values shown in Fig. 5.30-2 are substituted for s.

(a) $F(s) = \dfrac{1}{1 + 2s + s^2}$

(b) $F(s) = \dfrac{10}{s(1 + 6s)}$

(c) $F(s) = \dfrac{3}{-6.25 + 2.75s^2 + s^3}$

(d) $F(s) = \dfrac{1}{s^3 + 0.5s^2 + 0.5s + 1}$

(e) $F(s) = \dfrac{1 - s}{s(1 - 0.1s)(1 + 0.5s)}$

5-5. Plot the transfer function locus for the following open-loop functions. Determine N, P, and Z (where they have the meaning used in Section 5.50) for each function, and state whether the system represented by each function is stable or not.

(a) $F_o = \dfrac{50}{s(1 + 0.01s)}$

(b) $F_o = \dfrac{10}{s(1 + 0.5s)(1 + 0.8s)}$

(c) $F_o = \dfrac{2}{s^2(1 + 0.5s)(1 + 0.8s)}$

(d) $F_o = \dfrac{0.2(1 + 5s)}{s^2(1 + 0.5s)(1 + 0.8s)}$

(e) $F_o = \dfrac{1 + 2s}{-s(1 + 0.25s)}$

5-6. For what values of X is the relation in eq. (5.60-13) stable?

5-7. Determine the nature of the locus around the origin for the function in Fig. 5.50-2.

CHAPTER 6

APPLICATION OF THE NYQUIST CRITERION TO TYPICAL OPEN-LOOP TRANSFER FUNCTIONS

6.00 Introduction

The main results in the preceding chapter which must be fully understood are that the relation

$$N = P - Z \qquad (6.00\text{-}1)$$

is always true, and that for stability the open-loop polar plot must satisfy the relation

$$N = P \qquad (6.00\text{-}2)$$

where N, P, and Z are as defined in Section 5.50. These principles form the basis for control system analysis by frequency response techniques.

6.10 Stable polar plots

Open-loop equations may have the following factors which govern their general polar plot shape.

1. Order of s which may be factored out of the equation.
2. Number of denominator roots with positive real parts.

By expressing the open-loop equation in the K_o, G_o, and s form, general sketches of the frequency response transfer function plots may be developed. Figures 6.10-1 through 6.10-4 show examples of this. These cover practically every case which is encountered in practice. In each the sketch shows the general shape and not the specific shape of the example which an equation of that form must have for the control system it represents to be stable. Negative frequency points and the manner in which the loci close at $\omega = 0$ are not shown, so that the sketches may be kept simple.

The complete polar plot sketches for the examples in Figs. 6.10-1f, 6.10-2d, and 6.10-3e are given in Fig. 6.10-5. Closure between $\omega = 0^+$ and $\omega = 0^-$ for these cases follows the rule given in Section 5.50, namely, the locus is closed by circling clockwise from $\omega = 0^-$ to $\omega = 0^+$ $180n°$, where n is the order of s which can be factored out of the denominator. The example in Fig. 6.10-5a has s to the third order factored out of the denominator. Hence the locus traverses $540°$ clockwise from $\omega = 0^-$ to $\omega = 0^+$. The reader should apply this procedure to each example given in this section to satisfy himself that in each case $P = N$.

One cannot tell by inspection of the open-loop polar plot that a system is stable. He must know in addition the value of P in the open-loop equation. As an example, consider

$$F_0 = \frac{2}{s(1 + 0.3s)(1 + 0.01s)} \qquad (6.10\text{-}1)$$

and

$$F_0 = \frac{2}{s(1 + 0.3s)(1 + 0.01s)(1 - 0.01s)} \qquad (6.10\text{-}2)$$

When $j\omega$ is substituted for s in these and the polar plots are obtained, it will be found that both polar plots are almost identical, yet one system is stable and one is not. The reason is that P is zero in (6.10-1) and one in (6.10-2). Hence the system denoted by (6.10-2) is unstable. In order for this system to be stabilized, it must be manipulated and altered so that its polar plot looks like that in Fig. 6.10-2d. This could be accomplished by reversing the polarity of the system (see Section 4.53) and adding elements in the system which would produce numerator terms sufficient to "lead" the polar plot points around the -1 point.

The number of encirclements of the -1 point may be determined by the following method.

1. Sketch the complete locus for $F_0(j\omega)$.
2. Draw a radial line from the -1 point.
3. Wherever the radial line is cut by the $F_0(j\omega)$ locus, place an arrowhead denoting the direction of the locus for increasing frequencies.
4. Then N is equal to the number of counterclockwise directed arrowheads minus the number of clockwise directed arrowheads.

	F_o	Example of F_o	Stable polar plot shape*
a	$s^2 K_o G_o$	$\dfrac{10s^2}{(1+s)(1+2s)(1+3s)}$	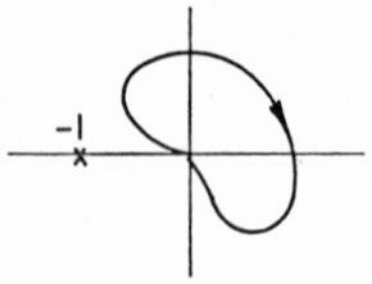
b	$s K_o G_o$	$\dfrac{5s}{(1+s)^2(1+2s)}$	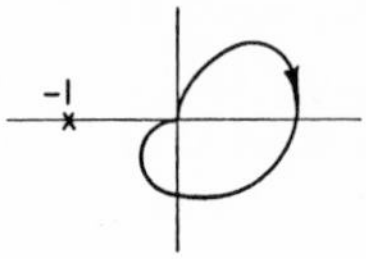
c	$K_o G_o$	$\dfrac{3}{(1+s+s^2)(1+2s)}$	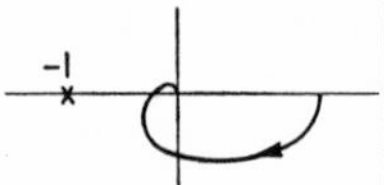
d	$\dfrac{K_o G_o}{s}$	$\dfrac{5}{s(1+0.1s)(1+0.01s)}$	
e	$\dfrac{K_o G_o}{s^2}$	$\dfrac{0.2(1+4s)}{s^2(1+0.4s)}$	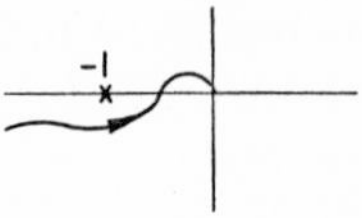
f	$\dfrac{K_o G_o}{s^3}$	$\dfrac{0.14(1+5s+9s^2)}{s^3(1+0.3s)}$	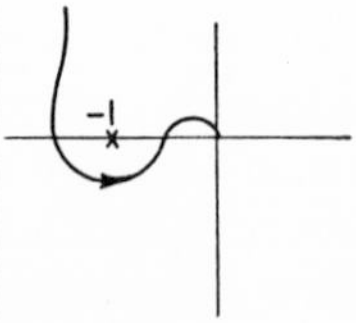

* For positive ω values, obtained by letting $s = j\omega$.

FIG. 6.10-1. Stable polar plot shapes for various open-loop equations having $P = 0$. Arrowheads indicate direction of increasing frequency.

	F_0	Example of F_0	Stable polar plot shape*
a	$s^2 K_0 G_0$	$\dfrac{0.1s^2}{(1 - 0.1s)(1 + 0.4s)}$	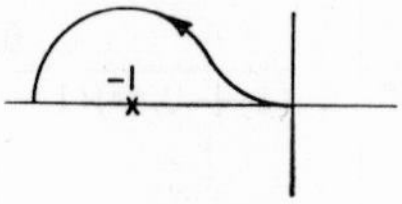
b	$s K_0 G_0$	$\dfrac{s}{1 - 0.5s}$	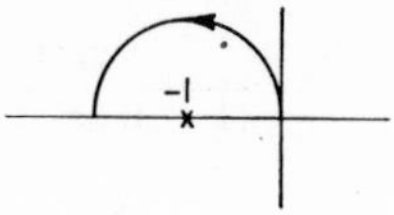
c	$K_0 G_0$	$\dfrac{-1.25}{(1 - 0.5s)(1 + 0.01s)}$	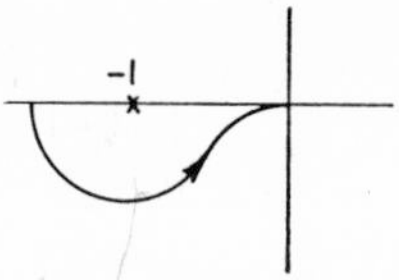
d	$\dfrac{K_0 G_0}{s}$	$\dfrac{-0.5(1 + 5s)}{s(1 - s)(1 + 0.01s)}$	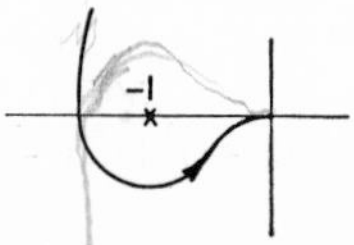
e	$\dfrac{K_0 G_0}{s^2}$	$\dfrac{-0.5(1 + 5s + 11s^2)}{s^2(1 + 4s)(1 - 0.267s)}$	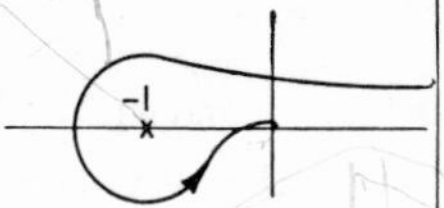
f	$\dfrac{K_0 G_0}{s^3}$	$\dfrac{-2(1 + 5s + 9s^2 + 7.5s^3)}{s^3(1 - 4s)(1 + 0.01s)}$	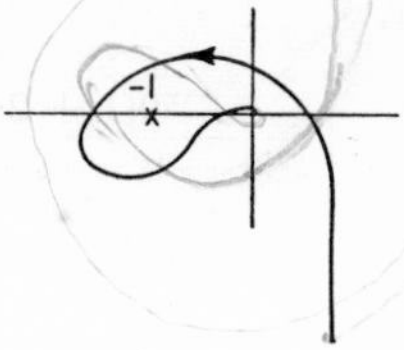

* For positive ω values, obtained by letting $s = j\omega$.

Fig. 6.10-2.   Stable polar plot shapes for various open-loop equations having $P = 1$. Arrowheads indicate direction of increasing frequency.

	F_o	Example of F_o	Stable polar plot shape*
a	$s^2 K_o G_o$	$\dfrac{0.5s^2}{(1 + 0.4s)(1 - 0.1s)(1 - 0.05s)}$	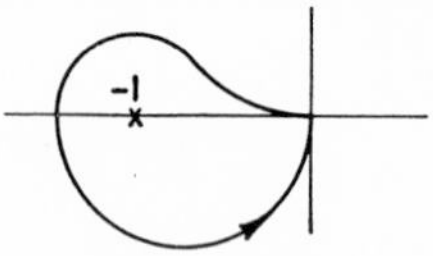
b	$s K_o G_o$	$\dfrac{2s(1 + 0.01s)}{(1 - 0.5s)(1 - s)(1 + 0.1s)}$	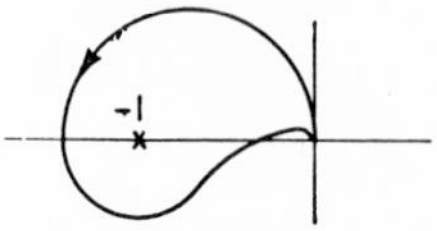
c	$K_o G_o$	$\dfrac{10(1 + s + s^2)}{(1 + 0.5s)(1 - 0.05s)(1 - 0.2s)}$	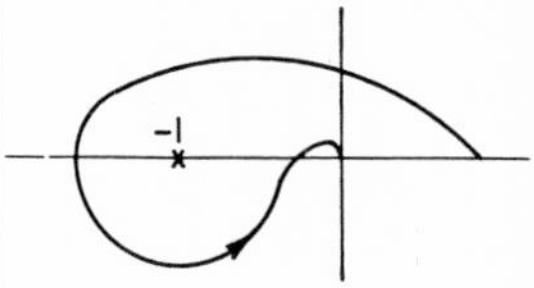
d	$\dfrac{K_o G_o}{s}$	$\dfrac{5000(1 + 0.025s)^2}{s(1 - 0.1s)(1 - 0.2s)(1 + 0.0025s)}$	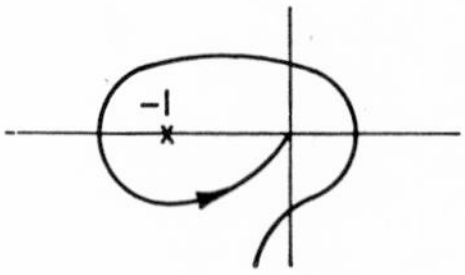
e	$\dfrac{K_o G_o}{s^2}$	$\dfrac{2500(1 + 2s)(1 + 0.025s)^2}{s^2(1 - 0.1s)(1 - 0.2s)(1 + 0.0025s)}$	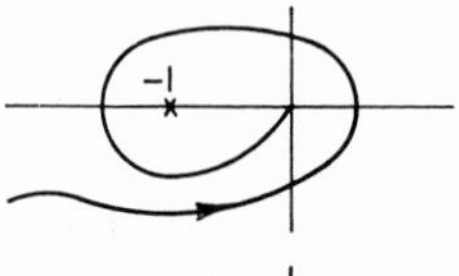
f	$\dfrac{K_o G_o}{s^3}$	$\dfrac{1250(1 + 2s)^2(1 + 0.025s)^2}{s^3(1 - 0.1s)(1 - 0.2s)(1 + 0.0025s)}$	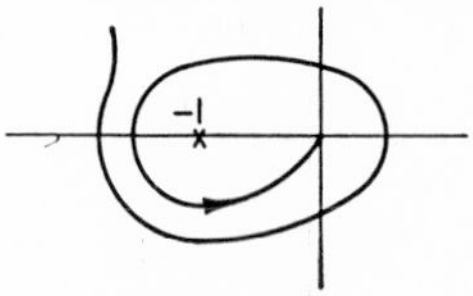

* For positive ω values, obtained by letting $s = j\omega$.

Fig. 6.10-3. Stable polar plot shapes for various open-loop equations having $P = 2$. Arrowheads indicate direction of increasing frequency.

	F_o	Example of F_o	Stable polar plot shape*
a	$s^2 K_o G_o$	$$\frac{20s^2(1 + 0.1s + 0.01s^2)}{(1 + 2s)(1 - 0.1s)(1 - 0.2s)(1 - 0.3s)}$$	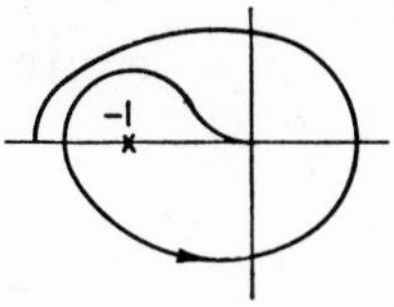
b	$s K_o G_o$	$$\frac{10s(1 + 0.1s + 0.01s^2)}{(1 - 0.1s)(1 - 0.2s)(1 - 0.3s)}$$	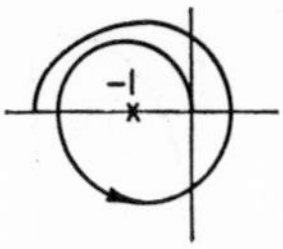
c	$K_o G_o$	$$\frac{-20(1 + 0.03s)^2(1 + 0.05s)}{(1 - 0.1s)(1 - 0.2s)(1 - 0.3s)(1 + 0.01s)}$$	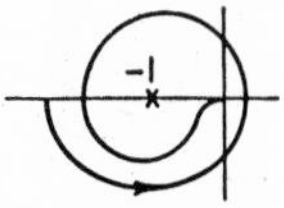
d	$\dfrac{K_o G_o}{s}$	$$\frac{-10(1 + 0.03s)^2(1 + 0.05s)(1 + 5s)}{s(1 - 0.1s)(1 - 0.2s)(1 - 0.3s)(1 + 0.01s)}$$	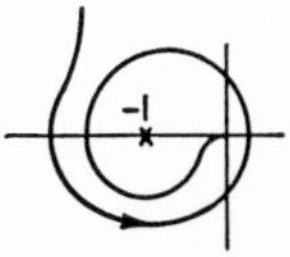
e	$\dfrac{K_o G_o}{s^2}$	$$\frac{-5(1 + 0.03s)^2(1 + 5s)^2(1 + 0.05s)}{s^2(1 - 0.1s)(1 - 0.2s)(1 - 0.3s)(1 + 0.01s)}$$	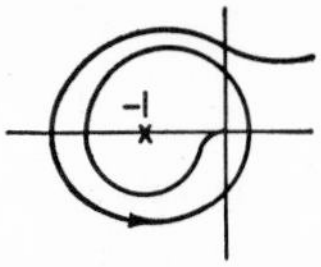
f	$\dfrac{K_o G_o}{s^3}$	$$\frac{-5(1 + 0.03s)^2(1 + 5s)^3(1 + 0.05s)}{s^3(1 - 0.1s)(1 - 0.2s)(1 - 0.3s)(1 + 0.01s)}$$	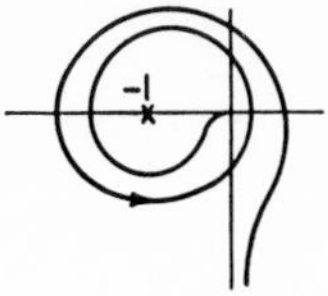

* For positive ω values, obtained by letting $s = j\omega$.

FIG. 6.10-4. Stable polar plot shapes for various open-loop equations having $P = 3$. Arrowheads indicate direction of increasing frequency.

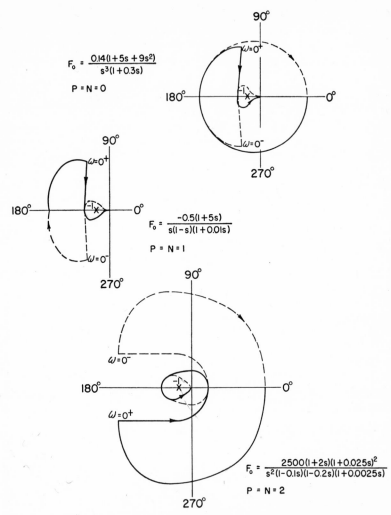

FIG. 6.10-5. Complete polar plots of stable open-loop functions (obtained by letting $s = j\omega$.) Arrowheads indicate increasing frequency.

Figure 6.10-6 is an example of this method. Two radial lines are shown. For line A there is one arrowhead counterclockwise, and therefore $N = 1$. Line B has two arrowheads counterclockwise and one clockwise, and again $N = 1$.

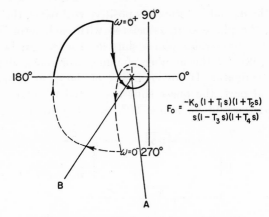

$$F_0 = \frac{-K_0\,(1 + T_1 s)(1 + T_2 s)}{s(1 - T_3 s)(1 + T_4 s)}$$

FIG. 6.10-6.   Method of determining N.

6.20 Nonminimum-phase functions

When $F(s)$ has one or more roots with positive real parts in either the numerator or denominator of a function, the function is called a nonminimum-phase function. Typical examples are all those shown in Figs. 6.10-2, 6.10-3, and 6.10-4. In addition, the following is a nonminimum-phase function.

$$F(s) = \frac{(1 + 2s)(1 - s)}{(1 + 3s)(1 + s)(1 + 0.5s)} \qquad (6.20\text{-}1)$$

This differs from the others in that the numerator, rather than the denominator, has a positive root. As the stability criterion is not affected by positive roots in the numerator of the open-loop function, less attention is given to these cases.

The term "nonminimum-phase" arises from consideration of the phase shift associated with a function of s when $j\omega$ is substituted for s. If both the numerator and denominator of an arbitrary function are factored, then

$$F(s) = K \frac{(1 + a_1 s)(1 + a_2 s)}{(1 + b_1 s)(1 + b_2 s)} \qquad (6.20\text{-}2)$$

Letting $s = j\omega$, eq. (6.20-2) becomes

$$F(j\omega) = \frac{K(1 + a_1j\omega)(1 + a_2j\omega)}{(1 + b_1j\omega)(1 + b_2j\omega)} \qquad (6.20\text{-}3)$$

If each of the a_n and b_n terms has positive real parts, then as ω goes to infinity, the phase shift associated with each term is *plus* 90°. Therefore the numerator phase shift at $\omega = \infty$ can be found by multiplying 90° by the number of numerator roots, and similarly for the denominator. However, if any of the a_n or b_n terms had a negative real part, the phase shift associated with that term as ω became large would be *minus* 90°, and the total numerator or

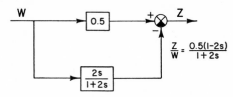

Fig. 6.20-1.   One method of obtaining a numerator nonminimum-phase function.

denominator phase shift at $\omega = \infty$ could no longer be found by multiplying the order of s by 90°.

Numerator nonminimum-phase functions may be obtained by operating on a function and adding the results in the desired polarity, as shown in Fig. 6.20-1. Denominator nonminimum-phase functions may be obtained by operating a servo loop so that it is unstable. In some cases this is desirable for an inner loop, with over-all system stability being maintained by an outer loop. An example is given in Section 6.40. In general, however, nonminimum-phase functions do not occur in most control systems.

6.30 Routh's criterion[43]

A method developed in 1877 by E. J. Routh is very useful in determining whether a function has roots with positive real parts. It is ideally suited to determining the value of P for open-loop equations, and it may also be applied to the system characteristic equation. When used for the latter, it provides a quick check on system stability; but as it lacks the clarity of the Nyquist method for system optimizing purposes, it is not widely used. For open-loop purposes, where only the exact value of P is desired, it is very valuable.

Let the equation, from which all zero roots ($s = 0$ factors) have been removed, be

$$a_0s^n + a_1s^{n-1} + a_2s^{n-2} + \ldots + a_{n-2}s^2 + a_{n-1}s^{n-1} + a_n = 0$$

$$(6.30\text{-}1)$$

where a_0 and n are positive, and all the a's are real. It should be noted that if any a's are zero or negative, the equation definitely has roots that are either purely imaginary or have positive real parts. If all the a's are positive, this may still be true, but not necessarily so.   Arrange the coefficients in an array of the following form.

$$
\begin{array}{cccc}
a_0 & a_2 & a_4 & a_6 \quad \cdots \\
a_1 & a_3 & a_5 & a_7 \quad \cdots \\
b_1 & b_2 & b_3 & \cdots \\
c_1 & c_2 & c_3 & \cdots \\
d_1 & d_2 & \cdots \\
e_1 & e_2 & \cdots \\
f_1 & \cdots \\
g_1 & \cdots
\end{array}
$$

where

$$b_1 = a_2 - \frac{a_0a_3}{a_1}, \quad b_2 = a_4 - \frac{a_0a_5}{a_1}, \quad b_3 = a_6 - \frac{a_0a_7}{a_1}, \quad \text{etc.}$$

$$c_1 = a_3 - \frac{a_1b_2}{b_1}, \quad c_2 = a_5 - \frac{a_1b_3}{b_1}, \quad c_3 = a_7 - \frac{a_1b_4}{b_1}, \quad \text{etc.}$$

$$d_1 = b_2 - \frac{b_1c_2}{c_1}, \quad d_2 = b_3 - \frac{b_1c_3}{c_1}, \quad d_3 = b_4 - \frac{b_1c_4}{c_1}, \quad \text{etc.}$$

$$e_1 = c_2 - \frac{c_1d_2}{d_1}, \quad e_2 = c_3 - \frac{c_1d_3}{d_1}, \quad \text{etc.}$$

The process is continued in each row and column until only zeros are obtained for additional coefficients. The number of changes in sign in the left-hand column is the number of roots with positive real parts. Any row may be multiplied by a positive constant without affecting the criterion.

As an example of Routh's criterion, let us start with an equation of known roots and show that the method gives the number of roots with positive real parts. Let the equation be

$$(s + 1)(s - 2)(s - 3) = s^3 - 4s^2 - 5s + 6 = 0 \quad (6.30\text{-}2)$$

From the original equation there are two roots with positive real parts, and likewise from the negative coefficients in the expanded equation, we know that there are roots with positive real parts. The coefficients array for (6.30-2) is

$$\begin{array}{cc} 1 & -5 \\ -4 & 6 \\ -3.5 & \\ 6 & \end{array}$$

Since there are two sign changes in the left column, by Routh's criterion there are two roots with positive real parts.

As a second example, consider

$$(s^2 - 0.5s + 1)(s + 1) = s^3 + 0.5s^2 + 0.5s + 1 = 0 \quad (6.30\text{-}3)$$

From the factored equation it is evident that there are two complex roots with positive real parts; but as all the coefficients in the expanded form are positive, it is not evident from a visual inspection that such roots exist. The coefficient array is

$$\begin{array}{cc} 1 & 0.5 \\ 0.5 & 1 \\ -1.5 & \\ 1 & \end{array}$$

Since there are two sign changes in the left column, there are two roots with positive real parts.

Occasionally it may be found that (1) the first coefficient in one row is zero, while the other coefficients are not zero, or (2) all the coefficients in a row are zero. When the first occurs, multiply the original equation by $(s + A)$, where A is an arbitrary positive real number which may have almost any value, and apply Routh's criterion to the new equation. When the second occurs, it indicates that there are factors in the original equation such as $(s + B)$ and $(s - B)$. The roots are of equal magnitude but with real parts of opposite polarities. The criterion may be applied to these cases by substituting for the zero row, the coefficients obtained by differentiating an assumed equation based on the row preceding the one with all zero coefficients. The highest order of s in the assumed equation is the order of the original equation plus one, less one for each satisfactory row. Lower order s terms in the assumed equation are s^{n-2}, s^{n-4}, s^{n-6}, etc., where n is the order of the assumed equation. The coefficients of the s terms are the coefficients of the row preceding the zero row.

An example will illustrate this. Let the equation be

$$(s + 2)(s - 2)(s^2 + 1)(s^2 + s + 1)$$
$$= s^6 + s^5 - 2s^4 - 3s^3 - 7s^2 - 4s - 4 = 0 \quad (6.30\text{-}4)$$

The Routh criterion array is

$$
\begin{array}{rrrr}
1 & -2 & -7 & -4 \\
1 & -3 & -4 & \\
1 & -3 & -4 & \\
0 & 0 & &
\end{array}
$$

Since the fourth row is zero, the assumed equation based on the third row is

$$s^4 - 3s^2 - 4 = 0 \qquad (6.30\text{-}5)$$

and the derivative with respect to s is

$$4s^3 - 6s = 0 \qquad (6.30\text{-}6)$$

These coefficients now form the fourth-row terms, and the completed array is

$$
\begin{array}{rrrr}
1 & -2 & -7 & -4 \\
1 & -3 & -4 & \\
1 & -3 & -4 & \\
4 & -6 & & \\
-1.5 & -4 & & \\
-16.7 & & & \\
-4 & & &
\end{array}
$$

Since there is one change of sign, one root with a positive real part is indicated, and that is the correct answer, as inspection of (6.30-4) shows.

Sometimes the zero row does not show up until near the end of the array, where there is only the first term left. Then, when multiplication of the original equation by a factor fails to remedy the trouble, differentiating as above will work.

6.40 Stable system with unstable inner loop

It is possible for a system to have an unstable inner loop and still be stable. This is logical since the only effect of an unstable inner loop is to introduce denominator roots with positive real parts in the over-all system open-loop equation, and it has been shown that a system may have any number of these roots in its open-loop

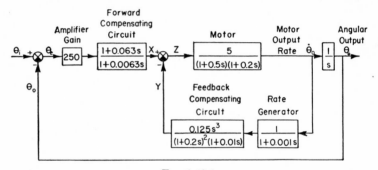

Fig. 6.40-1.

function and still be stable. Although systems are not generally of this type, there are some advantages, the principal one being that a high open-loop gain may be used, which enables better response performance.

An example is shown in Fig. 6.40-1. A rate generator is attached to the motor shaft, feeding a signal proportional to the output rate to a feedback compensating circuit whose output Y is combined with the forward signal X. The over-all open-loop polar plot with and without the inner loop feedback is shown in Fig. 6.40-2, the scale being distorted to show the complete loci shapes. Without the feedback the system gain is so high that the system is unstable. The polar points for both loci are the same at the very high and very low frequencies. In the intermediate frequencies the unstable inner loop shifts the open-loop locus, so that it has the form required by Fig. 6.10-3d.

The inner loop is Y/Z. Its transfer function locus is shown in Fig. 6.40-3. Since the encirclements for increasing frequencies are

clockwise, N is negative and

$$N = -2 \qquad (6.40\text{-}1)$$

The effect of the inner loop may be found by letting F_1 be the open-loop transfer function when there is no inner-loop feedback. Then

$$F_1 = \frac{1250(1 + 0.063s)}{s(1 + 0.5s)(1 + 0.2s)(1 + 0.0063s)} \qquad (6.40\text{-}2)$$

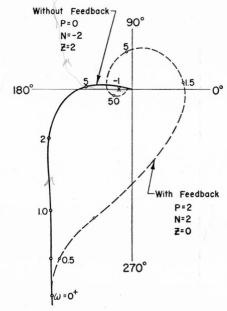

FIG. 6.40-2. θ_o/θ_e open-loop polar plot for Fig. 6.40-1. Not drawn to scale.

The inner-loop transfer function is

$$\frac{Y}{Z} = F_{o_1} = \frac{0.625s^3}{(1 + 0.5s)(1 + 0.2s)^3(1 + 0.01s)(1 + 0.001s)} \qquad (6.40\text{-}3)$$

Combining (6.40-2) and (6.40-3) gives the open-loop transfer function with feedback as

$$\frac{\theta_o}{\theta_e} = F_o = \frac{F_1}{1 + F_{o_1}} \qquad (6.40\text{-}4)$$

The frequency locus points for (6.40-4) may be determined graphically. For instance, on an accurate plot $1 + F_{o_1}$ at $\omega = 1.5$ is

$0.5\angle-174°$, so that F_1 is shifted 174° counterclockwise. Similarly, at $\omega = 5$, $1 + F_{o_1}$ is $11\angle-301°$, and F_1 is shifted 301° counterclockwise, etc.

With the unstable inner loop the over-all system has a frequency band pass of about 50 radians per second. Without the inner loop the system operation would be satisfactory if the amplifier gain were

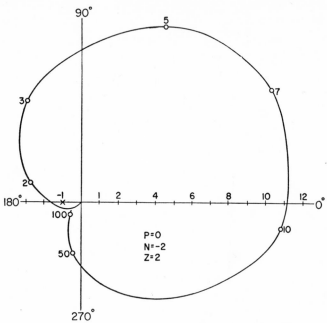

FIG. 6.40-3.   Transfer locus of unstable inner-loop Y/Z.

reduced from 250 to about 0.5, but the frequency band pass would then be about 1.5 radians per second.

The unstable loop appreciably improves the system performance. However, the performance also could have been improved without the inner-loop gain being so high that it made the inner loop unstable. Likewise, the inner-loop gain could have been so high that the system was completely unstable. This is illustrated by Figs. 6.40-4 and 6.40-5, which show satisfactory and unsatisfactory loci that F_{o_1} may have. In summary it may be stated that it is generally permissible for the inner-loop transfer function F_{o_1} locus to encircle the -1 point in the low-frequency range, but not in the high-frequency

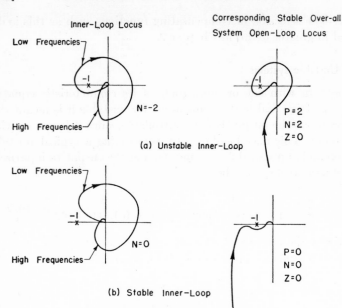

FIG. 6.40-4.   Satisfactory inner-loop loci.

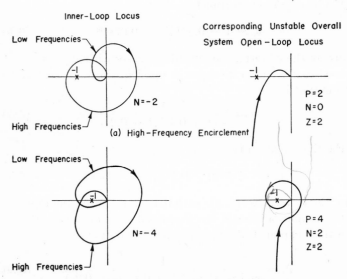

FIG. 6.40-5.   Unsatisfactory inner-loop loci.

range. The selection of compensating functions such as this is discussed in greater detail in Chapter 9.

6.50 Unstable systems

Any system with one or more roots of its characteristic equation having positive real parts is unstable. By unstable it is meant that for *any* input the output is not controllable, since it increases without bound. This may be shown by considering a typical unstable relation and applying different inputs. Let the output-to-input relation of a control system be

$$\frac{\theta_o}{\theta_i} = \frac{1}{1 - 0.1s - 0.02s^2} = \frac{1}{(1 + 0.1s)(1 - 0.2s)} \quad (6.50\text{-}1)$$

Because of the root $s = 5$, this system is termed unstable.

If a step input is applied to (6.50-1), the Laplace transform of θ_o is

$$\theta_o = \frac{1}{s(1 + 0.1s)(1 - 0.2s)} \quad (6.50\text{-}2)$$

and the inverse Laplace transform is

$$\theta_o = 1 - 0.33\epsilon^{-10t} - 0.67\epsilon^{+5t} \quad (6.50\text{-}3)$$

Because of the ϵ^{5t} term, the output increases without bound.

Likewise, if a unit rate input is applied, the Laplace transform of the output is

$$\theta_o = \frac{1}{s^2(1 + 0.1s)(1 - 0.2s)} \quad (6.50\text{-}4)$$

and the time solution is

$$\theta_o = t + 0.10 - 0.133\epsilon^{5t} + 0.033\epsilon^{-10t} \quad (6.50\text{-}5)$$

Again, the ϵ^{5t} term keeps the output from following the input.

A third input of interest is a sinusoidal wave of any frequency ω_1. When this is applied, the transform of the output is

$$\theta_o = \frac{1}{\omega_1(1 + s^2/\omega_1^2)(1 + 0.1s)(1 - 0.2s)} \quad (6.50\text{-}6)$$

and the time solution is

$$\theta_o = \frac{0.01\omega_1}{0.3(1 + 0.01\omega_1{}^2)} \, \epsilon^{-10t} - \frac{0.04\omega_1}{0.3(1 + 0.04\omega_1{}^2)} \, \epsilon^{5t}$$
$$+ \frac{\sin(\omega_1 t + \psi)}{[(1 + 0.01\omega_1{}^2)(1 + 0.04\omega_1{}^2)]^{1/2}} \quad (6.50\text{-}7)$$

where $\psi = -\tan^{-1} 0.1\omega_1 + \tan^{-1} 0.2\omega_1$. Again, the ϵ^{5t} term keeps the output from following the input, regardless of the frequency applied.

In using frequency analysis techniques, a misconception too often arises; namely, that frequency analysis procedures indicate only a band of input frequences for which the output is unstable. This is not true, as the foregoing demonstrates. If a system is unstable, meaning that it has roots of the characteristic equation with positive real parts, any input will show the instability.

An interesting exercise which is left to the reader is to plot the output in the above three cases and compare it with the input. This will demonstrate the high degree of instability existing in this example.

6.60 Calculation of polar points

As was discussed in Chapter 5, a polar plot is obtained by substituting $j\omega$ for s in a function of s and calculating the amplitude and phase for different values of ω. Considerable time may be saved by performing the calculations in a systematic manner and by utilizing dimensionless charts such as Figs. 2.26-1, 2.26-2, and 2.26-3.

Thought should also be given to the selection of frequency points. Frequency points for 100 and for 101 radians per second usually have approximately the same values, but points for 1 and 2 radians per second, which also have a difference of just one, may be widely separated in amplitude and phase. It will be found that for most applications, if each successive point is $1\frac{1}{2}$ times the preceding frequency, an adequate spacing occurs. Often, too, if points repeat themselves by a factor of ten (such as 0.02, 0.2, 2, 20, etc.), many of the calculations are simpler. The adoption of standard plotting frequencies has many advantages, and a useful set of these is

$$1 \times 10^n, \ 1.5 \times 10^n, \ 2.0 \times 10^n, \ 3.0 \times 10^n, \ 5 \times 10^n, \text{ and } 7 \times 10^n,$$

where n depends on the particular problem.

As an example, consider the case in Fig. 6.10-1d, where

$$F_o = \frac{5}{s(1 + 0.1s)(1 + 0.01s)} \tag{6.60-1}$$

One method of calculating this is to consider F_o as composed of factors as follows.

$$F_o = 5 \times \frac{1}{j\omega} \times \frac{1}{1 + 0.1j\omega} \times \frac{1}{1 + 0.01j\omega} \tag{6.60-2}$$

$$= \frac{5A_1A_2}{\omega} \angle \phi_1 + \phi_2 - 90° \tag{6.60-3}$$

$$= A \angle \phi \tag{6.60-4}$$

where $j\omega$ has been substituted for s,

$$A_1 \angle \phi_1 = \frac{1}{1 + 0.1j\omega}$$

$$A_2 \angle \phi_2 = \frac{1}{1 + 0.01j\omega}$$

Values for $A_1 \angle \phi_1$ and $A_2 \angle \phi_2$ may be found using Fig. 2.26-1. Here $A_1 \angle \phi_1$ has a "corner frequency" (when $\phi = -45°$) of 10 radians per second, and $A_2 \angle \phi_2$ has a corner frequency of 100 radians per second. The polar points of interest are:

1. All those necessary to show the locus shape around the 180° axis.

2. A few low-frequency points to show the nature of the locus as $\omega \to 0$.

3. A few high-frequency points to indicate how rapidly the locus amplitude approaches zero.

Since the corner frequencies are 10 and 100 radians per second, the 180° crossover will occur at some frequency between these two. Therefore, in order to include all sections of interest on the polar plot, the frequency points which would probably be sufficient are 5, 7, 10, 15, 20, 30, 50, 70, 100, 150. These are tabulated in Table 6.60-1.

Usually a two cycle chart, such as Fig. 2.26-1, contains a sufficient number of the points of interest. If it does not, the points may be either accurately calculated or the approximations below, which are adequate for most applications, may be used. Approximations for $A\angle\phi = 1/(1 + ju)$ are

1. For u less than 0.1

$$A = 1 \quad \text{and} \quad \phi = -57u \text{ degrees}$$

2. For u greater than 10

$$A = 1/u \quad \text{and} \quad \phi = -90 + 57/u \text{ degrees}$$

In this example the corner frequencies were even 10^n multiples, so that the amplitude and phase values could be read rather easily from the chart. In practice, corner frequencies may have any value, making the chart more difficult to use. This may be overcome by marking off on a piece of paper or ruler a logarithmic scale the same as the u scale, and sliding it along the chart until the corner frequency on the piece of paper is under the unity point on the u scale. Points may be read directly then.

A polar plot of the example in this section shows that the system is stable, and also that the velocity constant could be much higher than 5 without affecting the stability. In the next chapter methods for the adjustment of systems will be discussed.

TABLE 6.60-1

CALCULATING FORM FOR $F_0(s) = \dfrac{5}{s(1 + 0.1s)(1 + 0.01s)}$

$$F_0(j\omega) = \frac{5\angle -90°}{\omega} \times \frac{1}{1 + 0.1j\omega} \times \frac{1}{1 + 0.01j\omega}$$

$$= \frac{5\angle -90°}{\omega} \times A_1\angle\phi_1 \times A_2\angle\phi_2 = A\angle\phi$$

where $A = (5A_1A_2)/\omega, \qquad \phi = \phi_1 + \phi_2 - 90°$

ω	A_1	ϕ_1	A_2	ϕ_2	A	ϕ
0	1.000	0°	1.000	0°	∞	−90°
5	0.894	−26.6	0.999	−2.9	0.893	−119.5
7	0.819	−35.0	0.998	−4.0	0.584	−129.0
10	0.707	−45.0	0.993	−5.7	0.351	−140.7
15	0.555	−56.3	0.989	−8.5	0.183	−154.8
20	0.447	−63.4	0.981	−11.3	0.110	−164.7
30	0.316	−71.6	0.958	−16.7	0.050	−178.3
50	0.196	−78.7	0.894	−26.6	0.018	−195.3
70	0.141	−81.9	0.819	−35.0	0.008	−206.9
100	0.099	−84.3	0.707	−45.0	0.003	−219.3
150	0.066	−86.2	0.555	−56.3	0.001	−232.5

6.70 Conditionally stable systems

In every physical system, if the system gain is increased sufficiently, the system becomes unstable (see Sect. 7.50). In addition, if the gain is reduced sufficiently in some systems, the system also will become unstable. Such systems are called "conditionally stable," and a typical open-loop polar plot (for a $P = 0$ Type 1 system) is shown in Fig. 6.70-1.

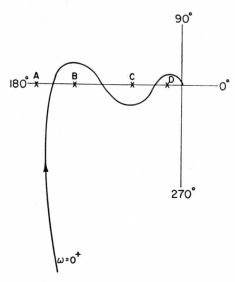

FIG. 6.70-1.   Open-loop polar plot for a conditionally stable system.

When this system is operated with the gain such that the -1 point is normally at C, the system is conditionally stable. Then either an increase in gain (making the -1 point around D) or a decrease in gain (making the -1 point around B) causes the system to be unstable. If the system were operated so that the -1 point was normally at A, it would not be a conditionally stable system, since a decrease in gain would not make it unstable.

When operated with either B or D as the -1 point, two encirclements of the -1 point exist. Since $P = 0$,

$$Z = 2 \qquad\qquad (6.70\text{-}1)$$

which indicates that the output would have two unstable roots in this condition.

The value of Z in an unstable system is very informative, for it indicates the nature of the instability. If $Z = 1$, the system has one unstable root, and its output will move in one direction only. If $Z = 2$, the system has two unstable roots, and its output is generally a divergent oscillation.

PROBLEMS

6-1. Sketch the complete locus (including negative frequency points and closure at $\omega = 0$) for the sketches shown in Figs. 6.10-1 through 6.10-4. Determine N, P, and Z for each case.

6-2. Calculate and plot the actual complete locus for each example in Figs. 6.10-1 through 6.10-4.

6-3. Determine the stable polar plot shapes for the case when $P = 4$ in the open-loop transfer function. Do the same six cases as those shown in Figs. 6.10-1 through 6.10-4.

6-4. Find the characteristic equation for each example in Figs. 6.10-1 through 6.10-4. Apply Routh's criterion to each characteristic equation to prove that each is stable.

6-5. Refer to the examples given in Figs. 6.10-1 through 6.10-4. Using the reasoning discussed in Section 6.60, state the frequency values which would probably be the most significant on the frequency-response locus for each example.

6-6. Which examples in Figs. 6.10-1 through 6.10-4 become unstable when the open-loop gain is sufficiently reduced?

6-7. Calculate and plot eq. (6.50-3). What is $\theta_e(t)$?

6-8. Calculate and plot eq. (6.50-5). What is $\theta_e(t)$?

6-9. Calculate and plot eq. (6.50-7) where $\omega_1 = 1$ radian per second. Repeat for $\omega_1 = 10$ radians per second.

CHAPTER 7

DESIGN CONSIDERATIONS

7.00 Introduction

The Nyquist criterion provides a very valuable tool in control system analysis. First, polar plots of the open-loop frequency response provide a method for determining system stability. Second, the polar plots indicate how an unstable system should be altered in order to achieve stability. Third, by correlating known transients with their open-loop frequency response plots, techniques may be developed so that the transient response may be predicted by inspection of the polar plot. This chapter introduces the correlation between the transient and frequency responses.

7.10 First-order systems

A first-order system is one characterized by the relation

$$\frac{\theta_o}{\theta_i} = \frac{1}{1 + Ts} \tag{7.10-1}$$

Although no physical system is this simple, a study of its transient and open-loop frequency responses provides a basis for a better understanding of complicated systems. If the input is a unit step, the output is

$$\theta_o = 1 - \epsilon^{-t/T} \tag{7.10-2}$$

As this transient has been discussed extensively in preceding sections, we may turn our attention to its open-loop frequency response characteristic.

The open-loop equation for (7.10-1) is

$$F_o(s) = \frac{\theta_o(s)}{\theta_e(s)} = \frac{1}{Ts} \tag{7.10-3}$$

or letting $s = j\omega$,

$$F_o(j\omega) = \frac{\theta_o(j\omega)}{\theta_e(j\omega)} = \frac{1}{Tj\omega} \tag{7.10-4}$$

Figure 7.10-1 shows the open-loop frequency response polar plot of this function. It should be noticed that the amplitude is unity at $\omega = 1/T$. Thus we have our first correlation; namely, the reciprocal of the frequency at unity amplitude is a measure of the system time constant. In higher order systems the actual time to reach 63% of the final value may be two or three times greater than the reciprocal of the unity crossover frequency. Thus this criterion is a measure, but not necessarily the exact value of the system time constant.

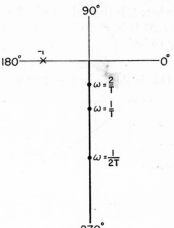

FIG. 7.10-1.   Open-loop polar plot for $\theta_o/\theta_e = 1/Tj\omega$.

7.20 Second-order systems

A second-order system is character-ized by the relation

$$\frac{\theta_o}{\theta_i} = \frac{1}{1 + as + bs^2} \qquad (7.20\text{-}1)$$

Usually it is desirable for second-order systems to be less than critically damped. That is, the denominator roots are complex, and (7.20-1) may be written

$$\frac{\theta_o}{\theta_i} = \frac{1}{1 + 2\zeta s/\omega_1 + s^2/\omega_1^2} \qquad (7.20\text{-}2)$$

The output of (7.20-2) for a step input is

$$\theta_o = 1 + \frac{1}{\sqrt{1 - \zeta^2}}\, \epsilon^{-\zeta\omega_1 t}\, \sin\,(\omega_1 \sqrt{1 - \zeta^2}\, t - \psi), \qquad (7.20\text{-}3)$$

where $\psi = \tan^{-1}\,[\sqrt{1 - \zeta^2}/(-\zeta)]$.

Transient response plots for various values of ζ were shown in Fig. 2.22-2. For small values of ζ, the system is highly oscillatory, and hence not satisfactory for control purposes. With large values of ζ, the system responds too slowly, and again is not properly adjusted.

Since each transient response has a unique frequency response, a correlation of the two will indicate methods of avoiding either oscillatory or slow responses. We can find the transient overshoot of

(7.20-3) by differentiating and setting $\dot{\theta}_o = 0$ to find the time θ_o is maximum. Laplace transform pair 00.001 gives this directly (see eq. 3.30-4) as

$$t_m = \frac{\pi}{\omega_1 \sqrt{1 - \zeta^2}} \tag{7.20-4}$$

where t_m is the time at which θ_o has its maximum value. Substituting (7.20-4) in (7.20-3) gives the maximum value of θ_o as a function of ζ to be

$$\theta_{o(\text{max})} = 1 + \epsilon^{-\zeta\pi/\sqrt{1-\zeta^2}} \tag{7.20-5}$$

This is shown in Fig. 7.20-1.

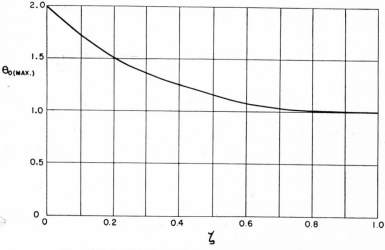

Fig. 7.20-1.   Maximum value of θ_o vs. ζ for (7.20-3).

We can also find the amplitude of θ_o for sinusoidal inputs. Figure 2.26-2 in Chapter 2 shows this for various values of ζ. We will now find the peak amplitude as a function of ζ. Letting $s = j\omega$, eq. (7.20-2) becomes

$$\frac{\theta_o}{\theta_i} = \frac{1}{1 - u^2 + 2j\zeta u} = M\angle\phi \tag{7.20-6}$$

where $u = \omega/\omega_1$.

$$M = \frac{1}{[(1 - u^2)^2 + 4\zeta^2 u^2]^{1/2}}$$

$$\phi = -\tan^{-1}\frac{2\zeta u}{1 - u^2}$$

The frequency u_p where M is a maximum occurs when $dM/du = 0$, and is

$$u_p = \sqrt{1 - 2\zeta^2} \qquad (7.20\text{-}7)$$

This indicates that the maximum closed-loop frequency response amplitude is greater than unity only when $\zeta < 0.707$. Substituting (7.20-7) into the expression for M gives the peak frequency response

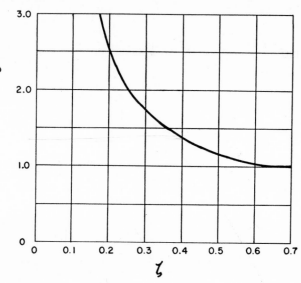

Fig. 7.20-2. M_p vs. ζ.

amplitude M_p as a function of ζ, shown in Fig. 7.20-2, to be

$$M_p = \frac{1}{2\zeta\sqrt{1 - \zeta^2}} \qquad (7.20\text{-}8)$$

This provides a means of correlating the peak $(\theta_o/\theta_i)(j\omega)$ frequency response amplitude and the transient overshoot. It was demonstrated in Section 4.40 that the transient response of a second-order equation will often approximate that of a more complex expression. As this is generally true, the frequency response characteristics of the second-order equation may be used as guides for more complex systems.

By definition, the minimum net system error occurs when the system is adjusted so that the time integral of $[\theta_e(t)]^2$ is a minimum.

For a second-order system this occurs when $\zeta = 0.5$, but for higher order systems no simple relation exists. However, for most systems if the transient overshoot is 20 to 30% for a step input, the system adjustment is approximately optimum. This corresponds to a ζ in a second-order system with a value between 0.36 and 0.50, and an M_p between 1.5 and 1.15.

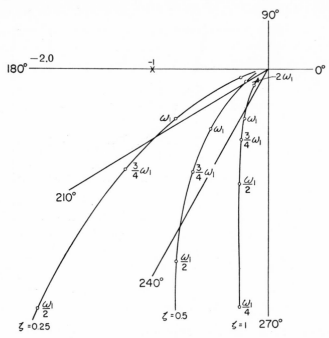

Fig. 7.20-3.   Polar plot of $\dfrac{\theta_o}{\theta_e} = \dfrac{1}{2\zeta j(\omega/\omega_1) - \omega^2/\omega_1{}^2}$.

The open-loop equation corresponding to (7.20-2) is

$$\frac{\theta_o}{\theta_e} = \frac{1}{2\zeta s/\omega_1 + s^2/\omega_1{}^2} \tag{7.20-9}$$

Polar plots, with $s = j\omega$, are shown in Fig. 7.20-3. As the value of ζ becomes smaller, the locus comes nearer the -1 point, and the system becomes more oscillatory. Again, the reciprocal of the open-loop frequency at unity amplitude is a measure (but not necessarily the time to reach 63%) of the system response time.

7.30 Constant magnitude and phase loci

The open- and closed-loop expressions are related by the equation

$$\frac{\theta_o}{\theta_i} = \frac{F_o}{1 + F_o} \qquad (7.30\text{-}1)$$

where F_o is the open-loop expression. In the preceding section it was shown that the peak magnitude of $(\theta_o/\theta_i)(j\omega)$ has a direct bearing on the transient overshoot. Since the open- and closed-loops are uniquely related, it is possible to develop loci (called M-circles)

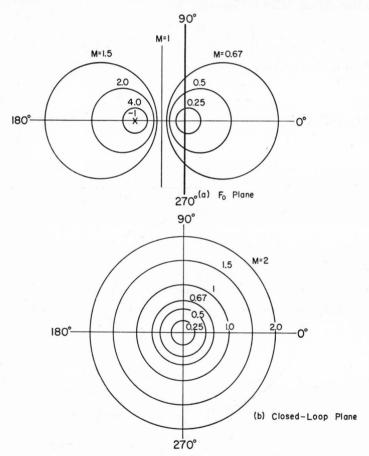

Fig. 7.30-1.   Family of M-circles.

on the open-loop plot which correspond to fixed magnitudes on a closed-loop plot. The relation between the two is found by expressing F_o in rectangular coordinates as

$$F_o = x + jy \qquad (7.30\text{-}2)$$

Then

$$M = \left| \frac{\theta_o}{\theta_i}(j\omega) \right| = \left| \frac{x + jy}{1 + x + jy} \right| \qquad (7.30\text{-}3)$$

$$= \left[\frac{x^2 + y^2}{(1 + x)^2 + y^2} \right]^{1/2} \qquad (7.30\text{-}4)$$

Rationalizing, (7.30-4) becomes

$$y^2 + \left[x + \frac{M^2}{M^2 - 1} \right]^2 = \frac{M^2}{(M^2 - 1)^2} \qquad (7.30\text{-}5)$$

which is the equation of a circle with the center at

$$x = \frac{M^2}{1 - M^2}, \qquad y = 0 \qquad (7.30\text{-}6)$$

and a radius of

$$r = \left| \frac{M}{1 - M^2} \right| \qquad (7.30\text{-}7)$$

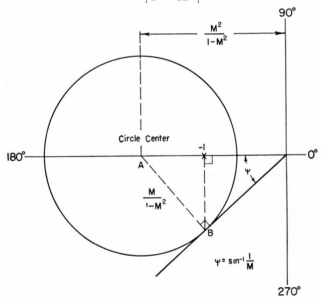

FIG. 7.30-2. M-circle in the F_o plane.

A family of these loci in both the closed- and open-loop planes is shown in Fig. 7.30-1. Thus if it is desired to keep the amplitude of the closed-loop function less than a given value for any input frequency, the open-loop transfer function locus must not have any points within the corresponding M-circle. Construction of a single M-circle is shown in Fig. 7.30-2. It is seen that a definite angle ψ is associated with each circle. These angles are valuable in determining M in the analysis of a system. Table 7.30-1 summarizes these results.

TABLE 7.30-1

M-CIRCLE DATA FOR THE F_o PLANE

M	Center $y = 0$ $x = \dfrac{M^2}{1 - M^2}$	Radius $r = \left\lvert \dfrac{M}{1 - M^2} \right\rvert$	$\psi = \sin^{-1} \dfrac{1}{M}$
0.5	0.33	0.67	. . .
0.67	0.80	1.20	. . .
1.0	∞	∞	90°
1.1	−5.76	5.24	65.4°
1.2	−3.27	2.73	56.4°
1.3	−2.45	1.88	50.3°
1.4	−2.04	1.46	45.6°
1.5	−1.80	1.20	41.8°
1.6	−1.64	1.03	38.7°
1.7	−1.53	0.90	36.0°
1.8	−1.45	0.80	33.7°
2.0	−1.33	0.67	30.0°
2.5	−1.19	0.48	23.6°
3.0	−1.13	0.38	19.5°
4.0	−1.07	0.27	14.5°
5.0	−1.04	0.21	11.5°
6.5	−1.02	0.16	8.9°
7.5	−1.02	0.14	7.7°
10.0	−1.01	0.10	5.7°

Similarly, constant phase-shift loci for the F_o plane, called "N-circles," can be obtained. Let ϕ be the phase shift in $(\theta_o/\theta_i)(j\omega)$, the closed-loop plane. Then from (7.30-3),

$$\phi = \tan^{-1}\frac{y}{x} - \tan^{-1}\frac{y}{1+x} \qquad (7.30\text{-}8)$$

or

$$\tan \phi = N = \frac{y}{x^2 + x + y^2} \qquad (7.30\text{-}9)$$

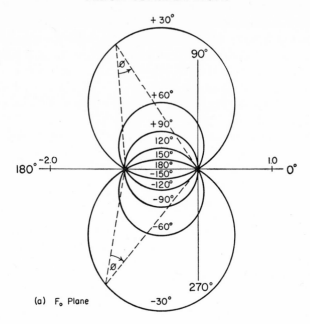

(a) F₀ Plane

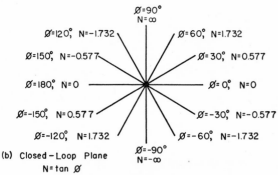

(b) Closed – Loop Plane
$N = \tan \phi$

Fɪɢ. 7.30-3. Family of N-circles.

which is the equation of a circle with the center at

$$x = \frac{-1}{2}, \qquad y = \frac{1}{2N} \qquad (7.30\text{-}10)$$

and a radius of

$$r = 0.5 \sqrt{1 + \frac{1}{N^2}} \qquad (7.30\text{-}11)$$

A family of these loci are shown in Fig. 7.30-3, and their results are summarized in Table 7.30-2. Unlike the M-circles, the N-circles

TABLE 7.30-2

N-CIRCLE DATA FOR THE F_o PLANE

		Radius	Center	
$\phi \pm 180° n$	N	$r = \frac{1}{2}\sqrt{1 + (1/N^2)}$	$x = -\frac{1}{2}$	$y = 1/2N$
−90	− ∞	0.500	−0.5	0
−75	−3.732	0.518	−0.5	−0.134
−60	−1.732	0.577	−0.5	−0.289
−45	−1.000	0.707	−0.5	−0.500
−30	−0.577	1.000	−0.5	−0.866
−15	−0.268	1.931	−0.5	−1.866
0	0	∞	−0.5	∞
15	0.268	1.931	−0.5	1.866
30	0.500	1.000	−0.5	0.866
45	1.000	0.707	−0.5	0.500
60	1.732	0.577	−0.5	0.289
75	3.732	0.518	−0.5	0.134
90	∞	0.500	−0.5	0

are not unique. That is, the loci for $\phi = 60°$ and $-120°$ apparently are the same. As this is impossible, it is necessary for the user to determine which part of the locus is associated with which angle. As shown in Fig. 7.30-3a, it is the x-axis, or real axis, which is the dividing line. No confusion should result by remembering that on the $F_o(j\omega)$ plane ϕ is the angle between the lines from the -1 point and the origin to the N-circle locus, with counterclockwise rotation for positive angles. Both the magnitude and phase are defined by the equation

$$M\angle\phi = \frac{F_o(j\omega)}{1 + F_o(j\omega)} \qquad (7.30\text{-}12)$$

7.40 Selection of the proper system gain

Two important items in the design of a control system are:

1. Selection of the proper system gain
2. Use of compensating functions

The selection of the proper gain is accomplished by adjusting the gain so that the $F_o(j\omega)$ locus is tangent to a given M-circle, the particular M-circle being chosen on the basis of the transient response for a second-order system. This is discussed in this section.

Compensating functions are used to improve the system operation by altering such things as the speed of response, static gain characteristic, effect of external disturbances, etc. These are discussed in Chapter 9.

The selection of the proper system gain is accomplished rather simply by plotting $K_o^{-1}F_o(j\omega)$ instead of $F_o(j\omega)$, where

$$K_o^{-1}F_o(j\omega) = \frac{F_o(j\omega)}{K_o} \qquad (7.40\text{-}1)$$

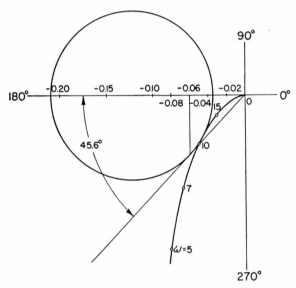

FIG. 7.40-1.   Polar plot of $K_o^{-1}F_o = 1/j\omega(1 + 0.1j\omega)$, showing method of selecting K_o for $M_p = 1.4$.

As different values of K_o merely change the amplitude and not the phase of locus points. M-circles based upon the angle ψ may be drawn on the $K_o^{-1}F_o(j\omega)$ plot and the necessary gain value K_o determined. A constant which is a factor of K_o may be used also, and sometimes this is more convenient. An example is shown in Fig. 9.20-4.

An example will illustrate the procedure. If the output-to-error is

$$\frac{\theta_o}{\theta_e}(s) = F_o(s) = \frac{K_o}{s(1 + 0.1s)} \qquad (7.40\text{-}2)$$

then
$$K_o^{-1}F_o(j\omega) = \frac{1}{j\omega(1 + 0.1j\omega)} \qquad (7.40\text{-}3)$$

Assume that the value of K_o is to be determined so that M_p for $(\theta_o/\theta_i)(j\omega)$ is a given value, which for this example we will select as $M_p = 1.4$. A plot of (7.40-3) is shown in Fig. 7.40-1. Also shown

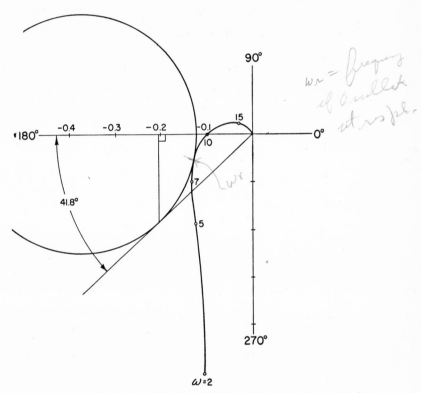

FIG. 7.40-2. Polar plot of $K_o^{-1}F_o = 1/j\omega(1 - 0.01\omega^2 + j0.1\omega)$, showing method of selecting K_o for $M_p = 1.5$.

is a line at the angle $\psi = \sin^{-1}(1/M) = 45.6°$ and a circle tangent to both the line and the $K_o^{-1}F_o(j\omega)$ locus. This circle fulfills two requirements of an $M_p = 1.4$ contour; namely, it is tangent to the angle ψ and to the $K_o^{-1}F_o(j\omega)$ locus, and no points of the $K_o^{-1}F_o(j\omega)$ locus are inside the circle. However, the perpendicular from the x-axis to the circle and angle ψ tangency is -0.06 instead of -1, as a comparison with Fig. 7.30-2 reveals. Therefore K_o should be $1/0.06 = 16.7$, so that the circle will be an M-circle with $M_p = 1.4$ in the $F_o(j\omega)$ plane. Since the circle is also tangent to the transfer locus and the transfer locus never crosses inside the contour at any other point, the system is properly adjusted for $M_p = 1.4$ when $K_o = 16.7$.

In general, all systems with one or more integrations in the open-loop equation (Types 1, 2, etc.), are adjusted so that M_p is between

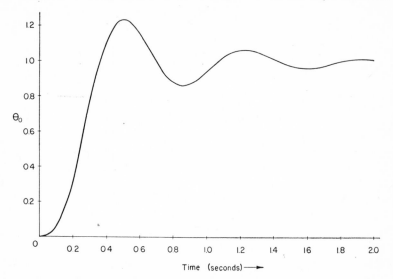

Fig. 7.40-3. Transient response of a third order system with $M_p = 1.5$, $\theta_o = 1 - 0.812\epsilon^{-6.37t} + 0.669\epsilon^{-1.815t} \sin (491t° - 163.9°)$.

1.15 and 1.5. The same reasoning is followed in the adjustment of Type 0 systems, but their proper M_p values are considerably different, as discussed in Section 7.60.

As an example of a higher order system, consider the case when

$$\frac{\theta_o}{\theta_e} (s) = F_o(s) = \frac{K_o}{s(1 + 0.1s + 0.01s^2)} \qquad (7.40\text{-}4)$$

For this case we will determine the value of K_o so that $M_p = 1.5$. Also, the transient response of $\theta_o(t)$ when a unit step $\theta_i(t)$ input is applied will be found. The function $K_o^{-1}F_o(j\omega)$ is shown in Fig. 7.40-2, along with the necessary construction for determining K_o. Since the perpendicular from the x-axis to the circle and angle ψ

tangency intersects the x-axis at -0.204, the value of K_o should be 4.9. Substituting this value into (7.40-4) and solving for the output-to-input relation gives

$$\frac{\theta_o}{\theta_i} = \frac{1}{1 + 0.204s + 0.0204s^2 + 0.00204s^3}$$

$$= \frac{1}{(1 + 0.157s)(1 + 0.047s + 0.013s^2)} \quad (7.40\text{-}5)$$

When θ_i is a unit step input, the transient solution for $\theta_o(t)$ is given by Laplace transform pair 00.111, where $T = 0.157$ sec, $\zeta = 0.207$, $\omega_1 = 8.77$ radians per sec. A plot of this is shown in Fig. 7.40-3. The peak transient output is 23% greater than the input. This is less than the overshoot would be for a quadratic with $M_p = 1.5$.

7.50 Phase margin, gain margin, and unity crossover frequency criteria

Three criteria often used in control analysis are the phase margin, gain margin, and unity crossover frequency. The phase margin is the angle between the negative x-axis and the F_o vector at which $|F_o|$ is unity. It is approximately equal to the angle ψ discussed in Section 7.30, and therefore is a measure of M_p. The gain margin is one minus the value of $|F_o|$ when F_o crosses the negative x-axis inside the -1 point. It is a measure of how much K_o could be increased before the system became unstable. In the first example of Section 7.40 the gain margin was 1.0, since $F_o(j\omega)$ never crossed the 180° axis. This is the maximum gain margin. In the second example it was 0.51, which is about the minimum value that the gain margin should have. The unity crossover frequency ω_u is the frequency at which $|F_o|$ is unity. It is a measure of the system speed of response, as the reciprocal of ω_u is approximately equal to the system time constant (see Sections 4.40 and 7.10).

Although the gain margin has a theoretical maximum value of one, it can never be so high in a physical system. There always exist higher order effects (such as the capacitance between two wires) which prevent a system from responding to an infinite range of frequencies. Because of this, caution should be exercised in using a controller whose performance depends upon the component characteristics at frequencies much higher than its normal operating range.

7.60 Proper adjustment of Type 0 systems

If
$$\frac{\theta_o}{\theta_i} = \frac{5}{1 + 2\zeta s/\omega_1 + s^2/\omega_1{}^2} \qquad (7.60\text{-}1)$$

then
$$\frac{\theta_o}{\theta_e} = \frac{5}{-4 + 2\zeta s/\omega_1 + s^2/\omega_1{}^2} \qquad (7.60\text{-}2)$$

which is an open-loop equation for a Type 0 control system, since there is no integrating term in the open-loop equation. A transient for (7.60-1) would be the same as a transient for (7.20-2), except that for (7.60-1) all variables would be five times larger. It may be assumed, therefore, that if an overshoot of 20% is permissible for a system described by (7.20-2), the same overshoot is permissible for a system described by 7.60-1.

If this is true, it will be found that, using frequency response techniques, (7.60-2) would have an M_p five times greater than (7.20-9) for the same type of transient. Therefore the gain adjustment techniques of the preceding sections should be altered, so that M_p is KM_p, where K is the steady-state gain factor between θ_o and θ_i.

7.70 Laboratory procedures

The frequency response of a component or system may be obtained by mathematical analysis, as has been discussed in preceding sections, or it may be obtained by laboratory measurement. Figure 7.70-1 shows a typical laboratory arrangement. Two synchros, A and B, have their rotors mechanically connected together and driven by a variable speed motor.

Synchro A is connected directly to a third synchro C, whose rotor position may be set by the phase shift dial. The phase shift dial shifts the phase of the signal being modulated by the rotation of the variable speed motor, as shown in Fig. 7.70-2. It is the modulated signal frequency, and not that of the carrier, which is used in control analysis. Usually the variable speed motor will drive the synchro rotors so that the modulation frequency is between 1 and 100 radians per second, the exact range depending on the components being analyzed.

Many control components are of two types, those whose input is an alternating current (a-c) and those whose input is a direct current (d-c). A typical a-c component is the 2-phase motor discussed in Chapter 4. The input voltage has an a-c carrier frequency, such as 60 or 400 c, and the control signal is a modulation of this carrier similar to the modulated synchro outputs. The output of an a-c component may be a shaft rotation (as in the case of a motor), another a-c signal (such as another synchro), or a d-c signal (such

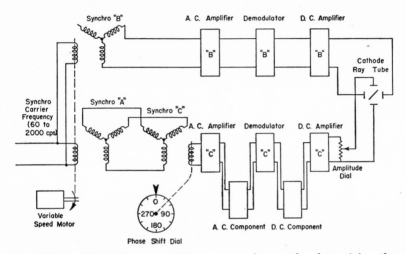

Fig. 7.70-1. Block diagram of laboratory equipment for determining the frequency response of a component.

as a mechanically positioned follow-up potentiometer). A typical d-c component is a d-c motor. Also, all the compensating circuits in Appendix 3 are d-c components. Other control components may be position (such as a gyro), fluid flow (such as an actuator), etc. The characteristics of these are usually measured by a-c or d-c voltage transducers.

The laboratory arrangement in Fig. 7.70-1 will measure the characteristics of either a-c or d-c components. Those which are a-c are inserted between the a-c amplifier and the demodulator, while d-c components are inserted between the demodulator and d-c amplifier. The outputs of the d-c amplifiers are applied to the deflection plates of the cathode ray tube. The variable speed motor is adjusted to a fixed modulation frequency (for example, 5 radians per second). If both the d-c amplifier output signals are in phase, the pattern on the cathode ray tube is a straight line. If they are not in phase, it indicates that some phase shift occurs in the component being tested. They may be brought into phase by turning

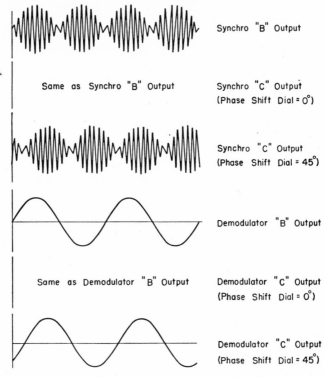

Synchro "B" Output

Same as Synchro "B" Output

Synchro "C" Output
(Phase Shift Dial = 0°)

Synchro "C" Output
(Phase Shift Dial = 45°)

Demodulator "B" Output

Same as Demodulator "B" Output

Demodulator "C" Output
(Phase Shift Dial = 0°)

Demodulator "C" Output
(Phase Shift Dial = 45°)

FIG. 7.70-2.   Laboratory equipment waveforms with no component phase shift.

the phase shift dial, the amount the dial must turn being the phase angle through which the component has shifted the signal for that frequency. The amplitude change is measured by adjusting the gain dial until a prescribed amplitude on the cathode ray tube is obtained. The procedure is then repeated for other modulation frequency inputs until a complete range of readings has been obtained.

PROBLEMS

7-1. Determine the value of K_o so that $M_p = 1.5$ for the following open-loop functions.

(a) $F_o = \dfrac{K_o}{s(1 + 0.1s)(1 + 0.01s)}$

(d) $F_o = \dfrac{K_1}{s(s + 0.2)}$

(b) $F_o = \dfrac{K_o(1 + 25s)}{s^2(1 + 0.5s)(1 + 0.8s)}$

(e) $F_o = \dfrac{K_o}{s(1 + 0.02s + 0.01s^2)}$

(c) $F_o = \dfrac{K_o}{s(1 + 5s)}$

7-2. Find θ_o/θ_i for each of the cases in Problem 7-1.

7-3. If θ_i is at unit step input, find $\theta_o(t)$ for each case in Problem 7-1.

7-4. What is the phase margin for each case in Problem 7-1? What is the gain margin? What is the unity crossover frequency?

7-5. Repeat Problem 7-1, finding K_o when $M_p = 1.2$.

CHAPTER 8

OTHER METHODS OF ANALYZING THE OPEN-LOOP FUNCTION

8.00 Introduction

It was shown in the preceding three chapters that the Nyquist criterion, when applied to the polar plot of the open-loop transfer function, is a powerful tool. The principal merits of the open-loop polar plot are:

1. System stability can be determined easily.

2. Proper adjustment of the system gain is not difficult.

3. The type of system is apparent from the low-frequency asymptote.

4. System speed of response can be approximated by the frequency band pass.

5. Laboratory results can be used as well as analytical equations.

6. Methods for improving the system can be evaluated graphically.

Most of these merits also apply to other analysis methods, which are discussed in this chapter. Two of these methods, the polar plot of the inverse transfer function (called the inverse F_o polar plot) and the log-decibel plot, are based on the Nyquist criterion. The third, the root-locus method, is based on working directly with the system roots.

Each method has individual advantages. The inverse F_o polar plot is particularly adapted for multiloop systems. Also, the closed-loop function can be obtained directly from the open-loop function, and the M-circles all have the same center. The log-decibel plot has the advantage of requiring very little calculating of points. In it, the locus may be sketched with adequate accuracy, using only a straightedge and semilogarithmic paper. The root-locus method also requires little calculation. The location of the open-loop function roots are plotted on rectangular coordinate paper and used to determine graphically the location of the closed-loop equation roots as a function of the system gain. The transient response equation may also be determined graphically from the same plot.

The polar plot of the open-loop transfer function (often called the Nyquist locus) is used throughout this book for most of the examples. This does not mean that Nyquist loci are easier to use than the other methods discussed in this chapter. Instead, for simple systems, the log-decibel method yields similar results in a fraction of the time required by the Nyquist loci method. Similarly, each of the other methods possesses certain advantages. The choice of the Nyquist loci method is, therefore, arbitrary, and it is used in this text for consistency, because the theory was originally developed from this method, and because it is applicable (though sometimes time-consuming) to all systems. The reader will note that in many cases the same problems are worked out in detail in this text using each of the different methods.

8.10 Inverse F_o plot

Since the open- and closed-loops are related by

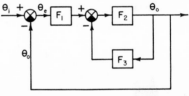

FIG. 8.10-1.   Multi-loop system.

$$\frac{\theta_i}{\theta_o} = 1 + \frac{1}{F_o} = 1 + F_o^{-1} \quad (8.10\text{-}1)$$

a polar plot of F_o^{-1} yields the inverse closed-loop plot merely by shifting the axis one unit. If the system has an inner loop, such as the one in Fig. 8.10-1, then the system relations (see eq. 4.30-12) are

$$\frac{\theta_i}{\theta_o} = 1 + \frac{1}{F_1 F_2} + \frac{F_3}{F_1} = 1 + F_o^{-1} \quad (8.10\text{-}2)$$

It is seen that F_o^{-1} is the sum of two terms, or

$$F_o = \frac{F_1 F_2}{1 + F_2 F_3} \quad (8.10\text{-}3)$$

All the relations that were developed in the preceding chapters could be applied to F_o^{-1} as well as they were to F_o. Hence the answer to which function should be used for analysis depends on such factors as computation time, flexibility, and ease of handling. As this is often determined by the particular problem, the answer is not always the same.

8.11 STABILITY RELATIONS FOR F_o^{-1}. The Nyquist stability relation for F_o^{-1} is different from the relation for F_o. The evolution of the stability relation follows the same procedure as in Section 5.50. If

$$\frac{\theta_o}{\theta_e} = F_o = \frac{F_a}{F_b} \tag{8.11-1}$$

then
$$\frac{\theta_o}{\theta_i} = \frac{F_o}{1 + F_o} = \frac{F_a}{F_a + F_b} \tag{8.11-2}$$

For stability there must not be any roots with positive real parts in the characteristic equation, $F_a + F_b = 0$. In Section 5.50 we let

$$F(s) = 1 + F_o = \frac{F_a + F_b}{F_b} \tag{8.11-3}$$

where $F(s)$ is a rational fraction in s, and therefore $F(s)$ always conforms to the basic relation of eq. (5.40-2) or (5-24) in Appendix 5.

Using F_o^{-1} rather than F_o, let

$$F_x(s) = 1 + F_o^{-1} = \frac{F_a + F_b}{F_a} \tag{8.11-4}$$

As in (8.11-3), the numerator of (8.11-4) is also the system characteristic equation, and $F_x(s)$ conforms to (5.40-2) and (5-24). Likewise, since encirclements of the origin of $F_x(s)$, as s assumes the values shown in the locus of Fig. 5.30-2, are the same as encirclements of the -1 point of F_o^{-1}, the Nyquist stability criterion for the inverse F_o can be determined.

Stated in summary form, the Nyquist criterion for the inverse transfer function F_o^{-1} is as follows.

1. Given the inverse open-loop transfer function F_o^{-1} as a function of s.

2. Let $s = j\omega$, and plot F_o^{-1} for values of ω from $-\infty$ to 0 to $+\infty$. (In practice, as the negative frequencies are the mirror image of the positive frequencies, they are generally omitted.)

3. Then N will always equal $C - Z$, but if the system is stable, Z must equal zero, and N must equal C, where N is the number of encirclements of the -1 point of $F_o^{-1}(j\omega)$ polar plot, (N is positive when going counterclockwise for increasing frequencies). C is the

number of denominator roots of $F_o^{-1}(s)$ with positive real parts (this is the same as the numerator roots of $F_o(s)$ with positive real parts). Z is the number of numerator roots with positive real parts of $1 + F_o^{-1}(s) = 0$ (or $F_a + F_b = 0$).

4. There may be some doubt about how the locus is closed between $\omega = +\infty$ and $\omega = -\infty$ when the amplitude is infinite. The locus

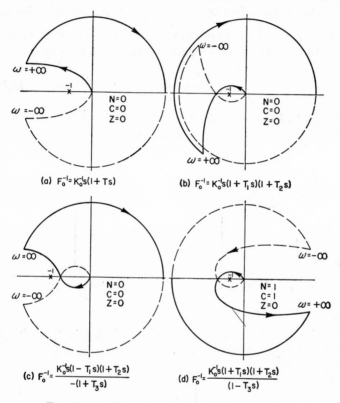

(a) $F_o^{-1} = K_o^{-1}s(1 + Ts)$

(b) $F_o^{-1} = K_o^{-1}s(1 + T_1 s)(1 + T_2 s)$

(c) $F_o^{-1} = \dfrac{K_o^{-1}s(1 - T_1 s)(1 + T_2 s)}{-(1 + T_3 s)}$

(d) $F_o^{-1} = \dfrac{K_o^{-1}s(1 + T_1 s)(1 + T_2 s)}{(1 - T_3 s)}$

Fig. 8.11-1.   Examples of stable F_o^{-1} polar plots.

should be closed by circling clockwise, from $\omega = +\infty$ to $\omega = -\infty$, $180n°$, where n is the difference between the order of s in the numerator and denominator of F_o^{-1}.

Because closure when the amplitude is infinite is a function of the order of the equation, it is difficult to classify the inverse open-loop equations as was done in Chapter 6. Application of the criterion is illustrated by the examples in Fig. 8.11-1. The quantity C has the same function as P did in Chapter 6, and is used to distinguish between the two. Here C is the number of numerator roots of F_o with positive real parts, whereas P is the number of denominator roots of F_o with positive real parts. Only rarely has C any value other than zero. The value of P does not affect the inverse criterion, and similarly, the value of C does not affect the F_o criterion. The same method shown in Fig. 6.10-6 may be used to determine N.

8.12 CONSTANT MAGNITUDE AND PHASE LOCI FOR F_o^{-1}. Since the inverse transfer function is related to the closed loop by

$$\frac{\theta_i}{\theta_o} = 1 + F_o^{-1} \qquad (8.12\text{-}1)$$

a polar plot of the closed-loop function can be obtained by merely shifting the x-axis one unit. This is illustrated by Fig. 8.12-1.

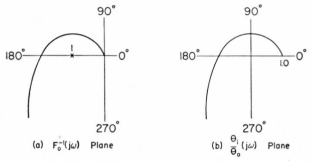

(a) $F_o^{-1}(j\omega)$ Plane   (b) $\dfrac{\theta_i}{\theta_o}(j\omega)$ Plane

FIG. 8.12-1.   Polar plots.

Likewise, constant magnitude loci, M-circles, in the θ_i/θ_o plane are related to M-circles in the F_o^{-1} plane by merely shifting the x-axis. Thus if

$$\left|\frac{\theta_o}{\theta_i}\right| = M \qquad (8.12\text{-}2)$$

then

$$\left|\frac{\theta_i}{\theta_o}\right| = \frac{1}{M} \qquad (8.12\text{-}3)$$

A family of M-circles is shown in Fig. 8.12-2. As the M-circle radius is $1/M$ and the circles are concentric about the -1 point in the F_o^{-1} plane, the same relationship for the angle ψ discussed in Section 7.30 exists, namely,

$$\psi = \sin^{-1} 1/M \qquad (8.12\text{-}4)$$

This may be shown by drawing two lines on the $F_o^{-1}(j\omega)$ plane. One from the origin tangent to a given M-circle, and the other from the -1 point to the tangency point. The geometry of the angle is such that (8.12-4) is satisfied.

Proper system adjustment is achieved utilizing F_o^{-1} in a manner similar to that discussed in Chapter 7 for F_o. The function $K_x F_o^{-1}$

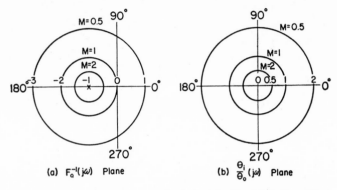

(a) $F_o^{-1}(j\omega)$ Plane   (b) $\frac{\theta_i}{\theta_o}(j\omega)$ Plane

FIG. 8.12-2.   Constant magnitude loci for $|(\theta_o/\theta_i)(j\omega)| = M$.

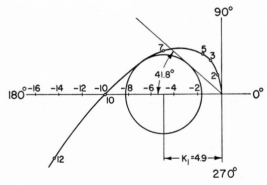

FIG. 8.12-3.   Polar plot of $K_1 F_o^{-1}(j\omega) = j\omega(1 - 0.01\omega^2 + 0.1j\omega)$ showing the method of selecting K_1 so that $M_p = 1.5$.

is plotted, where K_x is a system gain whose value is to be determined. The proper value of K_x is determined by drawing a circle tangent to both a given angle ψ and the $K_x F_o^{-1}(j\omega)$ locus. Then K_x is equal to the distance from the origin to the center of the circle. This is illustrated in Fig. 8.12-3. The example is the same as that used in Fig. 7.40-2.

Constant phase loci in the θ_o/θ_i plane are radial lines emanating from the origin for both the θ_o/θ_i and θ_i/θ_o planes and from the -1 point for the F_o^{-1} plane as shown in Fig. 8.12-4.

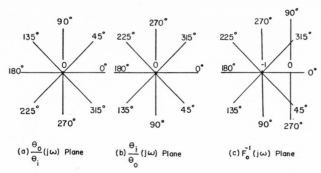

(a) $\dfrac{\theta_o}{\theta_i}(j\omega)$ Plane   (b) $\dfrac{\theta_i}{\theta_o}(j\omega)$ Plane   (c) $F_o^{-1}(j\omega)$ Plane

FIG. 8.12-4. Constant phase loci for the $(\theta_o/\theta_i)(j\omega)$ plane as they appear in other planes.

8.13 EXAMPLE USING F_o^{-1} METHOD. As an example of the application of the F_o^{-1} method, consider the system shown in Fig. 8.13-1, where

$$K_1 F_o^{-1} = 0.2s(1 + 0.1s + 0.01s^2) + \frac{0.4s}{1 + 0.0067s} \qquad (8.13\text{-}1)$$

The polar plot of this is shown in Fig. 8.13-2, where:

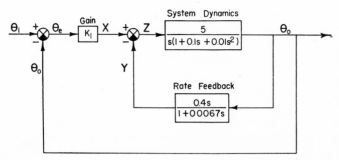

FIG. 8.13-1.

(1) Locus A is the polar plot of $0.2s(1 + 0.1s + 0.01s^2)$.

(2) Locus B is the polar plot of $0.4s/(1 + 0.0067s)$ for the low-frequency portion.

(3) Locus C is the polar plot of $K_1 F_o^{-1}$ which was obtained by graphically adding A and B.

The addition process is indicated by the dashed lines connecting A and C. The construction of an M-circle for $M_p = 1.5$ is also shown. Thus the proper value for K_1 is 3 when $M_p = 1.5$.

The addition of two loci may be accomplished quite simply with a pair of sliding straightedges. If the final result for F_o^{-1} is not of the desired shape, corrective measures are often evident when this

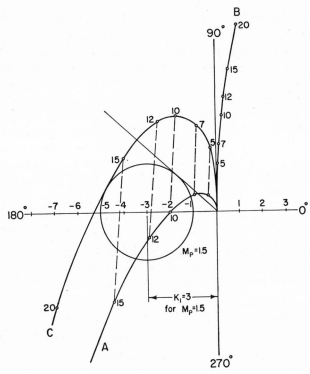

Fig. 8.13-2.   Polar plot of $K_1F_o^{-1}$ for (8.13-1).

method is used. Thus it is evident that the rate follow-up must have an amplitude of approximately 6 in order to move the 15 radians per second point sufficiently above the 180° axis, so that the M-circle will be tangent at a higher frequency.

Whether this is advantageous or not is another question. The system dynamics θ_o/Z has the same frequency-dependent term as the example in Section 7.40 (see eq. 7.40-4). No compensating term such as rate feedback was used there, and the transient with $M_p =$

1.5 was shown in Fig. 7.40-3. As the usual purpose of a compensating term is to improve the system response, we will determine the transient for this case. Letting $K_1 = 3$,

$$\frac{\theta_o}{\theta_i} = \frac{1 + 0.0067s}{1 + 0.2067s + 0.00711s^2 + 0.000711s^3 + 0.00000444s^4}$$

$$(8.13\text{-}2)$$

The denominator has two real roots and one pair of complex factors. Since the product of the real roots and the square of the natural frequency for the complex pair are not sufficiently separated, Lin's root finding method is difficult to apply to this example. In cases such as this the real roots may be found by the division process described in Appendix 2. As the frequency at M_p is considerably above the frequency where $F_o{}^{-1}$ is unity amplitude, a good approximation of one of the real roots is s equal to the unity crossover frequency. Also, the quadratic natural frequency is approximately the frequency at M_p. Knowing these, the roots may be determined. In factored form (8.13-2) is

$$\frac{\theta_o}{\theta_i} = \frac{1 + 0.0067s}{(1 + 0.188s)(1 + 0.0066s)(1 + 0.0117s + 0.00357s^2)}$$

$$(8.13\text{-}3)$$

The transient response for a unit input is given by Laplace transform pair 02.121 with $b = 0$. However, one of the denominator roots is approximately the same as the numerator root and may be canceled. The system relation then is

$$\frac{\theta_o}{\theta_i} = \frac{1}{(1 + 0.188s)(1 + 0.0117s + 0.00357s^2)} \qquad (8.13\text{-}4)$$

The transient response to a unit step input is given by Laplace transform pair 00.111, and is shown in Fig. 8.13-3.

This figure, compared with Fig. 7.40-3, shows the effect of rate feedback *in this case*. It is seen that the system response is faster with rate feedback, but a more pronounced oscillation exists. The oscillation is due to the existence of the high arch on the $F_o{}^{-1}(j\omega)$ locus at low frequencies.

Proper selection of compensating functions requires the recognition of desired and undesired polar loci shapes. These are discussed in greater detail in Chapters 9 and 11. At the present it may be stated that if the oscillatory response were due to the high arch, a compensating function which altered the arch would reduce the transient oscillation.

This may be accomplished on the F_o^{-1} plane by changing the Y/θ_o feedback from

$$\frac{Y}{\theta_o} = \frac{0.4s}{1 + 0.0067s} \tag{8.13-5}$$

to

$$\frac{Y}{\theta_o} = \frac{0.08s^2}{(1 + 0.0067s)(1 + 0.2s)} \tag{8.13-6}$$

The relation in (8.13-6) was selected by trial and error, after inspec-

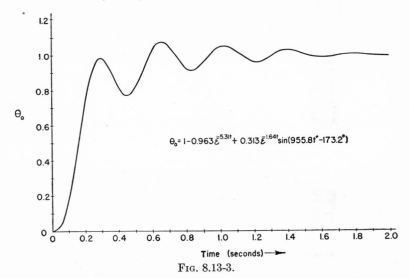

$$\theta_o = 1 - 0.963\bar{\varepsilon}^{5.31t} + 0.313\bar{\varepsilon}^{1.64t}\sin(955.81t^\circ - 173.2^\circ)$$

FIG. 8.13-3.

tion of Fig. 8.13-2 indicated how locus B should be altered. The polar plots are shown in Fig. 8.13-4, where:

(1) Locus A is the polar plot of $0.2s(1 + 0.1s + 0.01s^2)$.

(2) Locus B is the polar plot of $0.08s^2/(1 + 0.0067s)(1 + 0.2s)$.

(3) Locus C is the polar plot of $K_1F_o^{-1}$ and was obtained by adding A and B.

The M-circle for $M_p = 1.5$, also shown, indicates that K_1 should be 3.8. Using these values,

$$\frac{\theta_o}{\theta_i} = \frac{(1+0.0067s)(1+0.2s)}{1+0.2593s+0.03836s^2+0.001683s^3+0.0001157s^4+0.0000007s^5} \tag{8.13-7}$$

Lin's method may be used to find the roots quickly. Then

$$\frac{\theta_o}{\theta_i} = \frac{(1 + 0.0067s)(1 + 0.2s)}{(1 + 0.0066s)(1 + 0.2327s + 0.0282s^2)(1 + 0.02s + 0.00376s^2)}$$
(8.13-8)

Again, one of the numerator roots is approximately the same as the denominator real root and may be canceled. Laplace transform

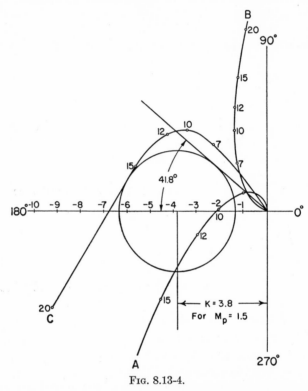

Fig. 8.13-4.

pair 02.102 (letting $b = 0$) may be used to find the output for a unit step input. The result is shown in Fig. 8.13-5. The system response time has been reduced, and the oscillation dies out faster. The overshoot, however, may be higher than is desirable. If so, reducing the gain slightly will reduce the overshoot without appreciably affecting the response time.

It is essential to correlate frequency and transient responses. Once the designer has a "feel" for this, the optimization of control systems may be accomplished rapidly. In this example the designer could tell from inspection of locus A the approximate form which locus B should have to improve the system operation. The inverse F_o polar plot has particular merits for parallel circuits, and also possesses most of the advantages of the F_o polar plot.

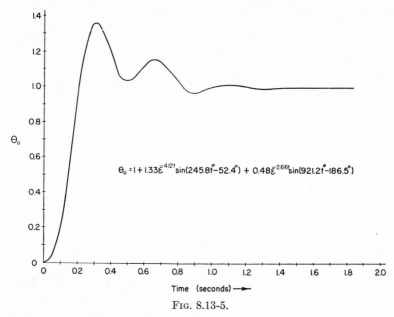

$$\theta_o = 1 + 1.33\varepsilon^{-4.12t}\sin(245.8t - 52.4°) + 0.48\varepsilon^{-2.66t}\sin(921.2t - 186.5°)$$

θ_o

Time (seconds) ⟶

FIG. 8.13-5.

8.20 Log-decibel method

The log-decibel method is often called the Bode method, after H. W. Bode, who developed many fundamental analysis theorems using this approach. The method is very useful for single-loop systems. It may be extended to multiloop systems, but becomes more involved. The amplitude of the open-loop function $F_o(j\omega)$ is expressed in decibels and plotted $vs.$ the frequency on a logarithmic scale. Since the locus is approximately a straight line whose slope changes at each corner frequency, a freehand sketch is often sufficient. The phase shift for $F_o(j\omega)$ is a separate locus and is composed of the phase contribution of each factor in $F_o(j\omega)$. Knowledge of the shape which both the amplitude and phase must have is often sufficient for the selection of both the system gain and compensating functions.

8.21 AMPLITUDE ASYMPTOTES. In the log-decibel method we plot 20 times the logarithm, to the base 10, of the amplitude. For example, if

$$F(j\omega) = \frac{1}{1 + jT\omega} = A \angle \phi \tag{8.21-1}$$

then the amplitude for a log-decibel plot is

$$A_{db} = 20 \log A \tag{8.21-2}$$

where A_{db} denotes the amplitude in decibels, log denotes the logarithm to the base 10, $A = 1/\sqrt{1 + T^2\omega^2}$. In this example

$$A_{db} = 20 \log \frac{1}{\sqrt{1 + T^2\omega^2}} \tag{8.21-3}$$

$$= -20 \log (1 + T^2\omega^2)^{1/2} \tag{8.21-4}$$

$$\simeq 0 \quad \text{(when } T\omega \text{ is less than 1)} \tag{8.21-5}$$

$$\simeq -20 \log T\omega \quad \text{(when } T\omega \text{ is greater than 1)} \tag{8.21-6}$$

The whole key to the log-decibel method is contained in eqs. (8.21-5) and (8.21-6). Since the logarithm of 1 is zero, A_{db} for (8.21-3) is a straight line from zero frequency until $T\omega$ is significant. As $T\omega$ becomes much larger than 1, the factor $(1 + T^2\omega^2)^{1/2}$ is approximately $T\omega$, as noted in (8.21-6).

It can be shown rather easily that if the frequency axis is logarithmic (8.21-6) also is a straight line. In a logarithmic axis the spacing is the same as the frequency is doubled. Thus the spacing is equal between the following.

$$\omega = 1/T \quad \text{and} \quad \omega = 2/T$$
$$\omega = 2/T \quad \text{and} \quad \omega = 4/T$$
$$\omega = 4/T \quad \text{and} \quad \omega = 8/T$$
$$\omega = 8/T \quad \text{and} \quad \omega = 16/T, \text{ etc.}$$

Each doubling of the frequency is an octave. Application to (8.21-6) is as follows.

ω	A_{db}
$1/T$	$-20 \log 1 = 0$ db
$2/T$	$-20 \log 2 = -6.02$ db
$4/T$	$-20 \log 4 = -12.04$ db
$8/T$	$-20 \log 8 = -18.06$ db
$16/T$	$-20 \log 16 = -24.08$ db, etc.

This is shown graphically in Fig. 8.21-1 as the approximate amplitude locus. The slope at the higher frequencies is −20 db per decade, or approximately −6 db per octave.

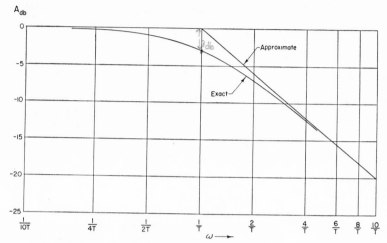

Fig. 8.21-1.   Log-decibel plot of $A_{db} = -20 \log (1 + T^2\omega^2)^{1/2}$.

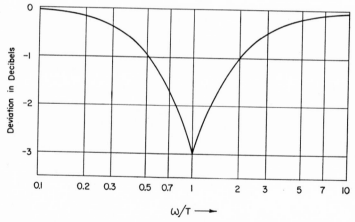

Fig. 8.21-2.   Deviation of actual amplitude locus from the asymptote amplitude locus for $A_{db} = -20 \log (1 + T^2\omega^2)^{1/2}$.

The straight-line amplitude asymptotes differ from the actual by a maximum of 3.01 db at the corner frequency. One octave away the error is 0.97 db. Two octaves away the error is only 0.263 db, and at wider separations the error is negligible. This is shown in Fig. 8.21-2, which shows the difference between the straight-line approximation and the actual amplitude locus for functions like (8.21-1). The phase angle associated with (8.21-1) is the same as that shown in Fig. 2.26-1.

When a function contains several factors, the result is the sum of the amplitude and phase curves for each factor. Thus if

$$F(s) = \frac{1 + 0.5s}{(1 + 0.2s)(1 + 0.04s)} = A \angle \phi \qquad (8.21\text{-}7)$$

then

$$A_{db} = 20 \log [1 + (0.5\omega)^2]^{1/2} - 20 \log [1 + (0.2\omega)^2]^{1/2}$$
$$- 20 \log [1 + (0.04\omega)^2]^{1/2} \qquad (8.21\text{-}8)$$

The amplitude asymptote approximation is shown in Fig. 8.21-3. Additional examples of amplitude asymptotes are provided by the

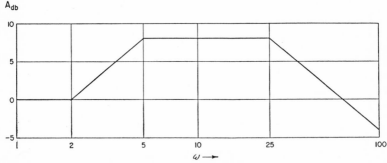

Fig. 8.21-3.   Log-decibel amplitude asymptotes for
$$F(j\omega) = \frac{1 + 0.5j\omega}{(1 + 0.2j\omega)(1 + 0.04j\omega)}.$$

compensating functions in Appendix 3.

If the function contains an s factor, then a 6 db per octave slope exists at the low frequencies. However, as the frequency axis is logarithmic, the zero point is never shown. These functions are represented by evaluating A_{db} at some convenient low frequency, and proceeding with the amplitude asymptotes at the higher frequencies. As an example, consider

$$F(s) = \frac{3}{s(1 + 0.2s)} = A \angle \phi \qquad (8.21\text{-}9)$$

Here $$A_{db} = +20 \log \frac{3}{\omega} - 20 \log [1 + (0.2\omega)^2]^{1/2} \qquad (8.21\text{-}10)$$

The corner frequency is 5 radians per second for the real root factor. Evaluating the first part of (8.21-10) at a lower frequency, such as $\omega = 1$, gives a starting point for the amplitude locus as

$$A_{db} = +20 \log 3 = +9.54db \qquad \text{(at } \omega = 1) \quad (8.21\text{-}11)$$

The complete locus is shown in Fig. 8.21-4.

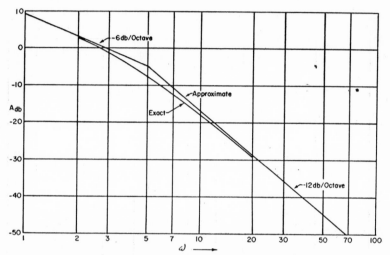

Fig. 8.21-4. Log-decibel plot for $F(j\omega) = \dfrac{3}{j\omega(1 + 0.2j\omega)}$.

Quadratic factors with the damping ratio ζ less than unity, such as

$$F(s) = \frac{1}{1 + 2\zeta s/\omega_1 + s^2/\omega_1{}^2} \qquad (8.21\text{-}12)$$

are a little more difficult to handle. The low-frequency amplitude asymptote is 0 db, and the high-frequency asymptote has a slope of -12 db per octave. But at ω_1, the corner frequency, the deviation may be appreciable, as shown in Figs. 8.21-5 and 8.21-6. The phase is the same as that shown in Fig. 2.26-3.

A chart showing the relation between A and A_{db} is shown in Fig. 8.21-7.

8.22 PHASE ANGLE CHARACTERISTICS. The phase angle for the log-decibel method is calculated in the normal manner. It is plotted *vs.* frequency so that each $F(j\omega)$ is represented by two loci, one for the amplitude and the other for the phase angle.

Several significant relationships between the amplitude and the phase become apparent in this method. A function such as (8.21-1) has a -6 db per octave slope and a $-90°$ phase shift at the high frequencies. One like (8.21-12) has a -12 db. per octave slope and a $-180°$ phase shift at the high frequencies (when ζ is positive).

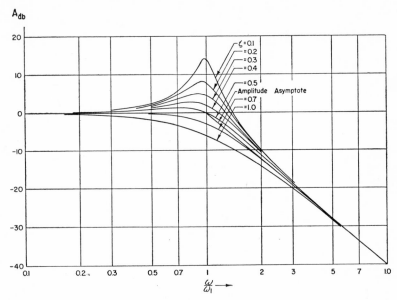

FIG. 8.21-5.   Log-decibel chart for $A_{db} = -20 \log [(1 - \omega^2/\omega_1^2)^2 + 4\zeta^2(\omega^2/\omega_1^2)]^{1/2}$.

Similarly, for all minimum-phase functions the phase tends toward $-90°$ for each -6 db per octave amplitude slope.

Therefore, in plotting A_{db} for a minimum-phase function, it is possible to judge the approximate phase shift visually. A minor exception occurs in the narrow zone around the natural frequency of a quadratic factor. These cases are easily recognized. This is a valuable analysis tool. The amplitude locus can be sketched using asymptotes. Then the phase angle can be judged from the amplitude slope. Thus in a matter of minutes the designer can gain valuable insight into the system operation.

The technique may be applied also to nonminimum-phase functions. But the designer must remember that the amplitude slope does not have the same relation to the phase as in the minimum-phase function cases. The designer usually can keep track of the approximate phase angle without much difficulty. One method is to write on the amplitude asymptote locus the total phase angle

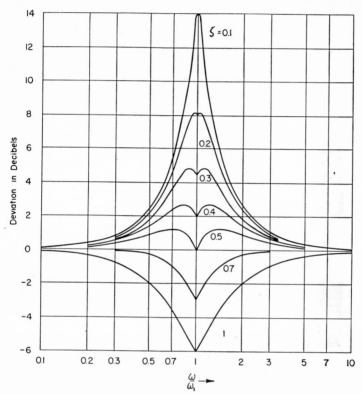

Fig. 8.21-6. Deviation of actual amplitude locus from the asymptote amplitude locus for $A_{db} = -20 \log [(1 - \omega^2/\omega_1^2)^2 + 4\zeta^2(\omega^2/\omega_1^2)]^{1/2}$.

associated with that function up to each corner frequency. As an example, if

$$F_o(s) = \frac{K_o(1 + 2s)}{s(1 + 0.1s)(1 + 0.01s)(1 + 0.005s)} = A_{db}\angle\phi \qquad (8.22\text{-}1)$$

the designer would write $-90°$ on the amplitude locus between $\omega = 0$ and $\omega = 0.5$, $0°$ between $\omega = 0.5$ and $\omega = 10$, $-90°$ between $\omega = 10$ and $\omega = 100$, $-180°$ between $\omega = 100$ and $\omega = 200$, and

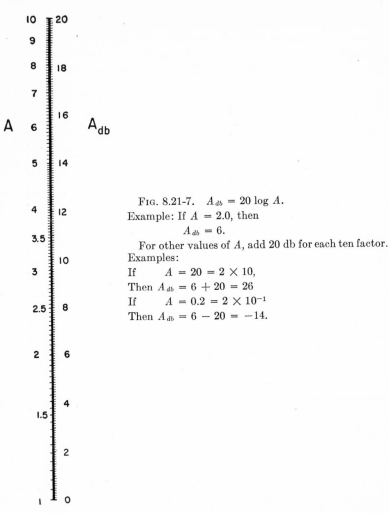

Fɪɢ. 8.21-7. $A_{db} = 20 \log A$.
Example: If $A = 2.0$, then
$$A_{db} = 6.$$
For other values of A, add 20 db for each ten factor.
Examples:
If $A = 20 = 2 \times 10$,
Then $A_{db} = 6 + 20 = 26$
If $A = 0.2 = 2 \times 10^{-1}$
Then $A_{db} = 6 - 20 = -14$.

$-270°$ above $\omega = 200$. Since the example is of the form shown in Fig. 6.10-1d, stability exists only if the amplitude is less than unity (or 0 db) when the phase angle becomes 180°. Therefore the value of A_{db} around and above 100 radians per second determines stability.

A nonminimum-phase function example is

$$F_o(s) = \frac{-0.5(1 + 5s)}{s(1 - s)(1 + 0.01s)(1 + 0.005s)} = A_{db}\angle\phi \quad (8.22\text{-}2)$$

which is the type shown in Fig. 6.10-2d. For this the designer would write $+90°$ on the amplitude locus between $\omega = 0$ and $\omega = 0.2$, $180°$ between $\omega = 0.2$ and $\omega = 1$, $-90°$ between $\omega = 1$ and $\omega = 100$, $180°$ between $\omega = 100$ and $\omega = 200$, and $-270°$ above $\omega = 200$. Two amplitude zones are important in this case. In the low frequencies (around $\omega = 0.5$) where the locus first crosses the $180°$ axis, the amplitude must be greater than unity (A_{db} greater than 0 db). In the high frequencies, when the locus again crosses the $180°$ axis, the amplitude must be less than unity (A_{db} less than 0 db).

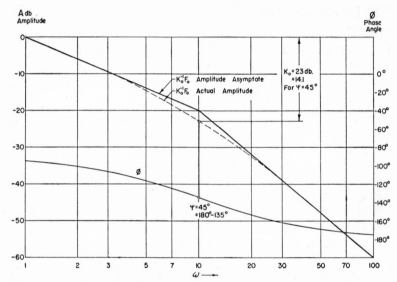

FIG. 8.23-1. Log-decibel and phase loci for $K_o^{-1}F_o = \dfrac{1}{j\omega(1 + 0.1j\omega)}$.

8.23 SYSTEM GAIN ADJUSTMENT. An open-loop function such as

$$F_o(s) = \frac{K_o}{s(1 + 0.1s)} \qquad (8.23\text{-}1)$$

may have its amplitude in decibels represented by

$$A_{db} = 20 \log K_o - 20 \log \omega - 20 \log (1 + 0.01\omega^2)^{1/2} \qquad (8.23\text{-}2)$$

Thus the gain merely changes the magnitude of A_{db}, and shifts the log-decibel locus vertically by a constant amount.

The proper gain is determined by plotting the function $K_o^{-1}F_o(j\omega)$

and selecting the value which K_o should have, so that the gain and phase margins (see Section 7.50) have acceptable values.

An example will illustrate the procedure. Figure 8.23-1 shows the amplitude and phase loci of $K_o^{-1}F_o(j\omega)$ for (8.23-1). At a phase margin of 45°, which corresponds approximately to $M_p = 1.4$, the $K_o^{-1}F_o$ amplitude is -23 db. Therefore if $K_o = 23$ db, the amplitude of F_o would be 0 db at this point. The 23 db gain setting is equivalent to a gain of 14.1, which compares favorably with the gain value of 16.7, determined in Section 7.40.

8.30 Root locus method

The root locus method is also called the Evans method after W. R. Evans of North American Aviation, Inc., who developed many of its basic techniques. The method uses the roots of the open-loop function $F_o(s)$ to find the roots of the closed-loop function. If the system contains inner loops, the open-loop expression of the inner loop is used to find its closed-loop expression in factored form. This expression is then used in the next open-loop function. Since the method deals directly with the system roots, and since all stability criteria are methods of determining the nature of these roots, a knowledge of the Nyquist criterion is not essential in understanding this method.

Stability in any linear system exists if, and only if, there are no roots with positive real parts in the characteristic equation. In the root locus method the values of the roots for $K^{-1}F_o(s)$ are plotted on the s-plane (see Section 5.20). Here K is the system gain. A locus called the "180° phase locus" is then determined graphically. This locus is such that the phase shift of $K^{-1}F_o(s)$ is 180° when s is equal to any point on the locus. Since

$$\frac{\theta_o}{\theta_i} = \frac{F_o(s)}{1 + F_o(s)} \qquad (8.30\text{-}1)$$

all the closed-loop denominator roots are located on the 180° phase locus. The exact position on the locus depends on the value of K. Thus as K is increased or decreased, the closed-loop root locations shift along the 180° phase locus, and K is selected so that the closed-loop denominator roots have acceptable values.

A further advantage exists in that the equation for the output response to any input signal may be determined graphically from a plot of the roots. Since the method yields the root locations, the same plot may be used to determine the equation for the output transient response.

All calculations are performed graphically. If a plastic tool called a "spirule" is used, the calculations may be performed rapidly and with a high degree of accuracy. In the following sections the basic principles of this method are discussed.

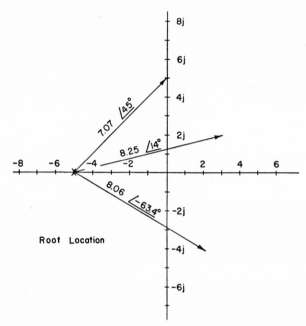

FIG. 8.31-1. s-Plane plot showing location of $s = -5$ and vectors between points.

8.31 GRAPHIC CALCULATIONS FOR AMPLITUDE AND PHASE. A function such as

$$F(s) = \frac{1}{1 + 0.2s} = A\angle\phi \qquad (8.31\text{-}1)$$

may be expressed in the form

$$F(s) = 5 \times \frac{1}{s + 5} \qquad (8.31\text{-}2)$$

The $1/(s + 5)$ portion of (8.31-2) may be represented on the s-plane by the point $s = -5$. As shown in Fig. 8.31-1, A and ϕ may be determined graphically for any value of s. Thus, using a protractor and a ruler, values such as the following may be obtained.

s	$F(s)$	A	ϕ
0	5/5	1.000	0°
2	5/7	0.714	0°
$5j$	$5/(7.07\angle 45°)$	0.707	−45°
$3 + 2j$	$5/(8.25\angle 14°)$	0.606	−14°
$2 - 4j$	$5/(8.06\angle -29.7°)$	0.620	+29.7°
−6	$5/-1$	5.000	180°

In the Nyquist method only the values of s along the imaginary axis were used. In the root locus method s may have any value, since the roots of s in both the open- and closed-loop expressions may have real as well as imaginary parts. Graphical calculation for $F(s)$ as s assumes any value may be performed simply, using the s-plane plot as was shown in Fig. 8.31-1.

If $F(s)$ is more complex, the procedure is the same. Accordingly, the function

$$F(s) = \frac{1}{s(1 + 0.1s + 0.01s^2)} = A\angle\phi \qquad (8.31\text{-}3)$$

may be expressed as

$$F(s) = \frac{100}{s} \times \frac{1}{s + 5 - 8.66j} \times \frac{1}{s + 5 + 8.66j} \qquad (8.31\text{-}4)$$

Figure 8.31-2 is a plot showing the root locations and the manner of graphic calculation for the following sample values of s.

s	$F(s)$	A	ϕ
$2 + 7j$	$\dfrac{100}{7.28\angle 74° \times 7.19\angle -13° \times 17.15\angle 66°}$	0.111	−127°
$-5 + 3j$	$\dfrac{100}{5.83\angle 149° \times 5.66\angle -90° \times 11.66\angle 90°}$	0.260	−149°

8.32 180° PHASE LOCUS. In the preceding section it was shown that the amplitude and phase of any factored $F(s)$ could be found by using the s-plane (or root locus) plot. For control analysis purposes a certain set of values for s is highly important. This set, called the "180° phase locus," consists of all the values of s which will make the phase angle for the open-loop function $F_o(s)$ equal to 180° or an

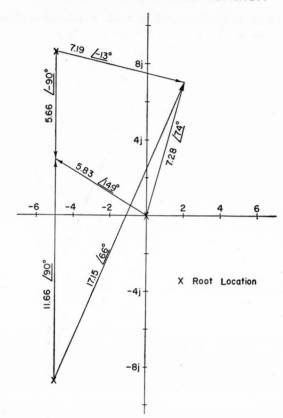

FIG. 8.31-2. s-Plane plot showing location of denominator roots for

$$F(s) = \frac{1}{s(1 + 0.1s + 0.01s^2)}$$

and vectors between points.

equivalent angle such as 540°, 900°, etc. These values are important, because if

$$F_o(s) = -1 = 1\angle180° \qquad (8.32\text{-}1)$$

then

$$1 + F_o(s) = 0 \qquad (8.32\text{-}2)$$

and the values of s which make $F_o(s) = -1$ are the denominator roots of the closed-loop function $(\theta_o/\theta_i)(s)$. The numerator roots of the closed-loop function are the same as the numerator roots of the open-loop function (see eq. 8.11-2).

Two requirements are imposed by (8.32-1). One is that the phase shift of $F_o(s)$ be 180°, and the other, that the amplitude be unity.

The root locus method considers each requirement separately. First, a locus is obtained for all values of s which make the phase shift of $F_o(s) = (1 + 2n)180°$, where n is any integer. Then the system gain is selected, so that the specific points on the 180° phase locus which make the amplitude of $F_o(s)$ unity are approximately the optimum.

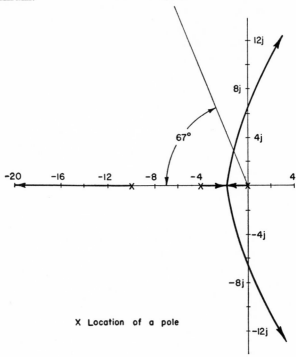

FIG. 8.32-1.   180° phase locus for $F_o = \dfrac{40K_o}{s(s + 4)(s + 10)}$.

Fortunately, the general shape of the 180° phase locus is usually evident from inspection of the particular $F_o(s)$. As an example, consider

$$F_o(s) = \frac{K_o}{s(1 + 0.25s)(1 + 0.1s)} = \frac{40K_o}{s(s + 4)(s + 10)} \quad (8.32\text{-}3)$$

The denominator roots, called "poles," are located at 0, −4, and −10, as shown in Fig. 8.32-1.

Considerable time may be saved in finding the 180° phase locus by studying the possibility of a portion of the locus occurring in the following places.

1. Anywhere along the positive real axis
2. Anywhere along the negative real axis
3. Along some positive or negative angle as s becomes a large value

In this case the locus cannot lie anywhere along the positive real axis, as the phase shift of each factor would be 0°. Hence the total phase shift would also be 0°. This is not true along the negative real axis. Between $s = 0$ and $s = -4$ the phase shift from the $s = 0$ root is 180°, and 0° from the $s = -4$ and $s = -10$ roots. Thus a portion of the 180° phase locus is located here. Between $s = -4$ and $s = -10$, the total phase shift is 360°, since the roots at 0 and -4 each contribute 180°, while the root at -10 contributes nothing. Therefore a portion of the locus is not located there. Between $s = -10$ and $s = -\infty$ the net phase shift is 540° which is equivalent to 180°, as each root factor has a 180° value when s is any value in this zone. This covers the possible locations suggested by items 1 and 2.

Item 3 indicates that another location for the 180° phase locus is along the plus or minus 60° vector. Thus if s has some large value (such as $100\angle+60°$), the phase shift of each root factor is about 60°. The total is 180° since there are three roots. Once the general location of the locus has been established, the specific points can be determined fairly rapidly. The reason for the vector at 67° (shown in Fig. 8.32-1) to the negative real axis is discussed in the next section.

As a second example, consider

$$F_o(s) = \frac{K_o}{s(1 + 0.1s + 0.01s^2)}$$

$$= \frac{100K_o}{s(s + 5 + j8.66)(s + 5 - j8.66)} \tag{8.32-4}$$

The poles shown in Fig. 8.32-2 are located at 0, $-5 - j8.66$, and $-5 + j8.66$. Again, the phase shift along the positive real axis is always 0°, and hence no portion of the 180° phase locus is there. However, anywhere along the negative real axis the phase shift is 180°, since the angle due to the zero root is 180°, and the angles due to the complex roots are of equal magnitude but of opposite

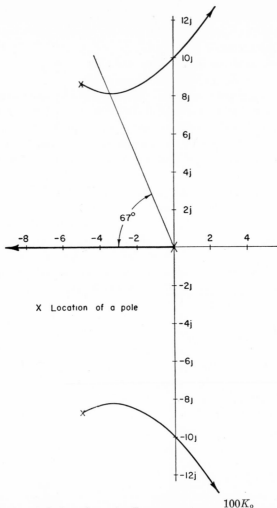

FIG. 8.32-2.   180° phase locus for $F_o = \dfrac{100K_o}{s(s+5+j8.66)(s+5-j8.66)}$.

sign. Again, if s is a large value along either the plus or minus 60°
vector, the phase shift for $F_o(s)$ would be 180°.

When $F_o(s)$ contains factors in the numerator, the procedure is the
same. An example of this type is

$$F_o(s) = \frac{K_o(1+0.5s)}{s(1+0.25s)(1+0.1s)} = \frac{20K_o(s+2)}{s(s+4)(s+10)} \qquad (8.32\text{-}5)$$

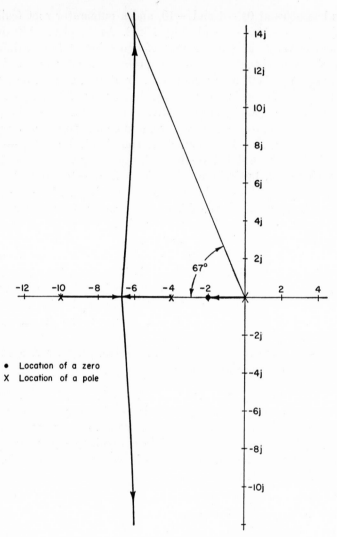

Fig. 8.32-3.   180° phase locus for $F_o = \dfrac{20K_o(s+2)}{s(s+4)(s+10)}$.

This has poles at 0, -4 and -10, and a numerator root (called a zero) at $s = -2$, as shown in Fig. 8.32-3. As the phase shift due to numerator terms is opposite that of denominator terms, different symbols are used to denote whether a root is a zero or a pole. Again, the phase shift is $0°$ along the positive real axis, so that no part of the $180°$ phase locus is there. Along the negative real axis there are two zones in which the locus occurs. Between 0 and -2 the phase shift is $180°$ due to the pole at zero, and $0°$ due to the other roots. Between -2 and -4 the net phase shift is $0°$. Between -4 and -10 the net phase shift is again $180°$, since the roots at 0, -2, and -4 each have a $180°$ phase, while the root at -10 has a $0°$ phase. Between -10 and $-\infty$ the net phase shift is $0°$. Since the phase shift of the zero cancels the shift of one pole when s assumes a large complex value, the remaining portion of the $180°$ phase locus occurs along the plus and minus $90°$ vectors.

It should be noted that in each example the $180°$ phase locus was symmetrical about the real axis. This is because the roots of the closed-loop function always occur in conjugate pairs. Therefore when the $180°$ phase locus departs from the real axis, it indicates that the closed-loop roots have a complex pair if the gain is sufficient.

If two or more roots have the same value, they are treated as if they were each separate roots.

8.33 Graphic Determination of Closed-Loop Roots. Once the $180°$ phase locus has been obtained, the designer studies it to select the system gain. Since the overshoot from a step input is usually due to roots with complex pairs in the closed-loop expression, a relation determining the damping ratio of these roots is valuable. The quadratic expression

$$F(s) = \frac{1}{1 + 2\zeta s/\omega_1 + s^2/\omega_1^2}$$

$$= \frac{\omega_1^2}{(s + \zeta\omega_1 + j\omega_1 \sqrt{1 - \zeta^2})(s + \zeta\omega_1 - j\omega_1 \sqrt{1 - \zeta^2})} \qquad (8.33\text{-}1)$$

has complex roots, as shown in Fig. 8.33-1. It is seen that the angle γ is determined by

$$\gamma = \cos^{-1} \zeta \qquad (8.33\text{-}2)$$

It was shown in Section 7.20 that $\zeta = 0.39$ in a quadratic factor corresponded to an overshoot of about 26% for a unit step input. This would be equivalent to $\gamma = 67°$.

In practice the designer decides the value of ζ which is permissible, and draws a vector at the corresponding angle γ to the intersection of the 180° phase locus. The exact value of γ depends on the

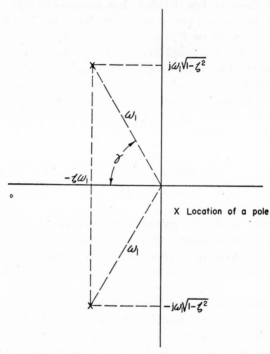

FIG. 8.33-1. Location of the complex roots of a quadratic equation on the s-plane.

system. Usually ζ should not be less than 0.36, but in high-order systems lower values are often permissible. This is because the transient contributions of the other root factors keep the low ζ term from causing the total overshoot to be excessive. One major advantage of the root locus method is that the output response equation can be determined quickly from the root locus plot. This is discussed in the next section. Hence the designer often tries one ζ (or γ value), finds its output response equation, and then selects either a higher or lower value, depending on the result.

Figures 8.32-1, 8.32-2, and 8.32-3 show γ vectors of 67°. This corresponds to $\zeta = 0.39$, which is a good central value. Thus if K_o is selected so that $F_o(s)$ is unity when s has the value at the γ intersection, the quadratic roots will have damping ratios of 0.39 and natural frequencies equal to the amplitude of the γ vector. The following examples will illustrate the procedure.

Once the designer has decided that a damping ratio of 0.39 is satisfactory, he draws a vector at 67°, as shown in Fig. 8.32-1. Next he determines the value K_o should have, so that the amplitude of $F_o(s)$ is unity when s is equal to the value at the intersection of the γ vector and the 180° phase locus. This is determined by substituting in (8.32-3) the magnitude of the vectors which are directed from each root to the point of intersection, and equating the result to unity. The result, for the case shown in Fig. 8.32-1, obtained by graphic measurements is

$$\frac{40K_o}{3.2 \times 4 \times 9.2} = 1 \qquad (8.33\text{-}3)$$

$$K_o = 2.94 \qquad (8.33\text{-}4)$$

Since the order of the denominator of F_o is 3 in this case, there are three closed-loop denominator roots. Two of these are complex conjugates and were determined by the γ vector. The other is a real root. The designer then determines the location of the remaining real root by trying sample points along the negative real axis, until one is found that makes F_o unity when K_o is 2.94. Again, using graphic calculations, it is found that when $s = -11.4$, the value of F_o is approximately unity.

As the gain is increased, the location of the roots along the 180° phase locus moves in the direction shown by the arrowheads. The reader may observe this by tracing the following root locations for the associated gains.

Gain	Denominator roots of θ_o/θ_i		
0.5	-0.63	-3.06	-10.31
1	$-1.71 + j0.935$	$-1.71 - j0.935$	-10.58
5	$-0.97 + j3.96$	$-0.97 - j3.96$	-12.06
10	$-0.37 + j5.5$	$-0.37 - j5.5$	-13.26
100	$+3.54 + j13.3$	$+3.54 - j13.3$	-21.1

The same method is used to select the gain for the example in Fig. 8.32-2. Thus the amplitude of the vectors from each of the roots to the γ vector and 180° phase locus intersection yields the value for the gain as

$$\frac{100K_o}{9 \times 1.6 \times 16.9} = 1 \qquad (8.33\text{-}5)$$

$$K_o = 2.44 \qquad (8.33\text{-}6)$$

The real root, evaluated graphically, is $s = -3.1$. The arrowheads on the 180° phase locus indicate the closed-loop root location as the gain is increased. Sample values are

Gain	Denominator roots of θ_o/θ_i		
0.5	$-4.74 + j8.52$,	$-4.74 - j8.52$,	-0.53
1.0	$-4.44 + j8.39$,	$-4.44 - j8.39$,	-1.11
10.	$j10$,	$-j10$,	-10
20.	$1.76 + j12$,	$1.76 - j12$,	-13.53

It is interesting to note that this is the same example as the second example in Section 7.40. There the gain was selected as 4.9 when $M_p = 1.5$.

Similarly, for the system in Fig. 8.32-3 the gain, determined graphically, is

$$\frac{20K_o \times 14.8}{15.5 \times 14.4 \times 14.8} = 1 \qquad (8.33\text{-}7)$$

$$K_o = 11.2 \qquad (8.33\text{-}8)$$

The real root is 1.86. Closed-loop denominator roots for various gain values are

Gain	Denominator roots of θ_o/θ_i		
0.5	-5.34,	-8.20,	-0.46
1	$-6.59 + j2.41$,	$-6.59 - j2.41$,	-0.82
10	$-6.08 + j13.4$,	$-6.08 - j13.4$,	-1.84
100	$-6.01 + j44.5$,	$-6.01 - i44.5$,	-1.98

8.34 GRAPHIC DETERMINATION OF TRANSIENT RESPONSE EQUATION. As demonstrated in Section 3.23, when an $F(s)$ is expressed in the partial fraction form,

$$F(s) = \frac{K_1}{s - r_1} + \frac{K_2}{s - r_2} + \frac{K_3}{s - r_3} + \dots \qquad (8.34\text{-}1)$$

the inverse transformation is

$$f(t) = K_1\epsilon^{r_1 t} + K_2\epsilon^{r_2 t} + K_3\epsilon^{r_3 t} + \ldots \qquad (8.34\text{-}2)$$

where
$$K_n = (s - r_n)F(s)\Big|_{s=r_n} \qquad (8.34\text{-}3)$$

The K_n coefficients may be evaluated graphically by substituting in (8.34-3) the amplitude and phase of the vectors which are directed from each numerator and denominator root to r_n.

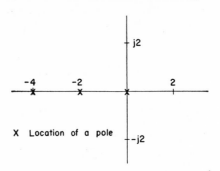

X   Location of a pole

FIG. 8.34-1. s-Plane plot showing root locations for

$$F(s) = \frac{1}{s(1 + 0.5s)(1 + 0.25s)}.$$

As an example, let

$$F(s) = \frac{1}{s(1 + 0.5s)(1 + 0.25s)} = \frac{8}{s(s + 2)(s + 4)} \qquad (8.34\text{-}4)$$

Then
$$f(t) = K_1 + K_2\epsilon^{-2t} + K_3\epsilon^{-4t} \qquad (8.34\text{-}5)$$

Here K_1 is equal to 8 divided by the product of the vectors from -2 to 0 and -4 to 0. Thus

$$K_1 = \frac{8}{2\angle 0° \times 4\angle 0°} = 1 \qquad (8.34\text{-}6)$$

Similarly,
$$K_2 = \frac{8}{2\angle 180° \times 2\angle 0°} = -2 \qquad (8.34\text{-}7)$$

and
$$K_3 = \frac{8}{4\angle 180° \times 2\angle 180°} = 1 \qquad (8.34\text{-}8)$$

The root locations for (8.34-4) are shown in Fig. 8.34-1.

Complex roots are handled in the same manner. If

$$F(s) = \cfrac{1}{s\left(1 + 2\zeta\,\dfrac{s}{\omega_1} + \dfrac{s^2}{\omega_1{}^2}\right)}$$

$$= \frac{\omega_1{}^2}{s(s + \zeta\omega_1 + j\omega_1\sqrt{1 - \zeta^2})(s + \zeta\omega_1 - j\omega_1\sqrt{1 - \zeta^2})} \quad (8.34\text{-}9)$$

then

$$f(t) = \frac{K_1}{s} + \frac{K_2}{s + \zeta\omega_1 + j\omega_1\sqrt{1 - \zeta^2}} + \frac{K_3}{s + \zeta\omega_1 - j\omega_1\sqrt{1 - \zeta^2}}$$

$$(8.34\text{-}10)$$

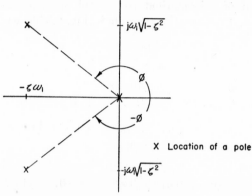

FIG. 8.34-2. s-Plane plot showing root locations for

$$F(s) = \frac{1}{s[1 + 2\zeta(s/\omega_1) + (s^2/\omega_1{}^2)]}.$$

The roots are shown in Fig. 8.34-2, and the coefficients, determined graphically, are

$$K_1 = \frac{\omega_1{}^2}{\omega_1\angle(180° - \phi) \times \omega_1\angle(\phi - 180°)} = 1 \quad (8.34\text{-}11)$$

$$K_2 = \frac{\omega_1{}^2}{\omega_1\angle{-\phi} \times 2\omega_1\sqrt{1 - \zeta^2}\,\angle{-90°}}$$

$$= \frac{1}{2\sqrt{1 - \zeta^2}}\angle(\phi + 90°) \quad (8.34\text{-}12)$$

$$K_3 = \frac{\omega_1{}^2}{\omega_1\angle\phi \times 2\omega_1\sqrt{1 - \zeta^2}\angle 90°}$$

$$= \frac{1}{2\sqrt{1 - \zeta^2}}\angle(-\phi - 90°) \quad (8.34\text{-}13)$$

where $\phi = \tan^{-1} \sqrt{1 - \zeta^2}/(-\zeta)$. Thus

$$f(t) = 1 + \frac{1}{2\sqrt{1 - \zeta^2}} \epsilon^{-\zeta\omega_1 t - j(\omega_1\sqrt{1-\zeta^2}t - \phi - \pi/2)}$$

$$+ \frac{1}{2\sqrt{1 - \zeta^2}} \epsilon^{-\zeta\omega_1 t + j(\omega_1\sqrt{1-\zeta^2}t - \phi - \pi/2)} \quad (8.34\text{-}14)$$

$$= 1 + \frac{1}{\sqrt{1 - \zeta^2}} \epsilon^{-\zeta\omega_1 t} \sin(\omega_1\sqrt{1 - \zeta^2}t - \phi) \quad (8.34\text{-}15)$$

which is the same as the result obtained in Section 3.23.

Application of this method to control problems may now be demonstrated. Consider the example in Fig. 8.32-3, where

$$\frac{\theta_o}{\theta_e} = F_o = \frac{20K_o(s + 2)}{s(s + 4)(s + 10)} \quad (8.34\text{-}16)$$

or

$$\frac{\theta_o}{\theta_i} = \frac{20K_o(s + 2)}{20K_o(s + 2) + s(s + 4)(s + 10)} \quad (8.34\text{-}17)$$

If K_o is 11.2, then using as denominator roots the values found in Section 8.33, eq. (8.34-17) becomes

$$\frac{\theta_o}{\theta_i} = \frac{224(s + 2)}{(s + 1.86)(s + 6.07 + j14.2)(s + 6.07 - j14.2)} \quad (8.34\text{-}18)$$

When θ_i is a unit step input, the Laplace transform for θ_o is

$$\theta_o(s) = \frac{224(s + 2)}{s(s + 1.86)(s + 6.07 + j14.2)(s + 6.07 - j14.2)} \quad (8.34\text{-}19)$$

which has the same form as (8.34-4) and (8.34-9). Hence

$$\theta_o(t) = K_1 + K_2\epsilon^{-1.86t} + K_3\epsilon^{-(6.07+j14.2)t} + K_4\epsilon^{-(6.07-j14.2)t} \quad (8.34\text{-}20)$$

where, by graphical measurement,

$$K_1 = \frac{224 \times 2}{1.86 \times 15.5\angle+67° \times 15.5\angle-67°} = 1 \quad (8.34\text{-}21)$$

$$K_2 = \frac{224 \times 0.14}{1.86\angle180° \times 14.85\angle73° \times 14.85\angle-73°} = -0.0765 \quad (8.34\text{-}22)$$

$$K_3 = \frac{224 \times 14.85\angle - 106°}{15.5\angle - 113° \times 14.85\angle - 107° \times 28.4\angle - 90°} = 0.509\angle 204°$$

$$(8.34\text{-}23)$$

$$K_4 = 0.509\angle - 204° \quad (K_3 \text{ and } K_4 \text{ are complex conjugates})$$

$$(8.34\text{-}24)$$

Substitution of the constants into (8.34-20) yields

$$\theta_o(t) = 1 - 0.0765\epsilon^{-1.86t} + 1.02\epsilon^{-6.07t} \cos (14.2t \text{ radians } - 204°)$$

$$(8.34\text{-}25)$$

All of the calculations necessary to find (8.34-25) were performed using graphical measurements. Therefore the values are not as exact as they would have been if the solution had been calculated using Laplace transform-pair 01.111. The variation between the exact solution to (8.34-19) and the graphic solution given by (8.34-25) is very small. As the time required for a graphic calculation is generally much less than for a numerical solution, the method has considerable merit.

PROBLEMS

8-1. Using the inverse F_o polar plot, find K_o so that $M_p = 1.5$ for the following cases.

(a) $F_o = \dfrac{K_o}{s(1 + 0.1s)(1 + 0.01s)}$ (d) $F_o = \dfrac{K_1}{s(s + 0.2)}$

(b) $F_o = \dfrac{K_o(1 + 5s)}{s^2(1 + 0.5s)(1 + 0.8s)}$ (e) $F_o = \dfrac{K_o}{s(1 + 0.02s + 0.01s^2)}$

(c) $F_o = \dfrac{K_o}{s(1 + 5s)}$

8-2. Repeat Problem 8-1, finding K_o when $M_p = 1.2$.

8-3. Plot the complete locus for

$$F_o^{-1} = \frac{20s(1 + 2s)(1 + 5s)}{(1 - 0.1s)}$$

Determine N, C, and Z. Is the system represented by this equation stable?

8-4. Plot the complete locus for

$$F_o^{-1} = 0.01s(1 + 0.1s)(1 + 0.05s)$$

Determine N, C, and Z. Is the system represented by this equation stable?

8-5. Draw the log-decibel method amplitude asymptotes for $K_o^{-1}F_o$ for each case in Problem 8-1. Visually estimate the approximate proper value of K_o and compare this result with the results obtained when Problems 7-1, 7-5, 8-1, or 8-2 were solved.

8-6. Plot the actual log-decibel method amplitude locus for each case in Problem 8-1.

8-7. Plot the phase for each case in Problem 8-1. Select K_o for each case so that the gain margin is 40°. How does the value of K_o selected in this manner compare with the value determined by Problems 8-1 and 8-2?

8-8. Find A_{db} when A has the following values.

$$5, 0.3, 28, 160, 0.32, 0.004, 75, 2, 0.0125, 80$$

8-9. Find the 180° phase locus for each case in Problem 8-1.

8-10. Determine K_o so that $\gamma = 67°$ for each case in Problem 8-9. Is it possible that in some cases γ must be greater than 67° for all values of gain? How do the values of K_o determined in this manner compare with those determined by other methods.

8-11. Find all the roots when $\gamma = 67°$ for each case in Problem 8-9. What is θ_o/θ_i in factored form for each case?

8-12. Use the method discussed in Section 8.34 to determine the transient response for a unit step input of each case in Problem 8-11.

CHAPTER 9

TYPES OF COMPENSATION

9.00 Introduction

We assumed in Chapters 7 and 8 that the systems under consideration were basically stable, and only the proper gain value needed to be determined. This is not always the case. The Type 2 example of eq. (4.54-3) in Chapter 4 is unstable for any value of gain, and so is the Type 1 nonminimum-phase example of eq. (6.10-2) in Chapter 6.

Therefore it is essential to be able to alter the frequency and phase characteristics of a system's transfer function. Elements which do this are called "compensating functions." They may consist of nothing more than a few inexpensive resistors and capacitors connected between amplifier stages, or they may be expensive rate gyros, as in the autopilot example in Fig. 4.30-1. In each case they are necessary for one or more of the following reasons:

1. System stability.
2. Better speed of response.
3. Enable K_o to have a higher value.
4. Reduce the effect of external disturbances.
5. Substitute a relatively steady feedback characteristic for an undesirable system characteristic.

Practically any rational $F(s)$ transfer function, both minimum- and nonminimum-phase, can be physically realized. The major limitation is that the denominator order of s in the output-to-input ratio must always be at least as high as the numerator order. Thus when an instrument is used to measure $\dot{\theta}$, the rate of a variable θ, the transfer function is not

$$V/\theta = s \qquad (9.00\text{-}1)$$

where V is a voltage representing $\dot{\theta}$. Instead, the instrument dynamic characteristics, at least to the first order, should be included.

The relation then becomes

$$\frac{V}{\theta} = \frac{s}{1 + Ts} \qquad (9.00\text{-}2)$$

where T is the first-order time lag of the rate instrument. Once the designer has assured himself that the instrument time lag T is so small that it cannot have an appreciable effect on the system operation, he often eliminates it. This enables the mathematic relations to be simplified without altering their solution much. The designer always recognizes, however, that when he uses an expression such as (9.00-1), he can never realize it with physical instruments.

In the design of a system the designer begins with an expression which describes the operation of the object he wishes to control. He then utilizes the techniques discussed in previous chapters to determine the proper gain setting. If the dynamics are such that operation with this gain setting is unsatisfactory, the designer studies the possibility of adding frequency-dependent terms in the system. These terms alter the open-loop transfer characteristic in a favorable manner and permit satisfactory operation to be obtained.

When compensators are inserted in the forward loop (i.e. between an amplifier and a servo motor), they are called "cascaded" compensators. When they are used to monitor output variables and insert signals in the control system as functions of those variables (i.e., a rate generator signal feedback), they are called "feedback" compensators. Either kind or any combination of the two may be used.

Cascaded compensation generally is the less expensive. Usually it consists of nothing more than a few resistors and capacitors inserted between amplifier stages. But if the system operates on an a-c carrier, it may require the addition of a demodulator and a d-c amplification stage. The compensating function is inserted between the demodulator and the d-c amplifier. Resistance and capacitance elements may also be used to form compensating functions for a-c signals without requiring demodulation. Parallel-T and bridge-T networks are used. However, these networks are difficult to adjust for most applications, and special characteristics are harder to realize. The theory for a-c compensators is the same as for d-c compensators, namely, the network characteristics must be symmetrical about the carrier frequency. The carrier frequency is

zero for d-c systems, and the compensator characteristics for negative frequencies are the mirror images of the positive frequency
characteristics.

Feedback (or parallel) compensators are usually larger and more
expensive than cascaded elements. This is not always the case.
Sometimes a voltage, such as the output of a motor-generator which
feeds into an output drive motor, is also fed back to the input
through a resistor, capacitor, and inductor circuit. Feedback compensation of this type is relatively simple and inexpensive. The
principal advantages of feedback compensators are that they may
be used to substitute the feedback element characteristic for the
forward characteristic, and that they are not so much affected by
changes in system dynamics.

9.10 Cascaded lead compensation

A proportional control system is one in which the magnitude of the
error signal is detected and a corrective signal proportional to it is

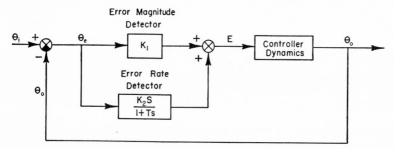

Fig. 9.10-1.   Proportional-plus-rate control system.

applied to the controller. If the rate of change of the error signal
is detected, as well as the magnitude, the system is a proportional-
plus-rate system. The advantage of such a system is evident. The
error signal now has anticipation. It not only knows the magnitude
of the error, but it also knows the probable magnitude in the future.
If the error rate is high, the error magnitude will change rapidly.
If the error rate is low, the magnitude change will be small. By
applying a signal having this information to a controller, the system
operation should be (and generally is) faster.

Figure 9.10-1 shows a simple block diagram with proportional
and rate channels. In equation form this becomes

$$E = K_1\theta_e + \frac{K_2 s}{1 + T_1 s}\theta_e \tag{9.10-1}$$

or
$$\frac{E}{\theta_e} = K_1\left(\frac{1 + \alpha T_1 s}{1 + T_1 s}\right) \tag{9.10-2}$$

where $\alpha T_1 = K_2/K_1 + T_1$. When $s = j\omega$ in (9.10-2), the phase shift is always positive, starting with a low value at the low frequencies, reaching a maximum at $\omega = 1/T_1\sqrt{\alpha}$, and then declining to $0°$ at $\omega = \infty$. The amplitude is K_1 at $\omega = 0$ and increases to αK_1 at $\omega = \infty$.

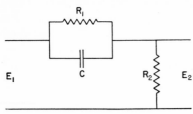

Fig. 9.10-2.   Lead circuit.

Functions such as (9.10-2) can be realized, except for a constant gain factor, by the simple resistance and capacitance network shown in Fig. 9.10-2. The transfer function is

$$\frac{E_2}{E_1} = \frac{R_2(1 + R_1 C s)}{R_1 + R_2 + R_1 R_2 C s} \tag{9.10-3}$$

By equating the coefficients of (9.10-2) and (9.10-3), it may be shown that

$$\alpha = \frac{1}{K_1} = \frac{R_1 + R_2}{R_2} \tag{9.10-4}$$

$$\alpha T_1 = R_1 C \tag{9.10-5}$$

$$\omega_m = \frac{\sqrt{\alpha}}{R_1 C} \tag{9.10-6}$$

where ω_m is the frequency at which maximum phase shift occurs. The derivation for this transfer function was given in Section 3.50, and different forms for representing the transfer relation were shown in Fig. 4.10-2.

Another useful form is

$$\frac{E_o}{E_1} = \frac{K(1 + \sqrt{\alpha}\, Ts)}{1 + Ts/\sqrt{\alpha}} \tag{9.10-7}$$

This has the advantage of having the maximum phase shift occur at $T\omega = 1$, and therefore this form is better for chart purposes.

The amplitude and phase characteristics for $K = 1$ and various values of α are shown in Fig. 9.10-3. The chart is used in the same manner as the nondimensional charts in Chapter 2. In practice α is usually between 5 and 10. Sometimes two or more lead circuits are used, but rarely does the product of the α factors exceed 25 in a system because of noise amplification.

A simple example of the improvement which is possible when a lead circuit is used may be seen by considering the function

$$\frac{\theta_o}{\theta_e} = F_o = \frac{K_o}{s(1 + 0.1s)} \tag{9.10-8}$$

In Chapter 7 the value of K_o for this example was determined to be 16.7 for $M_p = 1.5$. If a lead circuit were inserted in this system so that

$$F_o = \frac{1 + 0.1s}{1 + 0.02s} \times \frac{K_o}{s(1 + 0.1s)} \tag{9.10-9}$$

then K_o would be 83.5 for $M_p = 1.5$, and the system would respond to an input disturbance 5 times as fast. The lead circuit cancels the $(1 + 0.1s)$ factor in the original dynamics, substituting for it a factor whose time constant is much smaller. However, this example indicates a larger benefit than is normally obtained. The dynamics in (9.10-8) were such that a lead circuit could be peaked at any high frequency and a quicker response would result.

A more realistic example is

$$F_o = \frac{K_o G_1}{s(1 + 0.1s + 0.01s^2)} \tag{9.10-10}$$

where G_1 is the lead circuit characteristic which will be determined. When $G_1 = 1$, this is the same example that has been used in several previous sections. In Section 7.40 the gain for $M_p = 1.5$ was determined to be 4.9. This is a particularly stringent example in that the denominator contains a quadratic expression with complex roots. Thus the phase shift for (9.10-10) in the neighborhood of $\omega = 10$ (the quadratic natural frequency) is more rapid than a single lead circuit can counteract.

If a single lead compensator is used, it should have its peak phase shift around the frequency where the phase shift of (9.10-10) is slightly more negative than 180°. A reasonable value for α is between

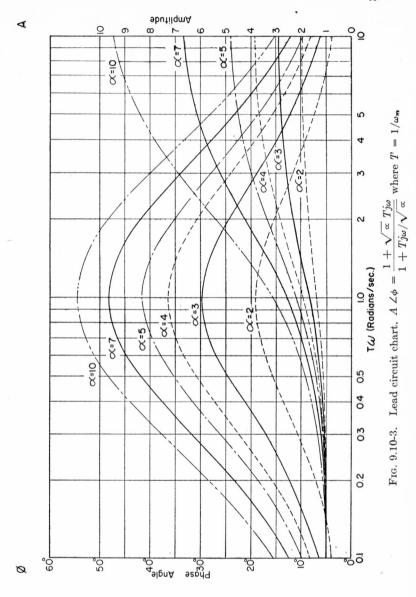

FIG. 9.10-3. Lead circuit chart. $A \angle \phi = \dfrac{1 + \sqrt{\alpha} \; T j \omega}{1 + T j \omega / \sqrt{\alpha}}$ where $T = 1/\omega_m$

5 and 10. Using a lead compensator peaked at $\omega_m = 12$ and with $\alpha = 5$, eq. (9.10-10) becomes

$$F_o = \frac{K_o(1 + 0.185s)}{s(1 + 0.037s)(1 + 0.1s + 0.01s^2)} \tag{9.10-11}$$

The polar plot is shown in Fig. 9.10-4. Here K_o is 4.45 for $M_p = 1.5$. With these values, the final result in factored form is

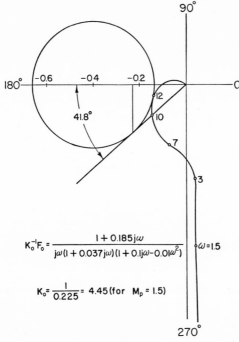

$$K_o^{-1}F_o = \frac{1 + 0.185j\omega}{j\omega(1 + 0.037j\omega)(1 + 0.1j\omega - 0.01\omega^2)}$$

$$K_o = \frac{1}{0.225} = 4.45 \,(\text{for } M_p = 1.5)$$

Fig. 9.10-4.

$$\frac{\theta_o}{\theta_i} = \frac{1 + 0.185s}{(1 + 0.344s)(1 + 0.034s)(1 + 0.032s + 0.0072s^2)} \tag{9.10-12}$$

The output response to a unit step input is given by Laplace transform pair 02.121 (with $b = 0$) as

$$\theta_o = 1 - 0.531\epsilon^{-2.91t} - 0.078\epsilon^{-29.4t}$$
$$+ 0.564\epsilon^{-2.24t} \sin (656t° - 136.5°) \tag{9.10-13}$$

This is shown in Fig. 9.10-5, along with the result when other compensating functions are used. It is seen that the improvement is not so great as that which resulted in (9.10-9). This is because the phase lead of the single lead circuit compensator is insufficient to overcome the system lags. Appreciable improvement in the speed of response could result only if additional phase lead were used (such as 2 lead circuits) in a manner so that the value of the unity crossover frequency would be appreciably increased.

The plot of (9.10-13) is interesting in that it shows the typical effect of lead compensation. As the output nears the final value,

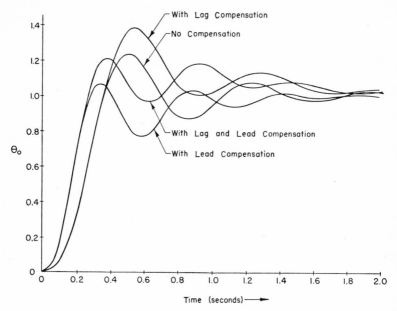

FIG. 9.10-5.   Output response to a unit step input when various compensation methods are used.

the rate signal from the lead circuit functions to keep the output from overshooting, and in doing this the output "undershoots" more than overshoots.

Another system input, which is often used in evaluating system operation, is a unit rate input. That is, if

$$\theta_i(t) = t \qquad\qquad (9.10\text{-}14)$$

then

$$\theta_i(s) = \frac{1}{s^2} \qquad\qquad (9.10\text{-}15)$$

Usually the magnitude of the error θ_e is plotted *vs.* time; $\theta_e(t)$ may be found in the following manner. When θ_i is a unit rate input, θ_o for the system given by (9.10-12) is

$$\theta_o(s) = \frac{1 + 0.185s}{s^2(1 + 0.344s)(1 + 0.034s)(1 + 0.032s + 0.0072s^2)} \qquad (9.10\text{-}16)$$

Using Laplace transform pair 02.221 (with $b = 0$), the output is

$$\theta_o(t) = t - 0.225 + 0.182\epsilon^{-2.91t} + 0.0026\epsilon^{-29.4t}$$
$$+ 0.0478\epsilon^{-2.24t} \sin (656t° - 238.1°) \qquad (9.10\text{-}17)$$

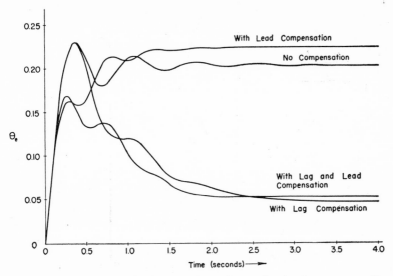

Fig. 9.10-6.   Error magnitude for a unit rate input when various compensation methods are used.

Since $\theta_e = \theta_i - \theta_o$, subtraction of (9.10-17) from (9.10-14) yields

$$\theta_e = 0.225 - 0.182\epsilon^{-2.91t} - 0.0026\epsilon^{-29.4t}$$
$$- 0.0478\epsilon^{-2.24t} \sin (656t° - 238.1°) \qquad (9.10\text{-}18)$$

This result is shown in Fig. 9.10-6, along with the results for the same basic dynamics when other compensating methods (discussed in later sections) are used.

It was shown in Section 4.53 that for Type 1 systems θ_e has a steady-state value of $1/K_o$ when a unit rate input is applied. In this example, the use of a lead compensator resulted in K_o being

4.45, against a value of 4.9 without any compensation. Thus Fig. 9.10-6 shows θ_e is larger in the steady state with lead compensation than it is without. This is undesirable, for θ_e should be as small as possible. Consequently, lead compensation does not aid this par-

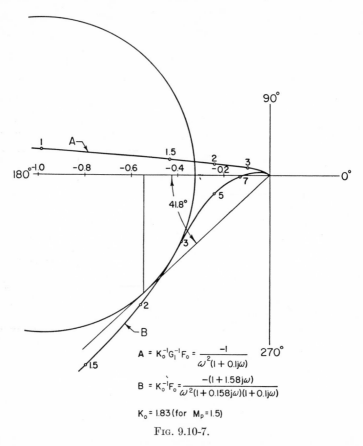

$$A = K_o^{-1}G_1^{-1}F_o = \frac{-1}{\omega^2(1 + 0.1j\omega)}$$

$$B = K_o^{-1}F_o = \frac{-(1 + 1.58j\omega)}{\omega^2(1 + 0.158j\omega)(1 + 0.1j\omega)}$$

$$K_o = 1.83 \,(\text{for } M_p = 1.5)$$

Fig. 9.10-7.

ticular system for rate inputs, unless more than one lead circuit is used. If two lead circuits (each with $\alpha = 5$ and $\omega_m = 22.4$) were used with the dynamics in (9.10-10), a polar plot of F_o would show that K_o could be 9.8 for $M_p = 1.5$, and the crossover frequency would be approximately 15 radians per second. The improvement which this compensation would provide for unit step and rate inputs is left as an exercise for the reader.

As an example of the use of a lead circuit to stabilize dynamics which otherwise would be unstable for any gain, consider

$$F_o = \frac{K_o G_1}{s^2(1 + 0.1s)} \qquad (9.10\text{-}19)$$

where G_1 represents a lead compensator whose value is to be determined. The system is unstable without G_1, as the F_o polar plot general shape should be like that in Fig. 6.10-1e for stability. The polar plot of $K_o^{-1}G_1^{-1}F_o$ is shown in Fig. 9.10-7 by locus A. If a single lead compensator with $\alpha = 10$ is used, it should be peaked around $\omega = 2$. This is determined by studying locus A, and remembering that the maximum phase shift when $\alpha = 10$ is 55°. The final locus should have a margin of about 40°, in order that a reasonably low value for M_p may be used. Therefore the lead circuit cannot be peaked at any frequency where the phase shift of $K_o^{-1}G_1^{-1}F_o$ is more negative than $-195°$. Selecting the lead circuit phase peak at $\omega = 2$, the valve of G_1 becomes

$$G_1 = \frac{1 + 1.58s}{1 + 0.158s} \qquad (9.10\text{-}20)$$

The resulting polar plot of $K_o^{-1}F_o$ is shown in Fig. 9.10-7 by locus B. Here K_o is 1.83 when $M_p = 1.5$.

Thus stability has been achieved in a relatively simple manner. The same approach is applied to most problems, namely, the dynamics are studied and compensating functions are selected based on the system needs. Lead circuits are one important type of compensation.

9.20 Cascaded lag compensation

In the preceding section it was demonstrated that a compensator having a leading phase characteristic is desirable. It might seem strange then, that in this section we will show that a lagging phase characteristic is also desirable. Each, of course, is only desirable for a particular set of conditions.

Proportional and proportional-plus-rate control systems were discussed in the preceding section. Suppose that instead of the error rate, we used the integral of the error signal in addition to the proportional factor. This is shown in Fig. 9.20-1. Is such a system desirable? It means that if θ_e has any value, the integrating action will cause E to increase until θ_e is driven to zero. Applications for small error systems are numerous. For instance, a multicolor printing press must have a very small register error. Hence a proportional-plus-integral control system is highly desirable for such applications.

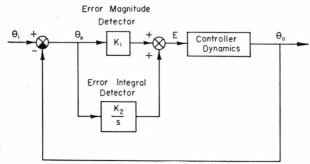

FIG. 9.20-1.   Proportional-plus-integral control system.

The relation between E and θ_e is

$$E = K_1\theta_e + \frac{K_2}{s}\theta_e \qquad (9.20\text{-}1)$$

or

$$\frac{E}{\theta_e} = K_2\frac{1 + Ts}{s} \qquad (9.20\text{-}2)$$

where

$$T = K_1/K_2$$

A purely integrating element usually involves the addition of several bulky and expensive components. Therefore if a resistor and capacitor circuit which approximated the proportional plus integrator effect would be adequate, it would present a cheaper and more compact solution. The answer is a circuit whose characteristic is the reciprocal of the lead circuit, namely,

$$\frac{E_o}{E_1} = \frac{1 + Ts/\sqrt{\alpha}}{1 + \sqrt{\alpha}\,Ts} \qquad (9.20\text{-}3)$$

or letting $T = \sqrt{\alpha}\,T_1$,

$$\frac{E_o}{E_1} = \frac{1 + T_1 s}{1 + \alpha T_1 s} \qquad (9.20\text{-}4)$$

The lead circuit chart in Fig. 9.10-3 may be used as a lag circuit chart by merely taking the reciprocal of the amplitude and the negative of the phase angle. Equation (9.20-3) has the advantage of having the peak phase shift occur at $T\omega = 1$, and (9.20-4) is a form which is easier to visualize.

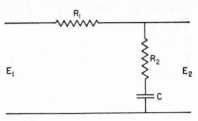

FIG. 9.20-2.   Lag circuit.

The transfer characteristic of (9.20-4) can be realized rather simply by the circuit in Fig. 9.20-2, where

$$\frac{E_2}{E_1} = \frac{1 + R_2Cs}{1 + (R_1 + R_2)Cs} \tag{9.20-5}$$

Equating coefficients with (9.20-4) yields

$$T_1 = R_2C \tag{9.20-6}$$

$$\alpha = 1 + \frac{R_1}{R_2} \tag{9.20-7}$$

$$\omega_m = \frac{1}{R_2C\sqrt{\alpha}} \tag{9.20-8}$$

where ω_m is the frequency at which the maximum phase shift occurs.

A comparison of the frequency response characteristics of a pure proportional-plus-integral characteristic, and α times (9.20-4) is shown in Fig. 9.20-3. It is seen that in the very high-frequency range both are unity. In the intermediate range they are somewhat the same, and at the low frequencies they are alike only in that all are greater than unity.

In practice a lag circuit is used to boost the system response at the very low frequencies. The circuit is selected so that the amplitude of α times (9.20-4) is approximately unity, and the phase is $-10°$ or less for all frequencies above ω_p, where ω_p is the peak response frequency which a properly adjusted system would have without the lag circuit. Inspection of Fig. 9.20-3 shows the advantage of this. All frequencies around and above ω_p are not affected much because the lag circuit (times α) is approximately unity. However, all frequencies below ω_p have their amplitude boosted.

If a true proportional-plus-integral element is used, the open-loop amplitude for zero frequency is boosted to infinity, and a normally Type 1 system is changed into a Type 2 system. If a lag circuit is used, the open-loop zero frequency point is boosted by a factor of α (actually only approximately α, since the system gain for a fixed M_p changes somewhat less than a factor of α).

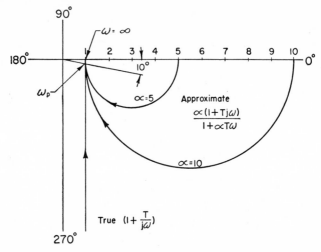

Fig. 9.20-3. Polar loci of true and approximate proportional-plus-integral compensator characteristics. Arrowheads indicate direction of increasing frequency.

An example will illustrate this type of compensation. Let the open-loop function be

$$F_o = \frac{K_1 K_2 G_1}{s(1 + 0.1s + 0.01s^2)} \tag{9.20-9}$$

where $K_1 G_1$ is a lag compensator whose value is to be determined. The function $K_1^{-1} K_2^{-1} G_1^{-1} F_o$ is shown in Fig. 9.20-4. The same dynamics have been used in several previous examples. Without any compensation, the proper gain was determined in Section 7.40 to be 4.9 for $M_p = 1.5$, and ω_p was approximately 8 radians per second.

A proper lag compensator for this case would be one which had little phase shift around and above $\omega = 8$, and whose amplitude was approximately unity for these high frequencies. At lower frequencies the compensator phase shift could be higher, as long as the final open-loop locus did not cut back into the system M_p-circle. The lag compensator amplitude should be much higher than one for the low frequencies. These are satisfied by selecting a lag circuit having

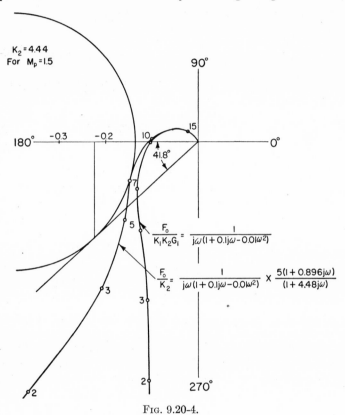

$$K_2 = 4.44$$
For $M_p = 1.5$

$$\frac{F_o}{K_1 K_2 G_1} = \frac{1}{j\omega(1 + 0.1j\omega - 0.01\omega^2)}$$

$$\frac{F_o}{K_2} = \frac{1}{j\omega(1 + 0.1j\omega - 0.01\omega^2)} \times \frac{5(1 + 0.896j\omega)}{(1 + 4.48j\omega)}$$

FIG. 9.20-4.

$\alpha = 5$ and $\omega_m = 0.5$. Then the phase shift is $-10°$ at $\omega = 5$, and less at higher frequencies. Letting

$$K_1 G_1 = \frac{5(1 + 0.896s)}{(1 + 4.48s)} \qquad (9.20\text{-}10)$$

the locus $K_2{}^{-1}F_o$ shown in Fig. 9.20-4 is obtained. Now K_2 may be selected for a specified M_p. When $M_p = 1.5$, $K_2 = 4.44$. This makes the total system open-loop gain $K_o = 22.2$, which is almost

5 times as large as the 4.9 value determined without a lag compensator. The final open-loop expression is

$$F_o = \frac{22.2(1 + 0.896s)}{s(1 + 4.48s)(1 + 0.1s + 0.01s^2)} \qquad (9.20\text{-}11)$$

and the closed-loop expression in factored form is

$$\frac{\theta_o}{\theta_i} = \frac{1 + 0.896s}{(1 + 0.674s)(1 + 0.21s)(1 + 0.057s + 0.0142s^2)} \qquad (9.20\text{-}12)$$

The output response to a unit step input is given by Laplace transform pair 02.121 as

$$\theta_o = 1 + 0.505\epsilon^{-1.48t} - 1.408\epsilon^{-4.76t} + 0.762\epsilon^{-2t} \sin (468t^\circ - 172.7^\circ) \qquad (9.20\text{-}13)$$

The result is shown in Fig. 9.10-5. It is seen that the output with lag compensation follows the output without any compensation for the first 0.35 second. Then the lag circuit overshoots more. Also, with lag compensation the output oscillates above the steady-state value as against below the steady-state value in the case of lead compensation, and about the steady-state value with no compensation. The integrating action of the lag circuit is responsible for the greater overshoot. It tends to sum the error *vs.* time. Thus when the output reaches the input, the integral of the error has a value which keeps the control signal from being reversed until a greater overshoot has occurred.

The major benefit which is obtained by the use of a lag circuit is that the open-loop gain K_o is higher. This is advantageous in minimizing the error with rate inputs. If a unit rate input is applied to the system given by (9.20-12), the system error is

$$\theta_e = 0.045 + 0.341\epsilon^{-1.48t} - 0.296\epsilon^{-4.76t}$$
$$- 0.0908\epsilon^{-2t} \sin (468t^\circ - 276.6^\circ) \qquad (9.20\text{-}14)$$

This is shown in Fig. 9.10-6, along with the response when other compensating methods are used. The error magnitude is approximately the same with lag compensation as it is without any compensation for the first 0.4 second. Then the integrating effect of the lag circuit becomes pronounced, and the error magnitude decays to its steady-state value of $1/K_o$.

9.30 Cascaded lag and lead compensation

Both the fast response benefit of lead compensation and the high K_o benefit of lag compensation may be obtained by inserting a compensating function with both characteristics in the system. The physical realization of combination compensating functions is discussed in Section 9.50. Design data for a number of typical circuits are given in Appendix 3.

In order that a comparison of the benefit may be made, the same dynamics that were used in Sections 9.10 and 9.20 will be used, namely,

$$F_o = \frac{K_1 G_1 K_2 G_2}{s(1 + 0.1s + 0.01s^2)} \tag{9.30-1}$$

where G_1 is the lead circuit characteristic, $K_2 G_2$ is the lag circuit characteristic, K_1 is a system gain adjustment. The same lead circuit characteristic used in (9.10-12) may be used in this example. Thus

$$G_1 = \frac{1 + 0.185s}{1 + 0.037s} \tag{9.30-2}$$

and Fig. 9.10-4 is the open-loop polar plot which may be used to select the lag circuit characteristics. Letting $\alpha = 5$ for the lag circuit, ω_m may be selected to be 1. Then the lag circuit phase shift is $-10°$ at $\omega = 10$, and at higher frequencies, the phase shift is less. Thus a reasonable value for the lag circuit is

$$K_2 G_2 = \frac{5(1 + 0.448s)}{(1 + 2.24s)} \tag{9.30-3}$$

The final open-loop function is

$$K_1^{-1} F_o = \frac{5(1 + 0.448s)(1 + 0.185s)}{s(1 + 2.24s)(1 + 0.037s)(1 + 0.1s + 0.01s^2)} \tag{9.30-4}$$

This is shown in Fig. 9.30-1. Here K_1 is 3.78 for $M_p = 1.5$. Since $K_o = K_1 K_2$, then K_o is 18.9 in the properly adjusted system. Using these values, the closed-loop relation in factored form is

$$\frac{\theta_o}{\theta_i} = \frac{1 + 0.633s + 0.083s^2}{(1 + 0.0341s)(1 + 0.616s + 0.158s^2)(1 + 0.0357s + 0.00817s^2)} \tag{9.30-5}$$

When the input is a unit step, the output is

$$\theta_o = 1 - 0.066\epsilon^{-29.3t} + 0.916\epsilon^{-1.95t} \sin(91t° - 39.7°)$$
$$+ 0.574\epsilon^{-2.2t} \sin(625t° - 142.5°) \tag{9.30-6}$$

When the input is a unit rate, the error is

$$\theta_o = 0.0529 - 0.00225\epsilon^{-29.3t} - 0.363\epsilon^{-1.95t} \sin (91t° - 180.5°)$$
$$- 0.0516\epsilon^{-2.2t} \sin (625t° - 243.9°) \quad (9.30\text{-}7)$$

Equation (9.30-6) is shown in Fig. 9.10-5, and eq. (9.30-7) is shown in Fig. 9.10-6. In each case the combined lag and lead compensated system possesses the most favorable characteristics.

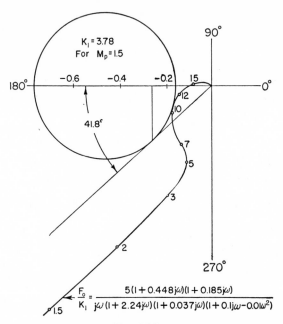

FIG. 9.30-1.

9.40 Selecting compensator characteristics with the log-decibel method

The proper lead and lag compensator characteristics can be selected rapidly, using the log decibel method. Generally only an amplitude asymptote sketch is needed to determine corner frequency values for the compensators. System gain is determined in the normal manner, either by adding the necessary correction factors to the amplitude asymptote locus, plotting the phase locus, and choosing an acceptable phase margin, or by using the polar plot to determine the gain for a desired M_p value.

Figure 9.40-1 shows the amplitude asymptotes for a lead and a lag compensator. It is seen that a lead compensator causes the amplitude asymptote to change from a 0 db slope to a positive 6 db per octave slope between the two lead circuit corner frequencies. Since we associate a positive 90° phase angle with a positive 6 db per octave slope, the phase shift of the lead circuit tends toward a maximum of 90°. The exact value of the maximum phase shift depends upon the spacing between corner frequencies, or α. It

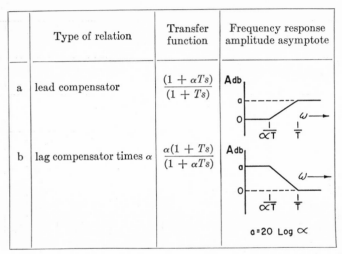

Fig. 9.40-1. Log-decibel amplitude asymptote sketches for lead and lag compensators.

occurs at ω_m, where ω_m is equal to the square root of the product of the corner frequencies. The lag compensator characteristics are similar to the lead circuit characteristics. Its amplitude asymptote has a negative 6 db per octave slope between the corner frequencies, and a negative phase angle.

The positive slope of the lead compensator amplitude asymptote and the negative slope of the lag compensator are used to alter the system open-loop dynamics, so that more favorable characteristics result.

When the log-decibel approach is used, it may be readily seen why the gain for the example given by (9.10-11) was not higher with a lead circuit than without. Also, the need for a double lead circuit to improve that example appreciably is apparent. These are shown by the loci in Fig. 9.40-2. The phase angle to which each amplitude asymptote slope will tend is shown on each straight-line segment. As the dynamics in this case are of the form in Fig. 6.10-1d, the system gain for stability should be such that the phase angle is no more negative than 180° when the open-loop amplitude is 0 db. Furthermore, for proper adjustment the system phase angle should be no more negative than about −140° (this allows a 40° phase margin) when the open-loop amplitude is 0 db.

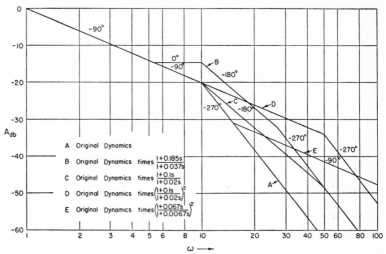

FIG. 9.40-2. Amplitude asymptotes for $1/s(1 + 0.1s + 0.01s^2)$ with various lead compensators.

Locus A in Fig. 9.40-2, which represents the original dynamics, has a −6 db per octave slope for all frequencies under 10 radians per second, and a −18 db per octave slope for all higher frequencies. The −6 db per octave slope corresponds to a −90° phase shift, and the −18 db per octave slope corresponds to a −270° phase shift. Therefore the phase for locus A starts at −90° in the low frequencies and changes rapidly around $\omega = 10$ to −270°. This information is sufficient, so that it may be stated that the proper system gain is such that the unity crossover frequency on the asymptote plot would be somewhat less than 10 radians per second. This conclusion may be reached rather easily by remembering that the amplitude correction factor for complex roots is positive, and that the phase shift due to the complex roots is $-90°$ at $\omega = 10$, making the total phase $180°$ at that frequency.

Locus B in Fig. 9.40-2 shows the amplitude asymptotes for $K_o^{-1}F_o$ of the system represented by (9.10-11). This differs from locus A in that it has a lead compensator with $\omega_m = 12$ and $\alpha = 5$. The lead compensator causes the amplitude slope to be zero between 5.4 and 10 radians per second. Then the amplitude drops off at -12 db per octave, which tends toward a $180°$ phase shift. Again, the amplitude asymptote locus contains sufficient information so that the designer can estimate the proper system gain setting. The amplitude correction factors for both the lead compensator corner frequency at $\omega = 5.4$ and the quadratic are positive. Therefore the proper open-loop 0 db level is very near to the zero amplitude asymptote slope between $\omega = 5.4$ and 10. Thus this lead compensator does not affect the final K_o value very much at all.

By changing the lead compensator corner frequencies so that the compensator is

$$G_1 = \frac{1 + 0.10s}{1 + 0.02s} \tag{9.40-1}$$

locus C is obtained. Now the unity crossover frequency in a properly adjusted system should be closer to 10 radians per second than it should be to locus A. Hence the system gain could be slightly higher with this lead circuit than without it.

However, the compensators in both loci B and C fail to provide the sizable system improvement which the designer usually seeks. Generally a designer does not rely upon a small gain change or a slightly different compensator characteristic to achieve the end results. In this case, an increased speed of response will result only if the unity crossover frequency is appreciably increased. This requires a compensator which will cause both a -6 db per octave slope and a phase angle which tends toward $-90°$ in the high-frequency zone. The -6 db per octave slope must be of sufficient duration so that the phase shift is adequate. Loci D and E illustrate examples.

Locus D was obtained by utilizing two lead compensators, each with the same characteristics as that in (9.40-1). Thus the numerator corner frequency cancels the denominator quadratic natural frequency (except for a small correction factor due to the different

ζ values). This enables the amplitude asymptote to continue at a
−6 db per octave slope to the lead circuit denominator corner
frequency.

In locus E a double lead circuit, each with corner frequencies
at $\omega = 15$ and 150, was used. This provides a -6 db per octave
shelf between 15 and 150 radians. The major disadvantage of this
locus is the high net α which is required by the lead circuit. The

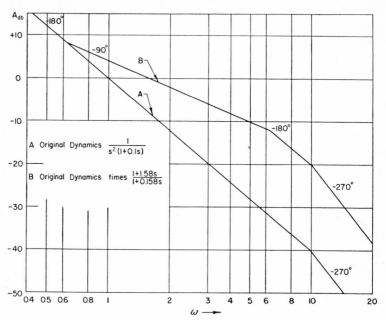

Fɪɢ. 9.40-3. Amplitude asymptote loci showing stabilizing effect of lead
compensation.

net α is the product of the lead circuit α factors, and is 100 in this
case. Factors of this magnitude often cause serious system noise
problems which are discussed in Chapter 10.

Locus A in Fig. 9.40-3 shows the amplitude asymptote for the
system expressed by (9.10-19) without lead compensation. This
system is unstable, since it does not satisfy the general shape shown
in Fig. 6.10-1e. Stability can be achieved in the same manner as
that in loci D and E of Fig. 9.40-2, namely, insert a lead compensator
which changes the asymptote slope to -6 db per octave over a
sufficient frequency zone, and select the system gain. Locus B shows

the amplitude asymptote when the lead compensator given by
(9.10-20) is used. It may be seen that the lead compensator corner
frequencies could not have been selected much higher, or a single
lead compensator would not be sufficient to effect stability.

Lag circuits are selected by making their highest corner frequency
approximately one-fifth that of the unity crossover frequency.
This keeps the negative phase of the lag compensator from appreciably affecting the system dynamics around the -1 point. Figure
9.40-4 shows the amplitude asymptotes for the example in Section
9.20. The selection of this compensator was discussed in that section.

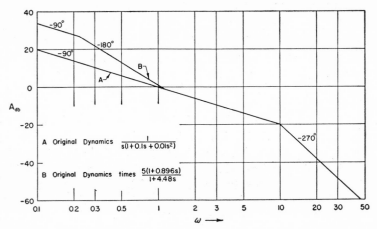

Fig. 9.40-4.   Amplitude asymptote loci showing effect of lag compensation.

Approximately these same characteristics would be chosen if the
lag compensator were selected on the basis of locus A in Fig. 9.40-4.
The steps are described below. Since the natural frequency of the
quadratic is 10 radians per second, the net phase shift at $\omega = 10$ is
$180°$ ($-90°$ from the -6 db per octave slope and $-90°$ from the
quadratic). Therefore the unity crossover frequency in a properly
adjusted system would be somewhat less than 10 radians per second.
Assume it is 7 radians per second. Then, allowing a spacing factor
of 5, the highest corner frequency of the lag circuit is 1.4 radians
per second, and the lag compensator characteristic times α for
$\alpha = 5$ is

$$KG = \frac{5(1 + 0.715s)}{(1 + 3.575s)} \qquad (9.40\text{-}2)$$

This, combined with the original dynamics, is approximately the same as locus B.

Knowledge of a functions' amplitude asymptote behavior plus the phase magnitude at a few important frequencies is usually sufficient to permit the designer to select the lead and lag compensator values. In addition, he can usually estimate the approximate proper system gain value and the unity crossover frequency.

9.50 Physical realization of compensating functions

Many lead and lag compensator characteristics (along with other characteristics which the designer may want) can be physically realized, except for a constant gain factor, by electric circuits composed of resistors, capacitors, and inductors. Appendix 3 summarizes design data for a number of typical functions. It will be noted that inductive elements are not used as frequently as resistive and capacitive elements. This is because the inductance of an element is often subject to undesirable temperature and current variations. However, when the advantages of using an inductance are appreciable and its characteristics are suitable, it should be employed without hesitation.

The physical realization of a given characteristic is obtained by comparing a general relation which has the form of the desired characteristic with an actual relation which expresses the transfer function of an electric circuit. Corresponding equation coefficients are equated, yielding as many equations as there are coefficients. If there are more electric components than there are equations, values are assumed for the excess electric components. Then the equations defining the value which the remaining electric components should have are found by simultaneous solution.

As an example to illustrate the procedure, we shall use the lead-lag compensator in (9.30-4), and designate it by G, where

$$G = \frac{(1 + 0.185s)(1 + 0.448s)}{(1 + 0.037s)(1 + 2.24s)} \tag{9.50-1}$$

This has a general form of

$$G = \frac{(1 + \alpha_1 T_1 s)(1 + T_2 s)}{(1 + T_1 s)(1 + \alpha_2 T_2 s)} \tag{9.50-2}$$

or
$$G = \frac{(1 + \alpha T_1 s)(1 + T_2 s)}{1 + (T_1 + \alpha T_2)s + \alpha T_1 T_2 s^2} \tag{9.50-3}$$

where $\alpha_1 = \alpha_2 = \alpha = 5$, $T_1 = 0.037$, $T_2 = 0.448$.

An electric circuit which has this same characteristic is shown in Fig. 9.50-1. Using Laplace transform notation and assuming there are no initial conditions, the transfer function between E_o and E_1 is found by solving the following equations.

$$E_1 = \left(R_2 + \frac{1}{C_1 s} + \frac{1}{C_2 s}\right) I_1 - \frac{1}{C_1 s} I_2 \qquad (9.50\text{-}4)$$

$$0 = \frac{-1}{C_1 s} I_1 + \left(R_1 + \frac{1}{C_1 s}\right) I_2 \qquad (9.50\text{-}5)$$

$$E_o = \left(R_2 + \frac{1}{C_2 s}\right) I_1 \qquad (9.50\text{-}6)$$

Simultaneous solution of (9.50-4) and (9.50-5) yields

$$\frac{I_1}{E_1} = \frac{(1 + R_1 C_1 s) C_2 s}{1 + (R_1 C_1 + R_1 C_2 + R_2 C_2)s + R_1 C_1 R_2 C_2 s^2} \qquad (9.50\text{-}7)$$

and combination of (9.50-6) and (9.50-7) gives the transfer function

$$\frac{E_o}{E_1} = \frac{(1 + R_1 C_1 s)(1 + R_2 C_2 s)}{1 + (R_1 C_1 + R_1 C_2 + R_2 C_2)s + R_1 C_1 R_2 C_2 s^2} \qquad (9.50\text{-}8)$$

Equating coefficients of (9.50-3) and (9.50-8), the following are obtained.

$$\alpha T_1 = R_1 C_1 \qquad (9.50\text{-}9)$$

$$T_2 = R_2 C_2 \qquad (9.50\text{-}10)$$

$$T_1 + \alpha T_2 = R_1 C_1 + R_1 C_2 + R_2 C_2 \qquad (9.50\text{-}11)$$

$$\alpha T_1 T_2 = R_1 C_1 R_2 C_2 \qquad (9.50\text{-}12)$$

Since the product of (9.50-9) and (9.50-10) is (9.50-12), only two of these three equations are independent. Therefore if we eliminate (9.50-12), we have three equations and four unknowns. The three equations are (9.50-9), (9.50-10), and (9.50-11), and the four unknowns are R_1, R_2, C_1, and C_2. We arbitrarily select one of the unknowns. Let it be C_1. Then, using (9.50-9),

$$R_1 = \frac{\alpha T_1}{C_1} \qquad (9.50\text{-}13)$$

Substituting this value for R_1, αT_1 for $R_1 C_1$, and T_2 for $R_2 C_2$ in (9.50-11), it is found that

$$C_2 = \frac{(\alpha - 1)(T_2 - T_1)}{\alpha T_1} C_1 \qquad (9.50\text{-}14)$$

Finally, (9.50-10) is used to find R_2. Thus

$$R_2 = \frac{T_2}{C_2} \tag{9.50-15}$$

Two assumptions were made in this derivation: one, that the source impedance is zero, so that no source impedance term is needed in (9.50-4); the other, that the output impedance is infinite, so that all the current I_1 passes through R_2 and C_2. These assumptions are generally legitimate in most applications.

Equations (9.50-13), (9.50-14), and (9.50-15) can now be used to select exact values for R_1, R_2, C_1, and C_2, so that the characteristics in (9.50-1) are realized. Assuming a value of $0.1\mu f$ for C_1, the other elements should be as follows.

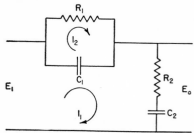

$$R_1 = 1.85 \text{ megohms}$$
$$R_2 = 0.504 \text{ megohm}$$
$$C_2 = 0.89\mu f$$

FIG. 9.50-1. Lag-lead circuit.

These are not standard values. Therefore since the *exact* characteristics of a compensator usually need not be realized, a good final set of standard values is

$$C_1 = 0.1\mu f$$
$$C_2 = 1.0\mu f$$
$$R_1 = 1.8 \text{ megohms}$$
$$R_2 = 0.47 \text{ megohm}$$

These values, substituted into (9.50-8), yield

$$\frac{E_o}{E_i} = \frac{(1 + 0.18s)(1 + 0.47s)}{(1 + 0.035s)(1 + 2.41s)} \tag{9.50-16}$$

which has a frequency response characteristic that is very similar to (9.50-1).

The circuit in Fig. 9.50-1 is subject to the limitation that the frequency of maximum phase shift for the lead compensator must be higher than that for the lag compensator. Otherwise T_1 is larger than T_2, so that negative values for C_2 and R_2 are required.

The derivation of the other compensating circuits in Appendix 3 is similar to that in this example.

9.60 Feedback compensation

The simplest type of feedback compensation is illustrated by the position feedback constant K_4 in Fig. 9.60-1. When $K_4 = 0$, the

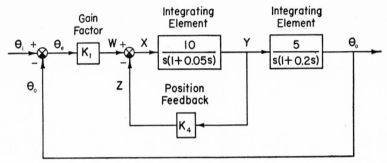

Fig. 9.60-1.   Example of an internal loop position feedback which changes the system from Type 2 to Type 1.

open-loop transfer function is

$$\frac{\theta_o}{\theta_e} = \frac{50K_1}{s^2(1 + 0.05s)(1 + 0.2s)} \tag{9.60-1}$$

This is the form of a Type 2 system. Stability may be obtained by using a lead compensator, as in locus B of Fig. 9.10-7. However, other methods of obtaining stability exist. The use of position feedback changes the open-loop transfer function to

$$\frac{\theta_o}{\theta_e} = \frac{5K_1}{K_4} \times \frac{1}{s(1 + 0.2s)(1 + as + 0.05as^2)} \tag{9.60-2}$$

where $a = 1/10K_4$.

This is now a conventional Type 1 system. Proper stable adjustment is achieved by selecting K_4 so that a reasonable M_p value exists in the inner-loop Z/X. This value of K_4 is substituted in (9.60-2), and K_1 is then selected in the normal manner.

Thus the designer has two methods of achieving stability in a system that is normally Type 2. One method, discussed in Section

9.10, uses lead compensation. The other method, described above, changes the system from Type 2 to Type 1. Each has its merits, which are usually evident in a particular application.

More complex feedback signals also may be used. The primary reason for them is that they substitute favorable feedback dynamics for unfavorable forward dynamics. This may be shown by the following considerations. Referring to Fig. 9.60-2, the transfer relation between Y and W may be written in either of the following forms.

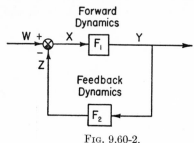

Forward Dynamics

Feedback Dynamics

FIG. 9.60-2.

$$\frac{Y}{W} = F_1 \cdot \frac{1}{1 + F_1 F_2} \qquad (9.60\text{-}3)$$

$$= \frac{1}{F_2} \cdot \frac{F_1 F_2}{1 + F_1 F_2} \qquad (9.60\text{-}4)$$

If the product of $F_1 F_2$ for a certain type of signal (such as a sinusoidal wave) is much smaller than 1, then (9.60-3) indicates that

$$\frac{Y}{W} \simeq F_1 \qquad (\text{for } F_1 F_2 < 1) \qquad (9.60\text{-}5)$$

Similarly, if $F_1 F_2$ is much larger than 1, then (9.60-4) indicates that

$$\frac{Y}{W} \simeq \frac{1}{F_2} \qquad (\text{for } F_1 F_2 > 1) \qquad (9.60\text{-}6)$$

This shows that when $F_1 F_2 > 1$, the feedback dynamics replace the forward dynamics.

If rate feedback were used and the instrumental time lags were negligible, so that

$$F_2 = Ks \qquad (9.60\text{-}7)$$

substitution into (9.60-6) yields

$$\frac{Y}{W} \simeq \frac{1}{Ks} \qquad (9.60\text{-}8)$$

Therefore with rate feedback the system open-loop frequency response tends toward the $-90°$ axis for all frequencies where the frequency response of $F_1 F_2$ is large.

If acceleration, instead of rate feedback, were used and the instrument lags were negligible,

$$\frac{Y}{W} \simeq \frac{1}{Ks^2}$$ (9.60-9)

in the frequency range where $F_1F_2(j\omega)$ is large. Therefore the system open-loop frequency response tends toward the 180° axis when acceleration feedback is used.

A particularly useful compensator is one with a constant phase shift over a wide band of some intermediate value between 0° and 90°. Then rate feedback can be cascaded with this constant phase

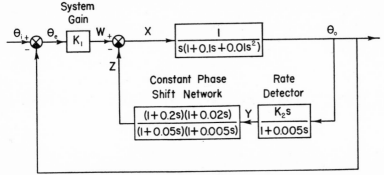

FIG. 9.60-3.   Control system with constant phase-shift feedback.

shift network to produce a feedback characteristic having a constant phase shift between 90° and 180°. This feedback characteristic would cause the system open-loop frequency response to have a uniform phase shift of, for example, $-140°$ over a wide band. An example using the system in Fig. 9.60-3 will illustrate the effect.

Constant phase shift over a limited frequency range is achieved by two lead compensators. Their frequencies of maximum phase shift are separated by a factor of 10, and each has the same value of α. The compensator in Fig. 9.60-3 has a phase characteristic of approximately 47° between 10 and 100 radians per second. The frequency response locus Z/X is shown in Fig. 9.60-4. When $K_2 = 6.25$, a reasonable degree of stability is achieved in the inner-loop θ_o/W. Then for all frequencies less than 50 radians per second, the amplitude of Z/X is greater than unity, so that the system open-loop locus θ_o/θ_e should tend to be the reciprocal of the feedback func-

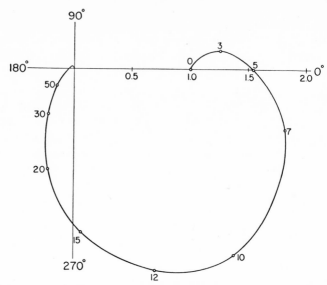

FIG. 9.60-4.   Frequency response locus of $(Z/K_2X)(j\omega)$ for Fig. 9.60-3.

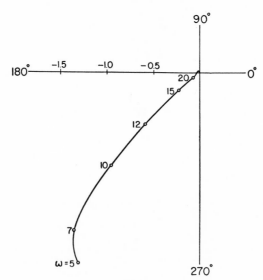

FIG. 9.60-5.   Frequency response locus of $(\theta_o/K_1\theta_e)(j\omega)$ for Fig. 9.60-3.

tion Z/θ_o. Accordingly, the θ_o/θ_e locus should be located along a radial line at $-137°$ ($47°$ from the phase shift network and $90°$ from the rate detector). Inspection of Fig. 9.60-5 shows that this is accomplished. This results in an M_p value of approximately 1.5 when the system gain K_1 is any value between 1.3 and 10. The designer then selects the gain on the basis of the frequency band pass he desires, rather than on the transient overshoot which he can tolerate. Furthermore, so long as the stability of the inner loop is maintained and the amplitude of the frequencies between 10 and 20 radians in the Z/X function is appreciably larger than 1, the θ_o/X dynamics can change in almost any manner without affecting the θ_o/θ_e locus. Thus the system in Fig. 9.60-3 shows an effective method of replacing a forward dynamic characteristic with a feedback characteristic.

9.70 Combined cascade and feedback compensation

Inspection of Fig. 9.60-5 indicates that if a lead compensator were cascaded with these dynamics, stable dynamics would be achieved with even very high K_1 gain values. This may be shown by changing the transfer relation between W and θ_e of Fig. 9.60-3 from K_1 to K_1G_1, where G_1 is a lead compensating function. Then if G_1 is a lead compensator with $\alpha = 3$ and $\omega_m = 100$ radians per second,

$$G_1 = \frac{1 + 0.0173s}{1 + 0.0058s} \tag{9.70-1}$$

and the open-loop transfer function becomes

$$\frac{\theta_o}{\theta_e} = F_o$$
$$= \frac{K_1(1+0.0173s)(1+0.05s)(1+0.005s)^2}{s(1+0.0058s)[(1+0.1s+0.01s^2)(1+0.05s)(1+0.005s)^2+6.25(1+0.2s)(1+0.02s)]} \tag{9.70-2}$$

The polar locus for $K_1^{-1}F_o$ is shown in Fig. 9.70-1.

Stable operation is now possible even with K_1 as high as 1000. With this gain, the unity crossover frequency is approximately 50 radians per second. Compared with the unity crossover frequencies that were found in Sections 9.10, 9.20, and 9.30 for the same basic dynamics, a sizable increase has been achieved by using combined cascade and feedback compensation.

A word of caution is in order. It is often possible to design "on paper" a system whose transient performance is significantly improved. However, closer inspection reveals other limitations. The magnitude of the signals in the system may be beyond the system capability. Hence saturations and nonlinearities must be considered. Furthermore, the transfer function equations may not be valid for the high frequencies used in the "paper" analysis.

This does not mean that the designer should hesitate to use complicated compensation methods. Rather, as the complexity of the

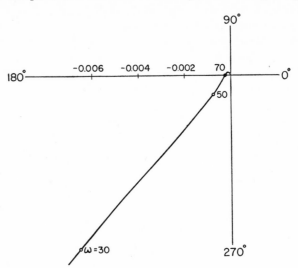

FIG. 9.70-1.   Frequency response locus of $(\theta_o/K_1\theta_e)(j\omega)$ for a system having combined cascade and feedback compensation.

system is increased, the designer should seek close correlation between design and practice. This includes laboratory models and the utilization of analytical techniques which include nonlinearity and saturation effects neglected by linear analysis. Chapters 12 and 13 discuss numerical integration and analog computers. Saturation and nonlinearity effects may be studied by both of these analysis tools.

PROBLEMS

9-1. Derive the output-to-input voltage ratio for each circuit in Appendix 3. Show that if the proper values for the resistors and capacitors are used, the general relations describe the operation of the circuits.

9-2. Find α and ω_m for the following lead compensator cases.

(a) $\dfrac{1 + 5s}{1 + 2s}$

(b) $\dfrac{1 + 10s}{1 + s}$

(c) $\dfrac{1 + 3s}{1 + 0.5s}$

(d) $\dfrac{1 + 9s}{1 + 0.1s}$

(e) $\dfrac{1 + 0.5s}{1 + 0.02s}$

(f) $\dfrac{1 + 0.01s}{1 + 0.005s}$

9-3. Select values of R_1, R_2, and C for the circuit in Fig. 9.10-2 in order to realize the frequency-dependent characteristics of the cases in Problem 9-2.

9-4. Find α and ω_m for the following lag compensator cases.

(a) $\dfrac{1 + 2s}{1 + 5s}$

(b) $\dfrac{1 + s}{1 + 10s}$

(c) $\dfrac{1 + 0.5s}{1 + 3s}$

(d) $\dfrac{1 + 0.1s}{1 + 9s}$

(e) $\dfrac{1 + 0.02s}{1 + 0.5s}$

(f) $\dfrac{1 + 0.005s}{1 + 0.01s}$

9-5. Select values of R_1, R_2, and C for the circuit in Fig. 9.20-2 in order to realize the frequency-dependent characteristics of the cases in Problem 9-4.

9-6. Plot the amplitude and phase loci for case C of Fig. 9.40-2. Select K_o so that the phase margin is 40°. Find θ_o/θ_i. Find $\theta_o(t)$ when θ_i is a unit step input. Find $\theta_o(t)$ when θ_i is a unit rate input.

9-7. Repeat Problem 9-6 for case D of Fig. 9.40-2.

9-8. Repeat Problem 9-6 for case E of Figure 9.40-2.

9-9. Repeat Problem 9-6 for case C of Fig. 9.40-2 and incorporate a lag circuit (with $\alpha = 5$) in the system.

9-10. Repeat Problem 9-9 for case D of Fig. 9.40-2.

9-11. Repeat Problem 9-9 for case E of Fig. 9.40-2.

9-12. Explain the differences in the transient responses shown in Fig. 9.10-5. In particular, state why the case with lead compensation does not overshoot as much as the rest, why the case with lag compensation over-shoots more than the others, and why the lead-compensated cases oscillate at a higher frequency than the other cases.

9-13. Explain the differences in the transient responses shown in Fig. 9.10-6.

9-14. Select a lead and a lag compensating circuit for the following.

(a) $F_o = \dfrac{K_o}{s(1 + 0.1s)(1 + 0.01s)}$

(b) $F_o = \dfrac{K_o}{s(1 + 0.02s + 0.01s^2)}$

9-15. Select K_o so that the phase margin is 40° and find $\theta_o(t)$ for unit step and rate inputs to the system developed in Problem 9-14.

9-16. The transfer functions that follow may be achieved by using a circuit in Appendix 3. State which circuit could be used, and select specific values for the resistors and capacitors which physically realize the characteristic. Ignore the constant gain factor K, as that may be realized by amplification or attenuation.

(a) $F = \dfrac{1 + s}{(1 + 5s)(1 + 0.1s)}$

(b) Solve part (a), using a different circuit.

(c) $F = \dfrac{(1 + 0.5s)(1 + s)}{(1 + 0.1s)(1 + 5s)}$

(d) $F = \dfrac{(1 + 0.1s)(1 + 0.5s)}{(1 + 0.02s)(1 + 5s)}$

(e) $F = \dfrac{(1 + 0.1s)(1 + 0.2s)}{(1 + 0.01s)(1 + s)}$

(f) $F = \dfrac{(1 + 5s)(1 + 0.5s)}{(1 + s)(1 + 0.1s)}$

(g) $F = \dfrac{(1 + 0.033s)(1 + 0.39s)(1 + 0.9s)}{(1 + 0.00165s)(1 + 0.13s)(1 + 3.375s)}$

(h) $F = \dfrac{s(1 + 5s)}{(1 + s)(1 + 0.1s)}$

(i) $F = \dfrac{s(1 + s)}{(1 + 0.1s)(1 + 0.01s)}$

(j) $F = \dfrac{s(1 + 0.1s)}{(1 + 0.01s)(1 + s)}$

(k) $F = \dfrac{s}{(1 + s)(1 + 0.1s)}$

(l) $F = \dfrac{s^2}{(1 + 0.01s)(1 + 0.05s)}$

(m) $F = \dfrac{1}{(1 + s)(1 + 2s)}$

9-17. Repeat Problem 9-14b, using combined feedback and cascaded compensation. Which is more effective, rate feedback or acceleration feedback?

CHAPTER 10

EFFECT OF NOISE AND OUTPUT
DISTURBANCES

10.00 Introduction

All systems are subject to spurious signals and output disturbances. They are due to changing load conditions, fluctuations in the power source, electrical pickup in the wiring, imperfect demodulation of a-c voltages, temperature changes, vibration, gearing imperfections, and other similar causes. Unfortunately, an automatic control system does not possess human judgment. Thus the system reacts to all input signals to the extent of its capability. This is undesirable for a number of reasons. It wastes power, reduces system accuracy, and shortens equipment life.

Therefore the designer designs the control system so that it favors certain input signals. He does this by studying the frequency spectrum of both the desired and the undesired input signals. Generally the undesirable signals are in the high-frequency range. A common signal of this type is 60 c a-c voltage pickup. As a result, the designer often incorporates electric filters in a control system and selects the system unity crossover frequency, so that only signals within the legitimate signal range are acted upon.

Output disturbances whose effect also must be minimized may occur in either the high- or low-frequency range. When they occur in the high-frequency range, filters will reduce their effect. However, when the output disturbances are either of constant magnitude or of a low frequency, filtering is not effective. Then the disturbance can usually be reduced by increasing the gain factor existing between the point of the disturbance input and the system error signal θ_e.

Analysis approaches for handling these problems are discussed in the following sections.

10.10 Low-pass filter characteristics

Two common electric filters which are often used in control systems are shown in Fig. 10.10-1. The transfer function of the resistance-capacitance (R-C) network in Fig. 10.10-1a is

$$\frac{E_o}{E_1} = \frac{1}{1 + RCs} = A \angle \phi \qquad (10.10\text{-}1)$$

The amplitude and phase of this function in terms of the dimensionless frequency operator u is given in Fig. 2.26-1. When E_1 is a sinusoidal wave of unity amplitude, E_o is also sinusoidal. The

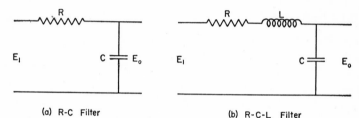

(a) R-C Filter   (b) R-C-L Filter

FIG. 10.10-1.   Electrical filter circuits.

magnitude of E_o is approximately unity for all frequencies up to the corner frequency ω_c, where

$$\omega_c = 1/RC \qquad (10.10\text{-}2)$$

Above ω_c the output amplitude may be approximated by

$$A = \omega_c/\omega \qquad (10.10\text{-}3)$$

Since the output amplitude decreases as the input frequency increases, the circuit is called a low-pass filter. That is, the low frequencies (those less than ω_c) pass through the filter without appreciable attenuation, while the high frequencies (those greater than ω_c) are attenuated.

Unfortunately, the phase shift of this function is appreciable in the low-frequency range. Phase as well as amplitude is important in system stability. Therefore when this filter is used in a control system, the location of its corner frequency ω_c is usually determined by phase considerations rather than by maximum noise attenuation. The examples discussed in Section 10.20 will illustrate this.

A more efficient low-pass filter is that shown in Fig. 10.10-1b. The transfer function of this resistance-capacitance-inductance

$(R$-C-$L)$ network is

$$\frac{E_o}{E_1} = \frac{1}{1 + RCs + LCs^2} \qquad (10.10\text{-}4)$$

The resistance R includes the resistance of the inductance, source impedance, and any resistance that might be added in the circuit. If the value of R is small enough so that the denominator roots of (10.10-4) are complex, the transfer relation may be expressed as

$$\frac{E_o}{E_1} = \frac{1}{1 + 2\zeta s/\omega_1 + s^2/\omega_1{}^2} = A\angle\phi \qquad (10.10\text{-}5)$$

where $\omega_1 = 1/\sqrt{LC}$, $\zeta = (R/2)\sqrt{C/L}$, and ζ is less than unity when the roots are complex. Frequency response loci for the amplitude and phase of this function in terms of the dimensionless frequency operator u are shown in Figs. 2.26-2 and 2.26-3. If the value of the resistance is so large that the denominator roots of (10.10-4) are not complex, this function has no significant advantage over two cascaded R-C circuits like that in Fig. 10.10-1a (see the filter-filter design sheet in Appendix 3).

The amplitude of (10.10-5) is approximately unity for all input frequencies up to the corner frequency ω_1. Above that the amplitude may be approximated by

$$A = \left(\frac{\omega_1}{\omega}\right)^2 \qquad (10.10\text{-}6)$$

Thus the R-C-L filter attenuates high frequencies by as much as 2 cascaded R-C filters. As in the case of the single R-C filter, phase considerations are important, and the complex roots (values of ζ less than unity) provide the advantage for the R-C-L filter.

As a simple example, suppose that the corner frequency was $\omega = 1$ for both an R-C-L filter and a double R-C filter. Then the phase shift at $\omega = 0.1$ is 5.8° when $\zeta = 0.5$ for the R-C-L filter, and 11.4° for the double R-C filter. For lower values of ζ the phase shift of the R-C-L filter becomes proportionately smaller. However, very small values of ζ are not only difficult to realize, but are also undesirable, since the amplitude response for the filter is increased around the corner frequency. A satisfactory range of ζ values is 0.3 to 0.6. The examples in the next section will illustrate the application.

10.20 Selection of filter characteristics

In the design of a control system, the designer must know the types of input signals which the system must follow accurately. This is obtained by determining the frequency spectrum of the input signals, and the magnitude of any rate or displacement signal which might be applied. The designer then determines the system characteristics, so that quantities such as the velocity constant and the unity crossover frequency are satisfactory.

Let us assume that this has been done for the system represented by Fig. 9.30-1. This is the system which has both a lead and a lag compensator, so that $K_v = 18.9$, and the unity crossover frequency (which is approximately the upper limit of the system band pass) is 7 radians per second. Suppose that this system has an undesirably high magnitude of high-frequency noise. Most of this noise is due to 60 c alternating voltage. We shall assume that all alternate means of improvement such as wire shielding, circuitry redesign, and the substitution of a higher frequency source have been fully explored. The problem, then, is the reduction of these noise frequencies in the control system by filtering and without appreciably affecting the band pass and open-loop gain setting.

Suppose that after studying the open-loop locus in Fig. 9.30-1, the designer decides that the system could stand a $-10°$ phase shift at $\omega = 10$ radians per second as long as the lower frequencies were not appreciably changed. He also decides to use one of the electric filter circuits in Fig. 10.10-1. He now wishes to compare the attenuation of 60 c signals which each would provide. The procedure follows.

Since
$$\omega = 2\pi f \tag{10.20-1}$$

60 c is the same as
$$\omega = 377 \text{ radians per second} \tag{10.20-2}$$

and all frequency measurements are now in radians per second. The chart in Fig. 2.26-1 may be used to determine the R-C filter characteristics. It is seen that the phase is $-10°$ at $u = 0.18$. Since the designer has specified that a $-10°$ phase shift may occur at $\omega = 10$, the corner frequency is

$$\omega_c = 55.6 \tag{10.20-3}$$

Substituting (10.20-3) in (10.10-3), it is found that this filter characteristic will attenuate 377 radians per second inputs by a factor of 6.8.

A similar relation will now be found for the R-C-L filter. Figure 2.26-3 may be used. When ζ is 0.5, the phase is $-10°$ at $u = 0.17$. Thus the quadratic corner frequency is

$$\omega_1 = 58.8 \qquad (10.20\text{-}4)$$

Substituting (10.20-4) in (10.10-6), it is found that this filter will attenuate the 377 radians-per-second noise signals by a factor of 41. If ζ is changed to 0.3, the quadratic corner frequency is 34.5, and the attenuation of the 377 radians-per-second signals is increased to a factor of 119.

The difference in filter attenuation factors would not be so great if a double R-C filter were used. However, the beneficial effect of a low damping ratio ζ is still significant. When the major noise frequency (such as 60 c) is relatively close to the control system frequencies, a filter with a low damping ratio is highly desirable. However, if the major noise frequency is appreciably higher than the control system frequencies, a single or double R-C low-pass filter is usually sufficient.

10.30 Effect of noise on compensators

Because compensators affect the frequency response amplitude as well as the phase, they may introduce serious noise disturbances.

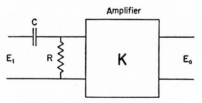

FIG. 10.30-1.   Rate compensator.

An example of this is the rate compensator shown in Fig. 10.30-1, whose transfer function is

$$\frac{E_o}{E_1} = \frac{KRCs}{1 + RCs} = A\angle\phi \qquad (10.30\text{-}1)$$

The frequency response of this function has an amplitude which increases from zero at $\omega = 0$ to K at $\omega = \infty$. Thus the higher frequencies are emphasized. In the case of the rate detector in Fig. 9.60-3, the amplitude of Y/θ_o at $\omega = \infty$ is 1250 when $K_2 = 6.25$. Yet only frequencies from $\omega = 0$ to $\omega = 70$ are used in the control system, and the amplitude of Y/θ_o at $\omega = 70$ is 410. Hence all the higher frequencies are boosted by a factor of as much as 3.

The same is true for lead compensators. Since the general equation of a lead compensator is

$$\frac{E_o}{E_1} = \frac{1 + \alpha Ts}{1 + Ts} = A\angle\phi \qquad (10.30\text{-}2)$$

the frequency response amplitude is α at $\omega = \infty$ compared with unity at $\omega = 0$. Thus all lead compensators boost the amplitude of high-frequency noise by a factor of α. Since two lead compensators are often cascaded together, high noise frequencies have their amplitude boosted by the product of the lead circuit α factors. Consequently, lead circuits are usually accompanied by filter circuits whose function is to attenuate all frequencies above those necessary in the control system.

As the general relation for a lag compensator is

$$\frac{E_o}{E_1} = \frac{1 + Ts}{1 + \alpha Ts} = A\angle\phi \qquad (10.30\text{-}3)$$

the frequency response amplitude of the high frequencies is attenuated by a factor of α. Hence lag compensators reduce the amplitude of high-frequency noise. Although lag compensators do not boost the magnitude of high-frequency noise, filters are sometimes combined with them. Again, the purpose is to attenuate all frequencies above those necessary in the control system.

Several typical circuits may be found in Appendix 3.

10.40 Multiple input systems

Once closed-loop system stability has been established for a θ_i input, other inputs may be injected into the system at any point without affecting the system stability. This is true so long as the linearity of the system is not disturbed, and the other inputs do not introduce additional closed-loop system paths. Figures 10.40-1 and 10.40-2 are examples of this.

Additional inputs, A, B, and C, are applied to the system in Fig. 10.40-1. Using conventional methods, the output is

$$\theta_o = \frac{1}{1 + 0.012s + 0.00024s^2} \left[\theta_i + \frac{1}{21} A + \frac{1 + 0.02s}{4.2(1 + 0.1s)} B \right.$$
$$\left. + \frac{s(1 + 0.02s)}{42(1 + 0.1s)} C \right] \quad (10.40\text{-}1)$$

The characteristic equation of this system is

$$1 + 0.012s + 0.00024s^2 = 0 \quad (10.40\text{-}2)$$

and since it does not contain any root of s with a positive real part, the system is stable. The steady-state effect on the output θ_o for

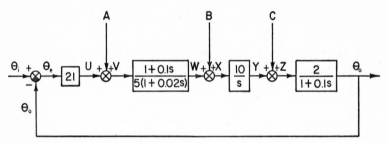

FIG. 10.40-1.   Block diagram of a multiple input system.

any input frequency may be found by plotting the amplitude of the frequency response between θ_o and the particular input. Thus an amplitude *vs.* frequency plot of

$$\frac{\theta_o}{A} = \frac{1}{21(1 + 0.012j\omega - 0.00024\omega^2)} \quad (10.40\text{-}3)$$

would show that θ_o is approximately $\frac{1}{21}$ for all unit-amplitude input frequencies applied at point A up to $\omega = 65$. Above $\omega = 65$, the amplitude of θ_o decreases rapidly. Similarly, an amplitude *vs.* frequency plot of

$$\frac{\theta_o}{B} = \frac{1 + 0.02j\omega}{4.2(1 + 0.1j\omega)(1 + 0.012j\omega - 0.00024\omega^2)} \quad (10.40\text{-}4)$$

would show that low-frequency signals applied at point B affect the output much more than they do when applied at point A. Input signals of constant magnitude applied at either A or B affect the output by the amount shown in their transfer equations when

$\omega = 0$. A constant input applied at point C does not affect the output in the steady state, but an oscillatory input will affect the output, as may be found by plotting the amplitude *vs.* frequency of

$$\frac{\theta_o}{C} = \frac{j\omega(1 + 0.02j\omega)}{42(1 + 0.1j\omega)(1 + 0.012j\omega - 0.00024\omega^2)} \quad (10.40\text{-}5)$$

The transient effect of inputs applied at A, B, or C may be found by determining the inverse Laplace transform of the output for a particular input.

Stable systems, which contain nonminimum-phase terms in either the numerator or denominator of the open-loop expression, are also

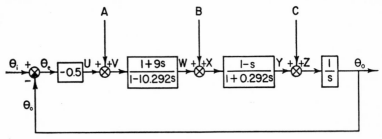

Fig. 10.40-2. Block diagram of a multiple input system that has nonminimum-phase terms.

stable when inputs are applied at any point in the system. Figure 10.40-2 represents an example of this, where

$$\theta_o = \frac{(1 + 9s)(1 - s)}{(1 + s)(1 + 2s)(1 + 3s)} \theta_i + \frac{-2(1 + 9s)(1 - s)}{(1 + s)(1 + 2s)(1 + 3s)} A$$
$$+ \frac{-2(1 - 10.292s)(1 - s)}{(1 + s)(1 + 2s)(1 + 3s)} B + \frac{-2(1 - 10.292s)(1 + 0.292s)}{(1 + s)(1 + 2s)(1 + 3s)} C$$
$$(10.40\text{-}6)$$

The characteristic equation for this system is

$$(1 + s)(1 + 2s)(1 + 3s) = 0 \quad (10.40\text{-}7)$$

Again, there are no roots of s with positive real parts. Hence the system is stable regardless of the signal input point. The steady-state magnitude of θ_o for different sinusoidal inputs may be found in the same manner as it was for the system represented by eqs. (10.40-3), (10.40-4), and (10.40-5).

It should be noticed that in each case, the transfer function between θ_o and the particular input is equal to the product of θ_o/θ_i

times the reciprocal of the forward transfer function between θ_e and the input junction. Thus

$$\frac{\theta_o}{A} = \frac{\theta_o}{\theta_i} \times \frac{\theta_e}{U} \tag{10.40-8}$$

$$\frac{\theta_o}{B} = \frac{\theta_o}{\theta_i} \times \frac{\theta_e}{W} \tag{10.40-9}$$

$$\frac{\theta_o}{C} = \frac{\theta_o}{\theta_i} \times \frac{\theta_e}{Y} \tag{10.40-10}$$

These principles provide a basis for determining the effect of those output disturbances which do not cause additional loop paths.

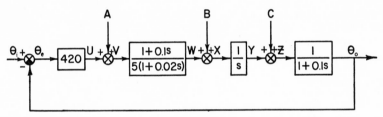

FIG. 10.40-3.   Block diagram of a multiple input system with a high gain between θ_e and U.

Disturbances of this type are a variation in the output load and a shift in an internal balance setting.

Since the characteristic between θ_e and the input junction point is a direct factor in the effect on the output, the designer often is able to improve the system by improving this characteristic. One method is the relocation of the system gain factors. An example is shown in Fig. 10.40-3. This system has the same θ_o/θ_i characteristic as that in Fig. 10.40-1. However, the gain factors are higher between θ_e and U. Thus

$$\theta_o = \frac{1}{1+0.012s+0.00024s^2}\left[\theta_i + \frac{1}{420}A + \frac{1+0.02s}{84(1+0.1s)}B + \frac{s(1+0.02s)}{84(1+0.1s)}C\right] \tag{10.40-11}$$

and the effect on θ_o of input signals applied at A, B, or C is appreciably reduced. This technique is not always possible, but its principle should not be overlooked. Another method is that of selecting open-loop compensating functions so an increased dynamic gain is obtained. Both lead and lag compensators are helpful. They are selected so that a gain as high as necessary exists between θ_o and an input point for all frequencies up to the θ_o/θ_e unity crossover frequency.

If the unwanted input signal introduces an additional signal path in the closed-loop system, it may seriously affect the system stability. An example of this is a structural vibration which causes a

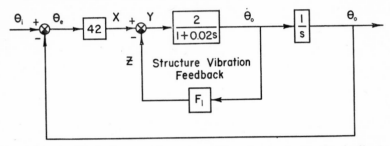

FIG. 10.40-4.   Block diagram of a system with a structural vibration feedback.

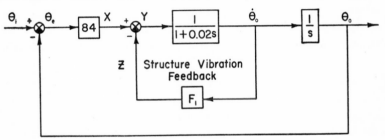

FIG. 10.40-5.   Block diagram of a system with a low-gain structural vibration feedback loop.

signal to be applied to the system as a function of the vibration. The system in Fig. 10.40-4 represents an example of this type. The closed-loop transfer function is

$$\frac{\theta_o}{\theta_i} = \frac{84}{84 + (1 + 2F_1)s + 0.02s^2} \qquad (10.40\text{-}12)$$

where F_1 is the structural feedback characteristic. If F_1 is a negative constant, instability results when the constant is greater than 0.5. If the constant is positive, a slower system results. The most satisfactory corrective measure, of course, is the elimination of the vibration feedback path. However, that is not always practical.

Some improvement is possible by altering the system arrangement. Thus if the gain factors are changed to those shown in Fig. 10.40-5, the closed-loop transfer function becomes

$$\frac{\theta_o}{\theta_i} = \frac{84}{84 + (1 + F_1)s + 0.02s^2} \qquad (10.40\text{-}13)$$

The effect of the structural feedback characteristic is reduced by a factor of 2 in this system. Similarly, compensating functions also may be used to reduce the effect of disturbances of this type.

It has been shown that output disturbances due to multiple inputs are reduced by increasing the gain in the open-loop function. On the other hand, noise disturbances are reduced by decreasing the gain. Thus the designer must arrive at a reasonable compromise in each system. If he increases the gain settings so that the output disturbance due to multiple inputs is negligible, he may find that he has created a serious noise problem. Conversely, if he eliminates the system noise, he may find that multiple inputs have a highly unfavorable effect. The usual compromise calls for increasing the system gains, both by constant factors and by frequency-dependent functions, up to the unity crossover frequency. Above this frequency high attenuation is usually desirable.

PROBLEMS

10-1. What is the velocity constant K_v when $M_p = 1.5$ for the system shown in Fig. 9.30-1, if the R-C filter given in eq. 10.20-3 is inserted in the open loop?

10-2. Repeat Problem 10-1, using the R-C-L filter given in eq. (10.20-4).

10-3. Repeat Problem 10-2, using $\zeta = 0.3$.

10-4. Repeat Problem 10-1 using a double R-C circuit. Select the corner frequency for each section of the R-C circuit, and state the attenuation which the filter provides for 60 c signals.

10-5. Select specific values of R, C, and L for the filters in Problems 10-1 through 10-4.

10-6. Given,

$$F = \frac{1 + 0.5s}{1 + 0.1s}$$

find the following.

(a) ω_m.

(b) An R-C filter circuit such that when it is cascaded with F the phase angle at ω_m is changed by $3°$. How much does this filter attenuate $\omega = 100$ and $\omega = 377$?

(c) An R-C-L filter circuit with $\zeta = 0.5$ such that when it is cascaded with F the phase angle at ω_m is changed 3°. How much does this filter attenuate $\omega = 100$ and $\omega = 377$?

10-7. The system shown in Fig. 10.40-1 is subjected to simultaneous unit step inputs of θ_i, A, B, and C. What is $\theta_o(t)$?

10.8. The system shown in Fig. 10.4-3 is subjected to simultaneous unit step inputs of θ_i, A, B, and C. What is $\theta_o(t)$?

10-9. If F_1 in Fig. 10.40-5 is a positive constant, and if the other elements have the characteristics shown, can F_1 produce an instability if it is very large? Explain your answer.

CHAPTER 11

INTERPRETING NYQUIST LOCI

11.00 Introduction

A major objective in control studies is the development of principles which govern the designer's thinking. The relative importance of each factor is considered and assigned to its proper echelon. First, the general function which an automatic control system might fulfill is recognized. Then the general control laws which will accomplish this need are evolved. This is followed by the development of the control system functional (or block diagram) arrangement. Tolerances are assigned to each function or block, and methods of physical realization combining reliability, economy, and accuracy are developed.

The preceding chapters have discussed many of the phases and techniques used in linear system analysis. Each step is not too complicated, but when all the detailed steps are combined, it is too easy to overlook the objective of developing principles. This chapter discusses the general interrelation of the preceding chapters. The general features of Nyquist loci (polar loci of the open-loop function) are discussed, and basic thoughts which the designer applies are developed.

11.10 Correlation of transient and frequency responses

In order to correlate closed-loop transient and open-loop steady-state frequency responses, the results for known output-to-input relations are compared. Section 7.10 compared the closed-loop transient response to a unit step input with the open-loop frequency response of a first-order system whose output-to-input relation was

$$\frac{\theta_o}{\theta_i} = \frac{1}{1 + Ts} \qquad (11.10\text{-}1)$$

Since systems usually cannot be represented by expressions so simple, this correlation is not too informative for design purposes.

A second-order system, which was discussed in Section 7.20, may be represented by

$$\frac{\theta_o}{\theta_i} = \frac{1}{1 + 2\zeta s/\omega_1 + s^2/\omega_1{}^2} \qquad (11.10\text{-}2)$$

This relation is much more representative of the output-to-input functions encountered in practice. Furthermore, the maximum transient overshoot to a unit step input is uniquely related to a maximum closed-loop frequency response amplitude.

Hence useful design criteria based on the relation between the open- and closed-loop transfer frequency response polar loci were developed. These include M-circles, N-circles, and unity crossover frequency values.

The reader may extend the correlation between the transient and frequency responses by analyzing transfer relations of higher complexity. For example, assume that a system is described by an output-to-input relation of the form

$$\frac{\theta_o}{\theta_i} = \frac{1}{(1 + Ts)(1 + 2\zeta s/\omega_1 + s^2/\omega_1{}^2)} \qquad (11.10\text{-}3)$$

Nondimensionalizing with respect to ω_1, eq. (11.10-3) becomes

$$\frac{\theta_o}{\theta_i} = \frac{1}{(1 + AU)(1 + 2\zeta U + U^2)} \qquad (11.10\text{-}4)$$

where $U = s/\omega_1$, $A = T\omega_1$. The inverse Laplace transform of (11.10-4) for a unit step θ_i input is given by transform pair 00.111 as

$$\theta_o = 1 - \frac{A^2}{1 - 2\zeta A + A^2}\, \epsilon^{-\omega_1 t/A} + \frac{\epsilon^{-\zeta\omega_1 t} \sin\left(\sqrt{1 - \zeta^2}\,\omega_1 t - \psi\right)}{[(1 - \zeta^2)(1 - 2\zeta A + A^2)]^{1/2}} \qquad (11.10\text{-}5)$$

where
$$\psi = \tan^{-1}\frac{\sqrt{1 - \zeta^2}}{-\zeta} + \tan^{-1}\frac{A\sqrt{1 - \zeta^2}}{1 - \zeta A}$$

The open-loop transfer function corresponding to (11.10-4), from which the Nyquist locus may be obtained, is

$$\frac{\theta_o}{\theta_e} = \frac{1}{(2\zeta + A)ju - (1 + 2\zeta A)u^2 - Aju^3} \qquad (11.10\text{-}6)$$

where ju has been substituted for U.

The correlation between the closed-loop transient response for a unit step input and the open-loop steady-state frequency response is found in the following manner.

1. Select a set of numerical values for A and ζ. (A may have any value, but ζ must be less than one if eq. 11.10-5 is used.)

2. Insert these values in (11.10-5), and plot θ_o as a function of $\omega_1 t$. This gives the transient response for a set of A and ζ values.

3. Insert the values for A and ζ in (11.10-6), and plot the polar vector of θ_o/θ_e for values of the dimensionless frequency operator u between 0 and ∞. This gives the Nyquist locus for a set of A and ζ values.

4. Compare the results of items 2 and 3.

5. Repeat the procedure, using other sets of values for A and ζ until a "feel" for the effect of each factor is obtained.

The same process may be repeated for other output-to-input relations. By being able to correlate transient and frequency responses, the designer is able to specify how a desired relation may be achieved. An example of this is discussed in Section 11.50, where it is shown that a system may be so designed that the output leads the input in the low-frequency range.

11.20 Characteristics of minimum-phase open-loop functions

The open-loop transfer function of most control systems contains only minimum-phase terms. That is, $F_o(s)$ has no roots with positive real parts. In order for the closed-loop system to be stable, the Nyquist locus must have one of the general shapes that are shown in Fig. 6.10-1.

The control system arrangement that is most common is the Type 1 system. Figure 11.20-1 shows the Nyquist locus for the Type 1 system, along with the loci for Types 0, 2, and 3. The difference in the system types is due to the number of integrators (or denominator s factors) in the open-loop function. This is discussed in Section 4.50. Thus a Type 0 system has no integration in its open-loop characteristic, a Type 1 system has one integrator, a Type 2 system has two integrators, etc. The integration is important, because if any error exists in the system, the integrating action causes the signal applied to the controller to increase until the error is reduced either to zero or to an equilibrium point. If a constant acceleration is applied to a Type 3 system, θ_e becomes zero in the steady state. On the other hand, if a constant acceleration is applied to a Type 2 system, an equilibrium point of $\theta_e = 1/K_a$ is reached in the steady state. Since both the Type 0 and 1 systems contain too few integrating elements, they are not able to respond accurately to prolonged acceleration inputs. However, constant acceleration

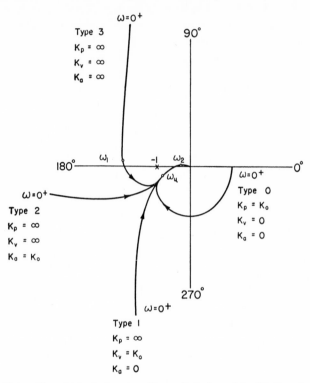

FIG. 11.20-1. Nyquist loci of system Types 0, 1, 2, and 3 with $P = 0$. Arrowheads indicate direction of increasing frequency.

inputs are very rare. Hence systems having as many integrating terms as Type 3 are not common.

Constant rate inputs, on the other hand, are quite common. Rate inputs may be accurately followed by either a Type 2 system or a Type 1 system with a high velocity constant. A typical transient for the error in a Type 1 system subjected to a constant rate input was shown in Fig. 9.10-6. The transient for a Type 2 system subjected to a constant rate input is similar to the transient for the lag-compensated case in Fig. 9.10-6, except that the steady state value of θ_e is zero.

Figure 11.20-2 shows the typical transient responses of systems Types 1, 2, and 3 subjected to a unit step input. The response for a Type 0 system is similar to that of a Type 1 system, except that the steady-state value is less than 1. This figure shows the same effect as that in Fig. 9.10-5, where the transient responses for a system with and without a lag compensator were compared. The lag compensator alters a Type 1 open-loop Nyquist locus (except at the

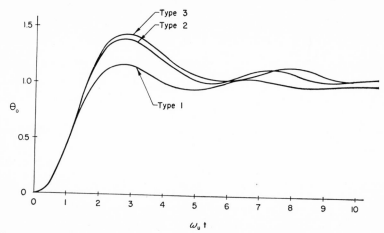

FIG. 11.20-2. Typical transient responses of Types 1, **2**, and 3 systems subjected to a unit step input. The unity crossover frequency is ω_u.

very low frequencies) in the same manner as an added integration factor that changes the system from Type 1 to Type 2.

The transient responses in Fig. 11.20-2 of the systems Types 2 and 3 are much the same. This is because their Nyquist loci are alike except for very low frequencies. As the transient contributions of low frequencies have large time constants, their effect is not evident until a considerable time interval has elapsed. Both system Types 2 and 3 are characterized by larger overshoots than Type 1 systems. This is because they tend to reduce to zero the integral of the error as well as the error signal.

Comparing Fig. 11.20-1 with Fig. 7.30-3a reveals an interesting property of Type 3 systems which is associated with all frequencies lower than ω_1, namely, the steady-state phase angle of the output is positive for sinusoidal inputs in the low-frequency range. It might appear that this is also true for all frequencies higher than ω_2. However, in that portion of the F_o plane, the phase angle lags in excess of 180°.

A leading output-to-input phase angle is often viewed as a mysterious effect. It infers that the output does what the input asks it to do before the input is applied. This is not entirely true. A more accurate description is that the output is proportional to the input plus the rate of change of the input when the input is a continuous and smooth function. Therefore the over-all system acts as a lead circuit, possessing prediction powers as long as the input does not change suddenly. If the input is suddenly changed, the output will continue on the basis of past inputs until the new input signals have been processed through the system. Thus temporary large errors may be encountered. However, as the input in most systems is a smooth function of time, a leading phase characteristic is often considered desirable.

The amount of positive phase angle that is usually found in a Type 3 system is generally very small, and the frequencies in which the lead occurs are very low. Therefore the designer usually investigates other methods of obtaining this characteristic when he desires it. Section 11.50 discusses other methods.

11.30 Typical open-loop functions for Type 1 systems

The most common automatic control system type is the Type 1 system which has no nonminimum-phase terms in the open-loop transfer function expression. These systems combine an adequate speed of response, accuracy, and simplicity for most applications. Fig. 11.30-1 shows the Nyquist loci for properly adjusted systems of this type. Locus A represents the shape for either uncompensated dynamics or lead-compensated dynamics. Locus B represents the shape when lag compensation is used. The system frequency having the maximum closed-loop amplitude response is ω_p, and ω_u denotes the unity crossover frequency. Usually ω_u and ω_p are so close together that they are approximately equal. Transient responses for a typical system subjected to a unit step input are shown in Fig. 9.10-5.

Sometimes the system dynamics are such that the Nyquist locus cuts back into the system M-circle, as shown in Fig. 11.30-2. This is often caused by the improper selection of lag compensator characteristics. The transient responses for systems like this are usually unsatisfactory. Two system resonant frequencies, each of high amplitude, exist. Their approximate frequencies are ω_1 and ω_2. Often two or more resonant frequencies occur in a system; but if the system is properly adjusted, the transient contribution of each

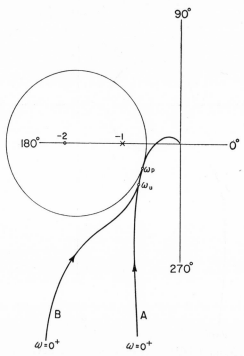

Fig. 11.30-1.   Typical Nyquist loci for properly adjusted Type 1 systems.

frequency is not excessive. The system represented by (9.30-5) is an example of a properly adjusted system having two resonant frequencies. Usually, if the Nyquist locus does not cut back into the system M-circle, the low-frequency portion may have any shape, provided K_v has a sufficient magnitude.

If a quadratic factor with a low damping ratio occurs in the denominator of a system's open-loop function, the Nyquist locus may have the form of that in Fig. 11.30-3. Nyquist loci having this shape are undesirable. The unity crossover frequency ω_u is much lower than ω_p. Hence the system transient response to a unit step input is approximately the same as that of a first-order system having a time constant of $1/\omega_u$ seconds and with a superimposed oscillation of the same frequency as ω_p. Fig. 8.13-3 provides an example of a transient like this, and its corresponding inverse open-loop polar locus is C in Fig. 8.13-2.

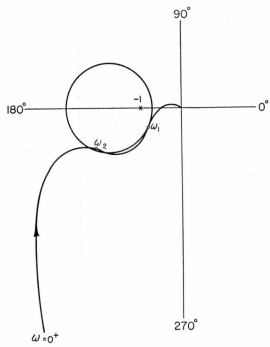

FIG. 11.30-2. Nyquist loci representing a system having two resonant frequencies.

The reader who has correlated the Nyquist loci and their transient responses for (11.10-4) will recognize that cases such as the one in Fig. 11.30-3 occur when A is large and ζ is very small. As an example, substitution of 8.25 for A and 0.04 for ζ in eqs. (11.10-4), (11.10-5), and (11.10-6) shows that $u_p \simeq 1$, $M_p \simeq 1.5$, and the dimensionless unity crossover frequency is approximately the reciprocal of A. The output transient equation is

$$\theta_o = 1 - 0.995\epsilon^{-0.121\omega_1 t} + 0.121\epsilon^{-0.04\omega_1 t} \sin (57.2\omega_1 t^\circ - 177.7^\circ)$$

$$(11.30\text{-}1)$$

Inspection of (11.30-1) reveals that the dominant contribution comes from the real root, which has approximately the same value as the unity crossover frequency. The contribution due to u_p adds little to the output response other than an oscillation of long persistency.

Since the unity crossover frequency is much lower than ω_p in systems whose Nyquist locus is like that in Fig. 11.30-3, the designer

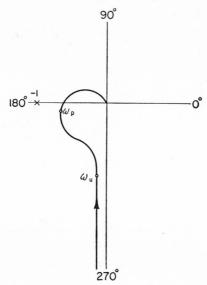

FIG. 11.30-3.   Nyquist locus representing a system having a quadratic factor with a low damping ratio in the open-loop expression.

is usually able to appreciably improve these systems with compensating functions. Effective compensating methods are:

1. Parallel feedback terms which substitute the feedback characteristic for the forward characteristic.

2. Double lead circuits which bend the "resonant bulge" toward the $-90°$ axis.

3. Lag circuits which bend the "resonant bulge" toward the $-270°$ axis.

11.40 Magnitude of system variables

The frequency response may be obtained between any two variables in a system. This is frequently done in order to determine the relative magnitude of the signals in a system. As an example of this technique, the following transfer functions exist for the system represented by Fig. 11.40-1.

$$\frac{\theta_o}{\theta_i} = \frac{1}{1 + 0.012s + 0.00024s^2} \tag{11.40-1}$$

$$\frac{\dot{\theta}_o}{\theta_i} = \frac{s}{1 + 0.012s + 0.00024s^2} \tag{11.40-2}$$

$$\frac{Z}{\theta_i} = \frac{s(1 + 0.1s)}{10(1 + 0.012s + 0.00024s^2)} \tag{11.40-3}$$

$$\frac{Y}{\theta_i} = \frac{s(1 + 0.02s)}{2(1 + 0.012s + 0.00024s^2)} \tag{11.40-4}$$

$$\frac{\theta_e}{\theta_i} = \frac{s(1 + 0.02s)}{84(1 + 0.012s + 0.00024s^2)} \tag{11.40-5}$$

All frequencies from 0 to ∞ are of interest. Thus (11.40-5) indicates that the amplitude ratio between θ_e and θ_i at infinite fre-

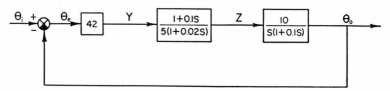

Fig. 11.40-1.

quency is unity. This follows logically from other considerations. If a sudden input (such as a unit step function) is applied, the error is initially the same as the input, because the system has not had time to respond. Similarly, if a very high frequency input is applied, the error is the same as the input, since the input changes before the system can respond.

The log-decibel method may be used to find the amplitude asymptotes of the frequency response between variables. These loci, together with a knowledge of the type of inputs that will be applied to a system, enable the designer to make reasonable approximations of the magnitude of system variables.

Table 11.40-1 tabulates the approximate maximum value of variables which are typical in most systems. The values were obtained by averaging the results of a number of transient responses, and therefore they serve as rough approximations which further correlate transient and frequency responses.

TABLE 11.40-1

APPROXIMATE MAXIMUM VALUE OF VARIABLES FOR UNIT STEP AND UNIT RATE
INPUTS

System input	Variable	Approximate maximum value of variable*
unit step	θ_o	$0.8M_p$ or 1.0, whichever is larger
unit step	$\dot{\theta}_o$	$0.7\omega_u$
unit step	$\ddot{\theta}_o$	$1.5\omega_u^2$
unit rate	θ_e	$1/\omega_u$ or $1/K_v$, whichever is larger
unit rate	$\dot{\theta}_o$	$0.8M_p$ or 1.0, whichever is larger
unit rate	$\ddot{\theta}_o$	$0.7\omega_u$

* K_v is the velocity constant, M_p is the maximum closed-loop amplitude response of a sinusoidal input, and ω_u is the open-loop unity amplitude crossover frequency.

Often the designer wants to know the approximate transient response of internal variables (such as Y and Z) without finding the inverse Laplace transform of the exact transfer function. Several simplifications can be made to accomplish this. One simplification is the approximation of the output-to-input function by a simple first-order time constant based on ω_u. Thus,

$$\frac{\theta_o}{\theta_i} = \frac{1}{1 + (s/\omega_u)} \tag{11.40-6}$$

and

$$\frac{\theta_e}{\theta_i} = \frac{s}{\omega_u + s} \tag{11.40-7}$$

where ω_u is the unity crossover frequency. Using this approximation and the actual relation between other variables, the following approximate transfer expressions can be written

$$\frac{Y}{\theta_i} = \frac{\theta_e}{\theta_i} \times \frac{Y}{\theta_e} = \frac{0.75s}{1 + 0.018s} \tag{11.40-8}$$

$$\frac{Z}{\theta_i} = \frac{\theta_e}{\theta_i} \times \frac{Z}{\theta_e} = \frac{0.15s(1 + 0.1s)}{(1 + 0.018s)(1 + 0.02s)} \tag{11.40-9}$$

where $\omega_u = 56$ for the example shown in Fig. 11.40-1.

The transient solution of (11.40-8) and (11.40-9) for a given θ_i input can be obtained fairly rapidly, and will approximate the actual response with reasonable accuracy.

The approximation in (11.40-7) can be used for most systems. More accurate approximations could be written, but they lose the simplicity associated with (11.40-7). An example of a more accurate approximation is

$$\frac{\theta_o}{\theta_i} = \frac{0.8\omega_u s + s^2}{\omega_u{}^2 + 0.8\omega_u s + s^2} \qquad (11.40\text{-}10)$$

which is based on a second-order output-to-input response with $\zeta = 0.4$ and a natural frequency of ω_u.

11.50 Synthesis of a desired function

Almost any transfer function, which in operational notation is a rational fraction in the operator s, may be realized. The major limitations are:

1. The order of the denominator of the output-to-input relation must be as high or higher than the numerator.

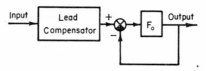

Fig. 11.50-1.

2. The system complexity may be prohibitively high.

Section 9.50 discusses the realization of minimum-phase real-root factors. Section 4.53 discusses a method of obtaining a denominator s factor, and numerator s factors may be physically realized by the method used for the rate compensator in Section 10.30. Nonminimum-phase numerator terms may be obtained by the method discussed in Section 6.20, and denominator nonminimum-phase terms may be realized by the methods discussed in Sections 6.20 and 11.60. Many additional methods exist for the realization of desired functions.

This makes it possible for the designer to stipulate and obtain a desired function. The desired function is selected on the basis of its transient or operational characteristics. For example, suppose the designer would like to have a system which has an appreciable phase lead in the low frequencies. Several methods exist. One method, shown in Fig. 11.50-1, cascades a lead compensator with the normal closed-loop controller.

Another method is the selection of the open-loop dynamics, so that the closed-loop relation has the characteristics of a lead com-

pensator. As an example, if it is desirable for the closed-loop
characteristic to be

$$\frac{\theta_o}{\theta_i} = \frac{1 + 0.5s}{1 + 0.1s} \qquad (11.50\text{-}1)$$

then the corresponding open-loop transfer relation is

$$\frac{\theta_o}{\theta_e} = \frac{-2.5(1 + 0.5s)}{s} \qquad (11.50\text{-}2)$$

The Nyquist locus for this function is shown in Fig. 11.50-2. Since
the frequency response of (11.50-2) is a finite amount at $\omega = \infty$,
this function can be only approximated by a control loop.

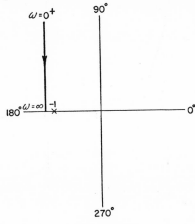

FIG. 11.50-2.

The general shape of Fig. 11.50-2 indicates the properties which a
control system must have in order for the closed-loop phase shift
to be positive in the low frequencies. The requirements for physical
realization may be determined by assuming an output-to-input
relation having the denominator order higher than the numerator
order. For example, if the closed-loop expression is

$$\frac{\theta_o}{\theta_i} = \frac{1 + 0.5s}{(1 + 0.1s)(1 + 0.05s)^2} \qquad (11.50\text{-}3)$$

the corresponding open-loop expression in factored form is

$$\frac{\theta_o}{\theta_e} = \frac{-3.33(1 + 0.5s)}{s(1 - 0.419s)(1 + 0.002s)} \qquad (11.50\text{-}4)$$

Fig. 11.50-3 shows the Nyquist locus of this function. It should be noted that this has the same form as that in Fig. 6.10-2d. A block diagram of a control system having this characteristic is shown in Fig. 11.50-4. The integrator has a low time constant, but other-

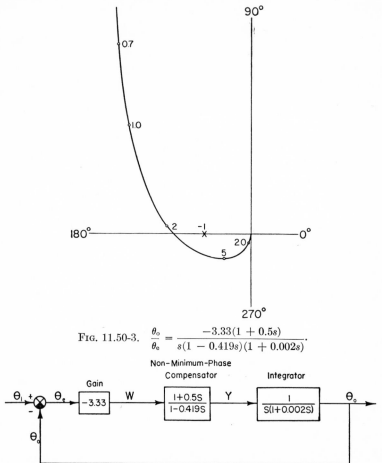

FIG. 11.50-3. $\dfrac{\theta_o}{\theta_e} = \dfrac{-3.33(1 + 0.5s)}{s(1 - 0.419s)(1 + 0.002s)}.$

FIG. 11.50-4. Block diagram of a control system having a positive phase shift for low-frequency input signals.

wise it is a conventional system element. The gain factor is nega-tive, which is always the case when an integration occurs in the open-loop function and $P = 1$ (see Fig. 6.10-2). Realization of the nonminimum-phase compensator Y/W characteristic can be obtained by two amplifiers and a resistance-capacitance network. This is discussed in the next section.

Thus methods exist for the synthesis of a control system which acts as a lead compensator for low-frequency inputs. Similarly, the synthesis of other desired functions can be accomplished.

11.60 Regenerative feedback loops

Figure 11.60-1 shows a simple arrangement which may be used to obtain desired characteristics. This figure differs from Fig. 9.60-2 in that the feedback variable Z is added to (rather than subtracted from) the input. These control loops are called "regen-

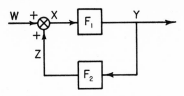

FIG. 11.60-1. Regenerative feedback system.

erative feedback loops." They are useful in obtaining desired control characteristics.

For example, the closed-loop expression for the system represented by Fig. 11.60-1 is

$$\frac{Y}{W} = \frac{F_1}{1 - F_1 F_2} \qquad (11.60\text{-}1)$$

If

$$F_1 = K_1 \qquad (11.60\text{-}2)$$

$$F_2 = \frac{K_2 s}{1 + Ts} \qquad (11.60\text{-}3)$$

then

$$\frac{Y}{W} = \frac{K_1(1 + Ts)}{1 + (T - K_1 K_2)s} \qquad (11.60\text{-}4)$$

Inspection of (11.60-4) reveals that it has the same form as that of the nonminimum-phase compensator in Fig. 11.50-4. Therefore, the Y/W characteristic in Fig. 11.50-4 can be realized by letting F_1 and F_2 in Fig. 11.60-1 have the following values.

$$F_1 = 1 \qquad (11.60\text{-}5)$$

$$F_2 = \frac{0.92s}{1 + 0.5s} \qquad (11.60\text{-}6)$$

Here F_1 may be realized by an amplifier having a unity gain factor, while F_2 may be realized by an amplifier cascaded with a resistance-capacitance network, as in Fig. 10.30-1.

Other characteristics may be realized by changing F_1 and F_2. Table 11.60-1 lists some of the possibilities. Because the feedback

TABLE 11.60-1

Y/W TRANSFER FUNCTIONS FOR VARIOUS F_1 AND F_2 CHARACTERISTICS

	F_1	F_2	Y/W	Special uses
a	K_1	$\dfrac{K_2 s}{1 + Ts}$	$\dfrac{K_1(1 + Ts)}{1 + (T - K_1K_2)s}$	If $K_1K_2 > T$, a nonminimum-phase denominator term occurs.
b	K_1	$\dfrac{K_2}{1 + Ts}$	$\dfrac{K_1(1 + Ts)}{1 - K_1K_2 + Ts}$	If $K_1K_2 = 1$, a proportional-plus-integral compensator results.
c	$\dfrac{K_1}{1 + Ts}$	K_2	$\dfrac{K_1}{1 - K_1K_2 + Ts}$	If $K_1K_2 = 1$, an integrator characteristic results. If $K_1K_2 > 1$, a nonminimum-phase denominator occurs.
d	$\dfrac{K_1}{s}$	1	$\dfrac{-1}{1 - s/K}$	Method of realizing a nonminimum-phase denominator term.

in a regenerative loop is positive rather than negative, these loops are often unstable by themselves. Therefore regenerative feedback loops find their widest application as internal loops in larger control systems, stability being maintained by the over-all system.

The system in Fig. 11.50-4 provides an excellent example. A regenerative feedback loop could be used to obtain the Y/W characteristic. The Y/W relation is unstable by itself. However, when it is an internal part of the over-all system in Fig. 11.50-4, complete stability is achieved.

The use of regenerative feedback inner loops enables the design of control characteristics such as those represented by the Nyquist loci in Figs. 6.10-2, 6.10-3, and 6.10-4.

11.70 Correlation with other analysis methods

The transient response, frequency response, and stability characteristics which have been discussed in this chapter for the Nyquist loci could be extended to other analysis methods. This is generally very informative. Different methods emphasize different characteristics. The root locus method closely correlates root location with transient characteristics; the log-decibel method reveals the simplicity which is possible in an analysis based on amplitude asymptote loci; and the inverse polar method exhibits the convenience associated with both concentric M-circles and a simple relation between the open- and closed-loop frequency responses.

Therefore the reader should extend the correlations discussed in this chapter to include these other methods. Then he will be able to use whichever method is best suited for his own particular analysis problems.

PROBLEMS

11-1. Calculate and plot the open-loop Nyquist of eq. 11.10-6, finding M_p for each case when the following values of A and ζ occur.

(a) $A = 0.1;\ \zeta = 0.01, 0.05, 0.1, 0.2, 0.3, 0.5, 0.9$
(b) $A = 0.5;\ \zeta = 0.01, 0.05, 0.1, 0.2, 0.3, 0.5, 0.9.$
(c) $A = 1;\quad \zeta = 0.01, 0.05, 0.1, 0.2, 0.3, 0.5, 0.9.$
(d) $A = 5;\quad \zeta = 0.01, 0.05, 0.1, 0.2, 0.3, 0.5, 0.9.$
(e) $A = 10;\ \zeta = 0.01, 0.05, 0.1, 0.2, 0.3, 0.5, 0.9.$

11-2. Find $\theta_o(\omega_1 t)$ for each case in Problem 11-1 when θ_i is a unit step input.

11-3. Answer the following for the closed-loop transfer functions given below.

What is the system type?
What is the open-loop function?
Is the open-loop function minimum-phase?
Which case in Figs. 6.10-1 to 6.10-4 corresponds to the open-loop function?
What are K_p, K_v, and K_a?
What are the Nyquist criterion values for N, P, and Z?
What are the inverse F_o criterion values for N, C, and Z?

(a) $\dfrac{1 + 5s}{(1 + s)(1 + 0.1s)}$

(b) $\dfrac{1 + 5s}{(1 + 2s)(1 + 3s)}$

(c) $\dfrac{1}{(1 + 0.1s)(1 + 0.01s)}$

(d) $\dfrac{1 + 5s}{(1 + s)(1 + 2s)(1 + 3s)}$

(e) $\dfrac{1 + s + s^2}{(1 + 0.1s + 0.01s^2)(1 + 0.9s)}$

(f) $\dfrac{(1 + s)(1 - 0.1s)}{(1 + 0.6s)(1 + 0.2s)(1 + 0.1s)}$

11-4. Given the open-loop expression,

$$F_o = \frac{5}{s(1 + 0.2s)}$$

(a) What is the closed-loop expression?
(b) What is $\theta_o(t)$ when θ_i is a unit step input?

(c) Select a proportional-plus-integral controller that changes the system from Type 1 to Type 2. What is $\theta_o(t)$ when θ_i is a unit step input?

(d) Select a second proportional-plus-integral controller that changes the system to Type 3. What is $\theta_o(t)$ when θ_i is a unit step input?

(e) Explain the difference between the $\theta_o(t)$ responses in parts (b), (c), and (d).

11-5. Select an open-loop function which has a frequency response like that in Fig. 11.30-2. Find the denominator roots of $(\theta_o/\theta_i)(s)$. Find $\theta_o(t)$ when θ_i is a unit step input.

11-6. Determine how well the approximate maximum values given in Table 11.40-1 describe the operation of systems which you have analyzed.

11-7. State how the open-loop expression of the following closed-loop relations could be realized.

(a) $\dfrac{1 + 0.5s}{(1 + 0.1s)(1 + 0.01s)^2}$

(b) $\dfrac{1 + 0.5s}{(1 + s)(1 + 0.2s)}$

(c) $\dfrac{10}{(1 + 0.1s)(1 + 0.4s)}$

(d) $\dfrac{10(1 + 5s)}{(1 + s)(1 + 0.1s)^2}$

(e) $\dfrac{10(1 + 0.1s)}{1 + s + s^2}$

(f) $\dfrac{10(1 + s)}{1 + s + s^2}$

CHAPTER 12

NUMERICAL INTEGRATION

12.00 Introduction[25,31,44]

It has been shown that the transient solution to control problems can be found by the use of Laplace transform tables or by conventional methods for differential equations. The solution also can be found by numerical integration. The process is one which applies pure mathematical logic. In fact, in many cases numerical integration is the only tool which the designer can use because of nonlinear effects such as variable coefficients and saturation limits. The process has several other important advantages:

1. The accuracy is adequate.
2. All the system variables are developed simultaneously.
3. The process can be adapted to machine solution.

The chief disadvantage is that in many complicated systems the method becomes too laborious. For these systems, automatic digital or analog computers should be used. However, even for complicated systems, it is often very valuable to perform a manual numerical integration.

Two methods of numerical integration are covered in this chapter. Both were selected because of their simplicity and accuracy. In addition another method, the Runge-Kutta, is covered in Appendix 1. The Runge-Kutta method has the advantage of requiring less computation time, but the disadvantage of requiring a more complicated set of integration formulas. The reader who is called upon to do extensive work of this type should consider the merits of all three methods before adopting one. In general, it will be found that each is more advantageous in certain applications, with Method 2 being the most applicable for general cases.

Logic plays the dominant part in solutions by this method. For example, an automobile driver who maintained his vehicle at 40 miles per hour for one-half hour knows that he has traveled 20 miles.

255

This is a simple integration problem, namely

$$\text{distance} = \int \text{speed } dt \tag{12.00-1}$$

Since the speed in this case was a constant, the equation is

$$\text{distance} = \text{speed} \times \text{time} \tag{12.00-2}$$

As a second example, suppose the driver was able to maintain a speed of 30 mph for the first 10 min, 40 mph for the following 15 min. and 60 mph for the next 5 min. How far would he have traveled in 5 min, 15 min, 30 min? These answers can be obtained by numerical integration. Let x be the distance traveled; then between 0 min and 10 min,

$$x = 30 \frac{t}{60} \tag{12.00-3}$$

where t is in minutes, x is in miles. Between 10 and 25 min, the equation is

$$x = \frac{40(t - 10)}{60} + 5 \tag{12.00-4}$$

where 5 is the distance traveled in the first 10 min. Between 25 and 50 min, the equation is

$$x = \frac{60(t - 25)}{60} + 15 \tag{12.00-5}$$

where 15 is the mileage traveled in the first 25 min.

12.10 Straight-line approximation (Method 1)

In this method for numerical integration, generally called the Euler method, the distance is calculated from the rate, the rate from the acceleration, the acceleration from the rate of acceleration, etc. By taking intervals so small that the change is gradual and summing the results, a close approximation to an actual differential equation solution can be found.

As an example, consider a system governed by the output to input relation

$$\frac{\theta}{\alpha} = \frac{1}{1 + 0.098s + 0.019s^2} \tag{12.10-1}$$

Let the system, initially at rest, be subjected to a unit step input so that

$$\alpha = \frac{1}{s} \tag{12.10-2}$$

The exact solution for θ is given by Laplace transform eq. 00.101.
It is

$$\theta = 1 + 1.07\epsilon^{-2.58t} \sin(388t° - 110.8°) \qquad (12.10\text{-}3)$$

A solution which closely approximates (12.10-3) can be found by numerical integration in the manner discussed below.

First, convert (12.10-1) back to differential equation form and solve for $\ddot{\theta}$. Thus

$$\ddot{\theta} = 52.6\alpha - 52.6\theta - 5.15\dot{\theta} \qquad (12.10\text{-}4)$$

Second, pick the initial conditions. For this the Laplace initial value theorem could be used, but since this system is relatively simple and initially at rest, the values can be written directly as

$$\theta = \dot{\theta} = 0 \qquad (12.10\text{-}5)$$

Also, it was given that

$$\alpha = 1 \qquad (12.10\text{-}6)$$

Therefore the system equation is

$$\ddot{\theta} = 52.6 - 52.6\theta - 5.15\dot{\theta} \qquad (12.10\text{-}7)$$

and a table with initial values may be set up as follows.

t	θ	$\dot{\theta}$	$\ddot{\theta}$
0	0	0	52.6

The initial value of $\ddot{\theta}$ was obtained by solving (12.10-7) at $t = 0$, when θ and $\dot{\theta}$ are zero. Section 12.30 discusses in greater detail how initial values are selected.

The next step is to determine the proper time interval. A very small time interval will produce very accurate results, whereas a large time interval will not. However the smaller the time interval, the greater the computation time required. Prior knowledge of a happy medium is therefore essential. Experience has shown that for this method the proper time interval is approximately 50 points per cycle of the *highest* system corner frequency. For this case there is only one system frequency. It can be found by expressing (12.10-1) in the nondimensional form.

$$\frac{\theta}{\alpha} = \frac{1}{1 + 2\zeta s/\omega_1 + s^2/\omega_1^2} \qquad (12.10\text{-}8)$$

Thus it is found that

$$\omega_1 = 7.25 \quad \text{radians per sec} \tag{12.10-9}$$

$$\zeta = 0.355 \tag{12.10-10}$$

Since

$$\omega = 2\pi f = 2\pi/P \quad \text{radians per sec} \tag{12.10-11}$$

where f = frequency in cycles per second, P = period of one cycle in seconds, the approximate interval to be used can be expressed as the general relation,

$$\Delta T = \begin{bmatrix} \text{approximate time interval} \\ \text{for Method 1} \end{bmatrix} = \frac{\pi}{25\omega_1} \tag{12.10-12}$$

$$\simeq \frac{1}{8\omega_1} \quad \text{sec}$$

In practice, the designer often starts with a smaller interval and changes to a larger interval than (12.10-12). However, unless one has had considerable experience, this is not advised, for it may indicate a false instability.

Applying (12.10-12) to the present example and rounding the result to an easier number to work with, the proper interval is

$$\Delta T = 0.02 \quad \text{sec} \tag{12.10-13}$$

The final step is to perform the actual numerical integration. This is done by solving (12.10-4) for $\ddot{\theta}$, using the value of $\ddot{\theta}$ to find the value of $\dot{\theta}$ at a time ΔT sec later, and using the value of $\dot{\theta}$ to find the value of θ at a time ΔT sec later. This may be expressed in equation form as follows.

$$\ddot{\theta} = 52.6 - 52.6\theta - 5.15\dot{\theta} \tag{12.10-14}$$

$$\dot{\theta} = \dot{\theta}_{-1} + \Delta T \ddot{\theta}_{-1} \tag{12.10-15}$$

$$\theta = \theta_{-1} + \Delta T \dot{\theta}_{-1} \tag{12.10-16}$$

where θ, $\dot{\theta}$, and $\ddot{\theta}$ are the values at a particular time, θ_{-1}, $\dot{\theta}_{-1}$, and $\ddot{\theta}_{-1}$ are values at a time ΔT sec earlier. Application of this method is illustrated by Tables 12.10-1, which shows the steps in the calculation of the first few values, and Table 12.10-2, which contains the time solution for the first 0.6 sec. Figs. 12.10-1, 12.10-2, and 12.10-3 show a comparison of the results of this method with the exact solution of (12.10-3) and with Method 2, having both a long

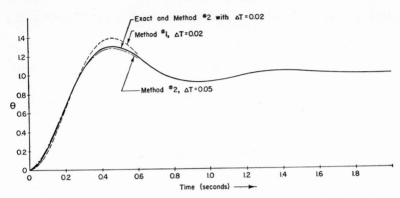

FIG. 12.10-1. Numerical integration results.

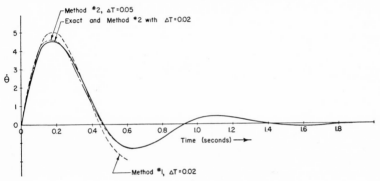

FIG. 12.10-2. Numerical integration results.

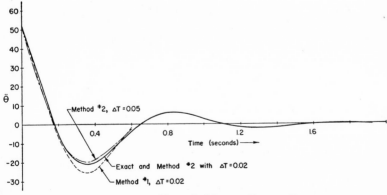

FIG. 12.10-3. Numerical integration results.

time interval and a short time interval. Table 12.10-3 contains the exact values of θ, $\dot{\theta}$, and $\ddot{\theta}$ for the first 1.0 sec.

TABLE 12.10-1
NUMERICAL INTEGRATION BY METHOD 1

System equation:

$$\frac{\theta}{\alpha} = \frac{1}{1 + 0.098s + 0.019s^2} \qquad \begin{aligned} \zeta &= 0.355 \\ \omega_1 &= 7.25 \end{aligned}$$

Disturbance: α = unit step input

Step-by-step equations:

$$\ddot{\theta} = 52.6 - 52.6\theta - 5.15\dot{\theta}$$

$$\dot{\theta} = \dot{\theta}_{-1} + \Delta T \ddot{\theta}_{-1}$$

$$\theta = \theta_{-1} + \Delta T \dot{\theta}_{-1} \qquad \Delta T = 1/8\omega_1 \simeq 0.02 \text{ sec}$$

t	θ	$\dot{\theta}$	$\ddot{\theta}$
0	0	0	$52.6 - 0 - 0$ $=52.6$
0.02	$0 + 0.02 \times 0$ $= 0$	$0 + 0.02 \times 52.6$ $= 1.052$	$52.6 - 52.6 \times 0 - 5.15 \times 1.052$ $= 47.18$
0.04	$0 + 0.02 \times 1.052$ $= 0.021$	$1.052 + 0.02 \times 47.18$ $= 1.996$	$52.6 - 52.6 \times 0.021 - 5.15 \times 1.996$ $= 41.22$
0.06	$.021 + 0.02 \times 1.996$ $= 0.061$	$1.996 + 0.02 \times 41.22$ $= 2.820$	$52.6 - 52.6 \times 0.061 - 5.15 \times 2.820$ $= 34.87$
0.08	$.061 + 0.02 \times 2.820$ $= 0.117$	$2.820 + 0.02 \times 34.87$ $= 3.518$	$52.6 - 52.6 \times 0.117 - 5.15 \times 3.518$ $= 28.32$

12.20 Weighted average method (Method 2)

The straight-line approximation method of the preceding section yielded a straightfoward and relatively easy method for obtaining transient response information. The main disadvantage of that method was the small interval required. The weighted average method presents a great improvement in that respect, for the number of points per cycle may be easily reduced from 50 to 20. Thus the proper time interval is approximately

$$\Delta T = 1/3\omega_1 \quad \text{sec} \qquad (12.20\text{-}1)$$

The basic weighted average method numerical integration equations for the case discussed in Section 12.10 are

$$\ddot{\theta} = 52.6 - 52.6\theta - 5.15\dot{\theta} \qquad (12.20\text{-}2)$$

$$\dot{\theta} = \dot{\theta}_{-1} + (3\ddot{\theta}_{-1} - \ddot{\theta}_{-2})\frac{\Delta T}{2} \qquad (12.20\text{-}3)$$

$$\theta = \theta_{-1} + (\dot{\theta} + \dot{\theta}_{-1})\frac{\Delta T}{2} \qquad (12.20\text{-}4)$$

TABLE 12.10-2

NUMERICAL INTEGRATION BY METHOD 1

System equation:

$$\frac{\theta}{\alpha} = \frac{1}{1 + 0.098s + 0.019s^2}$$

$\zeta = 0.355$

$\omega_1 = 7.25$

Disturbance: α = unit step input

Step-by-step equations:

$$\ddot{\theta} = 52.6 - 52.6\theta - 5.15\dot{\theta}$$

$$\dot{\theta} = \dot{\theta}_{-1} + \Delta T \ddot{\theta}_{-1}$$

$$\theta = \theta_{-1} + \Delta T \dot{\theta}_{-1} \qquad \Delta T = 1/8\omega_1 \simeq 0.02 \text{ sec}$$

t	θ	$\dot{\theta}$	$\ddot{\theta}$	t	θ	$\dot{\theta}$	$\ddot{\theta}$
0	0	0	52.6	0.32	1.1792	2.9903	−24.826
0.02	0	1.052	47.182	0.34	1.2390	2.4938	−25.414
0.04	0.021	1.9956	41.218	0.36	1.2889	1.9855	−25.421
0.06	0.0609	2.8200	34.874	0.38	1.3286	1.4771	−24.891
0.08	0.1173	3.5175	28.315	0.40	1.3581	0.9793	−23.879
0.10	0.1877	4.0838	21.695	0.42	1.3777	0.5017	−22.451
0.12	0.2694	4.5177	15.163	0.44	1.3877	0.0527	−20.664
0.14	0.3598	4.8210	8.846	0.46	1.3880	−0.3606	−18.594
0.16	0.4562	4.9979	2.865	0.48	1.3816	−0.7325	−16.300
0.18	0.5562	5.0552	− 2.690	0.50	1.3670	−1.0585	−13.853
0.20	0.6573	5.0014	− 7.731	0.52	1.3458	−1.3356	−11.311
0.22	0.7573	4.8468	−12.195	0.54	1.3191	−1.5618	− 8.741
0.24	0.8542	4.6029	−16.036	0.56	1.2879	−1.7366	− 6.200
0.26	0.9463	4.2822	−19.229	0.58	1.2532	−1.8606	− 3.736
0.28	1.0319	3.8976	−21.751	0.60	1.2160	−1.9353	− 1.395
0.30	1.1099	3.4626	−23.613				

TABLE 12.10-3

EXACT VALUES OF EQUATION 12.10-3 FOR FIRST SECOND

t	θ	$\dot{\theta}$	$\ddot{\theta}$
0	0	0	52.6
0.1	0.215	3.751	21.888
0.2	0.652	4.446	− 4.683
0.3	1.048	3.216	−19.132
0.4	1.267	1.160	−20.031
0.5	1.293	−0.518	−12.699
0.6	1.193	−1.312	− 3.353
0.7	1.058	−1.272	3.527
0.8	0.954	−0.753	6.286
0.9	0.911	−0.270	5.528
1.0	0.919	0.276	2.802

where θ, $\dot{\theta}$, and $\ddot{\theta}$ are values at a particular time, θ_{-1}, $\dot{\theta}_{-1}$, and $\ddot{\theta}_{-1}$ are values at a time ΔT sec earlier, and θ_{-2}, $\dot{\theta}_{-2}$, and $\ddot{\theta}_{-2}$ are values at a time $2\Delta T$ sec earlier. Comparison of the above eqs. with (12.10-15) and (12.10-16) shows important differences. Eq. (12.20-3) shows that the rate term is obtained from the latest two acceleration terms, giving greater weight to the last term. Eq. (12.20-4) shows that a value of θ will occur as soon as $\dot{\theta}$ occurs. Also, θ is obtained by the latest two rate terms rather than just the preceding term. Using the last two terms enables a much better approximation of the system than that obtained by Method 1.

Application of this method is illustrated by Table 12.20-1, which shows the steps in the calculation of the first few values with an

TABLE 12.20-1

NUMERICAL INTEGRATION BY METHOD 2

System equation:

$$\frac{\theta}{\alpha} = \frac{1}{1 + 0.098s + 0.019s^2} \qquad \begin{aligned} \varsigma &= 0.355 \\ \omega_1 &= 7.25 \end{aligned}$$

Disturbance: $\alpha =$ unit step input

Step-by-step equations:

$$\ddot{\theta} = 52.6 - 52.6\theta - 5.15\dot{\theta}$$

$$\dot{\theta} = \dot{\theta}_{-1} + (3\ddot{\theta}_{-1} - \ddot{\theta}_{-2})\Delta T/2$$

$$\theta = \theta_{-1} + (\dot{\theta} + \dot{\theta}_{-1})\Delta T/2 \qquad\qquad \Delta T = 0.02 \text{ sec}$$

t	θ	$\dot{\theta}$	$\ddot{\theta}$
0	0	0	52.6
0.02	$0+(1.052+0)\times0.01 = 0.01052$	$0+(3\times52.6-52.6)\times0.01 = 1.052$	$52.6-52.6\times0.01052-5.15\times1.052$ $= 46.629$
0.04	$0.01052+(1.925+1.052)\times0.01$ $= 0.04029$	$1.052+(3\times46.629-52.6)\times0.01$ $= 1.925$	$52.6-52.6\times0.04029-5.15\times1.925$ $= 40.568$
0.06	$0.04029+(2.676+1.925)\times0.01$ $= 0.08629$	$1.925+(3\times40.568-46.629)\times0.01$ $= 2.676$	$52.6-52.6\times0.08629-5.15\times2.676$ $= 34.282$
0.08	$0.08629+(3.298+2.676)\times0.01$ $= 0.14603$	$2.676+(3\times34.282-40.568)\times0.01$ $= 3.298$	$52.6-52.6\times0.14603-5.15\times3.298$ $= 27.932$

interval of 0.02 sec; Table 12.20-2, which contains the time solution for $\Delta T = 0.02$ sec; and Table 12.20-3, which contains the time solution for $\Delta T = 0.05$ sec.

In applying Method 2, the equations are not always of the second order, as (12.20-2) was. In these cases the method outlined below is used.

If the equation is of the first order, such as

$$\dot{\theta} = 5 - \theta \qquad\qquad (12.20\text{-}5)$$

TABLE 12.20-2

NUMERICAL INTEGRATION BY METHOD 2

System equation:

$$\frac{\theta}{\alpha} = \frac{1}{1 + 0.098s + 0.019s^2}$$

$\zeta = 0.355$
$\omega_1 = 7.25$

Disturbance: $\quad \alpha$ = unit step input

Step-by-step equations:

$$\theta = \theta_{-1} + (3\dot{\theta}_{-1} - \dot{\theta}_{-2})(\Delta T/2)$$

$$\theta = \theta_{-1} + (\dot{\theta} + \dot{\theta}_{-1})(\Delta T/2)$$

$$\ddot{\theta} = 52.6 - 52.6\theta - 5.15\dot{\theta} \qquad \Delta T = 0.02 \text{ sec}$$

t	θ	$\dot{\theta}$	$\ddot{\theta}$	t	θ	$\dot{\theta}$	$\ddot{\theta}$
0	0	0	52.6	0.32	1.10971	2.77767	−20.07575
0.02	0.01052	1.052	46.6288	0.34	1.16114	2.36525	−20.65700
0.04	0.04029	1.92486	40.56772	0.36	1.20426	1.94630	−20.76752
0.06	0.08629	2.67560	34.28181	0.38	1.23902	1.52984	−20.45113
0.08	0.14603	3.29838	27.93217	0.40	1.26556	1.12398	−19.75695
0.10	0.21695	3.79353	21.65175	0.42	1.28416	0.73578	−18.73608
0.12	0.29652	4.16376	15.55968	0.44	1.29523	0.37127	−17.44114
0.14	0.38230	4.41403	9.75877	0.46	1.29930	0.03540	−15.92549
0.16	0.47195	4.55120	4.33675	0.48	1.29697	−0.26795	−14.24068
0.18	0.56330	4.58371	− 0.63569	0.50	1.28893	−0.53592	−12.43773
0.20	0.65435	4.52127	− 5.10335	0.52	1.27590	−0.76665	−10.56409
0.22	0.74331	4.37453	− 9.02694	0.54	1.25864	−0.95920	− 8.66458
0.24	0.82860	4.15476	−12.38137	0.56	1.23791	−1.11350	− 6.77954
0.26	0.90888	3.87359	−15.15608	0.58	1.21447	−1.23024	− 4.94538
0.28	0.98304	3.54272	−17.35291	0.60	1.18906	−1.31081	− 3.19388
0.30	1.05020	3.17369	−18.98503				

the equation used to find θ is

$$\theta = \theta_{-1} + (3\dot{\theta}_{-1} - \dot{\theta}_{-1})(\Delta T/2) \qquad (12.20\text{-}6)$$

If the equation is of the third order, such as

$$\dddot{\theta} = 5 - \theta - 3.5\dot{\theta} - 3.5\ddot{\theta}, \qquad (12.20\text{-}7)$$

the equations used to find $\ddot{\theta}$, $\dot{\theta}$, and θ are

$$\ddot{\theta} = \ddot{\theta}_{-1} + (3\dddot{\theta}_{-1} - \dddot{\theta}_{-2})(\Delta T/2) \qquad (12.20\text{-}8)$$

$$\dot{\theta} = \dot{\theta}_{-1} + (\ddot{\theta} + \ddot{\theta}_{-1})(\Delta T/2) \qquad (12.20\text{-}9)$$

$$\theta = \theta_{-1} + (\dot{\theta} + \dot{\theta}_{-1})(\Delta T/2) \qquad (12.20\text{-}10)$$

For higher order equations, the method is similar. That is, an equation of the form (12.20-8) is used for the highest derivative, and for the subsequent lower derivatives the (12.20-9) type is used.

The weighted average method is based upon the assumption that a variable changes the same amount in the preceding interval as it

TABLE 12.20-3

NUMERICAL INTEGRATION BY METHOD 2

System equation:

$$\frac{\theta}{\alpha} = \frac{1}{1 + 0.098s + 0.019s^2}$$

$\zeta = 0.355$
$\omega_1 = 7.25$

Disturbance: α = unit step input

Step-by-step equations:

$$\theta = \theta_{-1} + (3\ddot{\theta}_{-1} - \ddot{\theta}_{-2})(\Delta T/2)$$

$$\theta = \theta_{-1} + (\dot{\theta} + \dot{\theta}_{-1})(\Delta T/2)$$

$$\ddot{\theta} = 52.6 - 52.6\theta - 5.15\dot{\theta} \qquad \Delta T = 1/3\omega_1 \simeq 0.05 \text{ sec}$$

t	θ	$\dot{\theta}$	$\ddot{\theta}$
0	0	0	52.6
0.05	0.06575	2.63	35.59705
0.10	0.23112	3.98478	19.92147
0.15	0.44546	4.58896	5.53566
0.20	0.67284	4.50610	− 5.99780
0.25	0.88344	3.91787	−14.04597
0.30	1.05675	3.01437	−18.50906
0.35	1.18154	1.97734	−19.73231
0.40	1.25498	0.96014	−18.35667
0.45	1.28090	0.07670	−15.17035
0.50	1.26776	−0.60216	−10.98305
0.55	1.22654	−1.04663	− 6.52586
0.60	1.16884	−1.26149	− 2.38431

does in the following interval. Using acceleration as an example,

$$\ddot{\theta} - \ddot{\theta}_{-1} = \ddot{\theta}_{-1} - \ddot{\theta}_{-2} \qquad (12.20\text{-}11)$$

or

$$\ddot{\theta} = 2\ddot{\theta}_{-1} - \ddot{\theta}_{-2} \qquad (12.20\text{-}12)$$

The average value throughout the interval from $\ddot{\theta}_{-1}$ to $\ddot{\theta}$ may be found by adding $\ddot{\theta}_{-1}$ to (12.20-12) and dividing by two. Thus

$$\text{average acceleration} = \frac{(\ddot{\theta} + \ddot{\theta}_{-1})}{2} = \frac{(3\ddot{\theta}_{-1} - \ddot{\theta}_{-2})}{2} \qquad (12.20\text{-}13)$$

This acceleration value is used to compute the rate associated with that particular time in a manner similar to Section 12.10. Therefore

$$\dot{\theta} = \dot{\theta}_{-1} + (3\ddot{\theta}_{-1} - \ddot{\theta}_{-2})(\Delta T/2) \qquad (12.20\text{-}14)$$

The average value of $\dot{\theta}$ throughout the interval from $\dot{\theta}_{-1}$ to $\dot{\theta}$ may be found by adding these values and dividing by two. This yields the basic θ equation as

$$\theta = \theta_{-1} + (\dot{\theta} + \dot{\theta}_{-1})(\Delta T/2) \qquad (12.20\text{-}15)$$

The derivation for equations of higher order follows the same procedure.

12.30 Initial values

Inclusion of the proper initial values in a numerical integration is highly important. First, erroneous values give the designer false data on the system performance. Second, if the system is not a linear one, erroneous values may or may not "trigger off" an instability. It has been stated elsewhere in this book that the initial values in a *linear* system affect the transient response, but do not affect the stability. However, as all physical systems are linear only

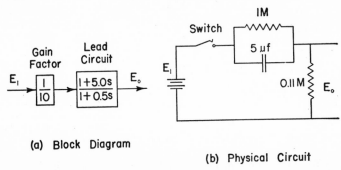

(a) Block Diagram

(b) Physical Circuit

Fig. 12.30-1.   Lead circuit.

within a given range, initial conditions may affect system stability. In the design of a complicated system the effect of saturations and signal limits must be included in the analysis, for frequently a nonlinearity (such as one due to saturation) can cause an otherwise stable system to oscillate violently when it is sufficiently disturbed. Linear analysis may be used to determine the approximate magnitude of system signal levels, but a complete analysis of their effect calls for prototypes, automatic computer simulation, or manual numerical integration techniques.

When a system is initially at rest, all variables, their rates, and their accelerations, are zero. Once the system is disturbed, however, the initial value of the variables, their rates, and accelerations, all may have values. Analysis of a simple lead circuit will show this. Fig. 12.30-1 shows both the block diagram expression and a physical realization of a lead circuit. Assume that the voltage E_1 is 1 volt.

When the switch is closed, the capacitor initially acts as a short circuit, so that the initial value of the output voltage E_o is unity. Then as the capacitor charges, the resistors act as a voltage divider, so that the output voltage eventually becomes one-tenth of the initial value. From these considerations we know that as soon as the switch is closed, the output voltage, its rate, acceleration, and all higher derivatives have values. The Laplace transform initial value theorem is a simple, straightforward method for evaluating these quantities.

Thus from Fig. 12.30-1,

$$\frac{E_o}{E_1} = \frac{(1 + 5s)}{10(1 + 0.5s)} \tag{12.30-1}$$

If E_1 is a unit step input,

$$e_o(t) = \mathcal{L}^{-1}E_o = \mathcal{L}^{-1}\frac{(1 + 5s)}{10s(1 + 0.5s)} = 0.1 + 0.9\epsilon^{-2t} \quad \text{volts}$$
$$\tag{12.30-2}$$

The Laplace initial value theorem is

$$f(0) = \lim_{s \to \infty} sF(s) \tag{12.30-3}$$

where $f(0)$ is the value of the function at $t = 0^+$, $F(s)$ is the Laplace transform of the function. Application of this to (12.30-2) yields

$$e_o(0) = \lim_{s \to \infty} s\frac{(1 + 5s)}{10s(1 + 0.5s)} = 1 \quad \text{volt} \tag{12.30-4}$$

To find the value of $\dot{e}_o$ at $t = 0$, it is necessary to obtain the Laplace transform of $\dot{e}_o(t)$. This is

$$\mathcal{L}\dot{e}_o(t) = s\mathcal{L}e_o(t) - e_o(0), \tag{12.30-5}$$

$$= \frac{1 + 5s}{10(1 + 0.5s)} - 1 \tag{12.30-6}$$

$$= \frac{-9}{10(1 + 0.5s)} \tag{12.30-7}$$

Use of (12.30-3) to (12.30-7) gives

$$\dot{e}_o(0) = \lim_{s \to \infty} \frac{-9s}{10(1 + 0.5s)} = -1.8 \quad \text{volts per sec} \tag{12.30-8}$$

Similarly, the Laplace transform of $\ddot{e}_o$ can be found. Thus

$$\mathcal{L}\ddot{e}_o(t) = s^2\mathcal{L}e_o(t) - se_o(0) - \dot{e}_o(0) \qquad (12.30\text{-}9)$$

$$= s\mathcal{L}\dot{e}_o(t) - \dot{e}_o(0) \qquad (12.30\text{-}10)$$

$$= \frac{-9s}{10(1 + 0.5s)} + 1.8 \qquad (12.30\text{-}11)$$

$$= \frac{18}{10(1 + 0.5s)} \qquad (12.30\text{-}12)$$

Hence the initial value result is

$$\ddot{e}_o(0) = \lim_{s \to \infty} \frac{18s}{10(1 + 0.5s)} = 3.6 \quad \text{volts per sec}^2 \qquad (12.30\text{-}13)$$

12.31 GENERAL INITIAL VALUE EQUATION. If a function $x(t)$ has as its Laplace transform a polynomial in s divided by another polynomial in s, a general equation for the initial value of x and of all the derivatives of x can be formulated. Thus the form of the Laplace transform may be expressed as

$$\mathcal{L}x(t) = \frac{a_{n-1}s^{n-1} + a_{n-2}s^{n-2} + a_{n-3}s^{n-3} + \ldots + a_o}{b_n s^n + b_{n-1}s^{n-1} + b_{n-2}s^{n-2} + \ldots + b_o} \qquad (12.31\text{-}1)$$

where all the a and b coefficients, except b_n, may be positive or negative, or zero. The coefficient b_n may be positive or negative, but it cannot be zero. Application of the initial value theorem yields the following general equations.

$$x(0^+) = \frac{a_{n-1}}{b_n} = K_{xo} \qquad (12.31\text{-}2)$$

$$\dot{x}(0^+) = \frac{a_{n-2}}{b_n} - \frac{b_{n-1}}{b_n} K_{xo} = K_{\dot{x}o} \qquad (12.31\text{-}3)$$

$$\ddot{x}(0^+) = \frac{a_{n-3}}{b_n} - \frac{b_{n-2}}{b_n} K_{xo} - \frac{b_{n-1}}{b_n} K_{\dot{x}o} = K_{\ddot{x}o} \qquad (12.31\text{-}4)$$

From the above three equations, the sequence pattern can be observed, so that the initial value equation for any derivative can be written down immediately.

The example of Section 12.30 may be used. Thus from (12.30-2)

$$\mathcal{L}e_o(t) = \frac{1 + 5s}{10s(1 + 0.5s)} = \frac{1 + 5s}{10s + 5s^2} \qquad (12.31\text{-}5)$$

Equating (12.31-5) to (12.31-1), the coefficients are

$$b_n = 5 \tag{12.31-6}$$

$$b_{n-1} = 10 \tag{12.31-7}$$

$$a_{n-1} = 5 \tag{12.31-8}$$

$$a_{n-2} = 1 \tag{12.31-9}$$

All other coefficients are zero.

Application of (12.31-2), (12.31-3), and (12.31-4) yields

$$e_o(0^+) = \tfrac{5}{5} = 1 \tag{12.31-10}$$

$$\dot{e}_o(0^+) = \tfrac{1}{5} - \tfrac{10}{5} \times 1 = -1.8 \tag{12.31-11}$$

$$\ddot{e}_o(0^+) = \tfrac{0}{5} - \tfrac{0}{5} \times 1 - \tfrac{10}{5} \times (-1.8) = 3.6 \tag{12.31-12}$$

These values are the same as those obtained in Section 12.30.

12.40 Control system example

The control system shown in Fig. 12.40-1 may be used as an example of equation formulation and initial value determination. The relation between variables is shown on the block diagram.

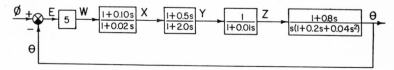

Fig. 12.40-1.

The first step in the solution calls for expressing the system relations as differential equations and solving for the highest order derivative in each case. These equations are

$$E = \phi - \theta \tag{12.40-1}$$

$$W = 5E \tag{12.40-2}$$

$$\dot{X} = 50(W - X) + 5\dot{W} \tag{12.40-3}$$

$$\dot{Y} = 0.5(X - Y) + 0.25\dot{X} \tag{12.40-4}$$

$$\dot{Z} = 100(Y - Z) \tag{12.40-5}$$

$$\ddot{\theta} = 25(Z - \dot{\theta}) + 20\dot{Z} - 5\ddot{\theta} \tag{12.40-6}$$

It should be noticed that, in order to solve (12.40-3), the term $\dot{W}$ is needed. This is found by taking the derivative of (12.40-2). In turn, $\dot{E}$ is required. Therefore the derivative of (12.40-1) is also needed. Then (12.40-1) and (12.40-2) become

$$\dot{E} = \phi - \dot{\theta} \tag{12.40-7}$$

$$\dot{W} = 5\dot{E} \tag{12.40-8}$$

The next step is to determine the initial value of all the variables in the preceding equations for a given input. The Laplace initial value theorem is very useful for this. It may be used in two ways. One method is to obtain the transfer function between each desired variable and the system input. The other method uses the transfer function between each desired variable and its preceding variable. Although the equations are more complicated in the first method, it is more straightforward. Its principal disadvantage is that it will not handle cases where variables exceed their maxima. A combination of the two methods is generally the easiest.

Using the techniques discussed in Chapter 4, the following transfer relation can be obtained.

$$\frac{\theta}{\phi} = \frac{F_{\circ}}{1 + F_{\circ}} \tag{12.40-9}$$

$$\frac{E}{\phi} = \frac{\theta}{\phi} \times \frac{E}{\theta} = \frac{1}{1 + F_{\circ}} \tag{12.40-10}$$

$$\frac{W}{\phi} = \frac{E}{\phi} \times \frac{W}{E} = \frac{5}{1 + F_{\circ}} \tag{12.40-11}$$

$$\frac{X}{\phi} = \frac{W}{\phi} \times \frac{X}{W} = \frac{5}{1 + F_{\circ}} \times \frac{(1 + 0.1s)}{(1 + 0.02s)} \tag{12.40-12}$$

$$\frac{Y}{\phi} = \frac{X}{\phi} \times \frac{Y}{X} = \frac{5}{1 + F_{\circ}} \times \frac{(1 + 0.1s)}{(1 + 0.02s)} \times \frac{(1 + 0.5s)}{(1 + 2s)} \tag{12.40-13}$$

$$\frac{Z}{\phi} = \frac{Y}{\phi} \times \frac{Z}{Y} = \frac{5}{1 + F_{\circ}} \times \frac{(1 + 0.1s)}{(1 + 0.02s)} \times \frac{(1 + 0.5s)}{(1 + 2s)} \times \frac{1}{(1 + 0.01s)} \tag{12.40-14}$$

where

$$F_{\circ} = \frac{5(1 + 0.1s)(1 + 0.5s)(1 + 0.8s)}{s(1 + 0.02s)(1 + 2s)(1 + 0.01s)(1 + 0.2s + 0.04s^{2})} \tag{12.40-15}$$

The initial values may now be determined for a given input. Suppose that the input is a unit step. Then

$$\phi(t) = 1 \quad \text{unit} \tag{12.40-16}$$

$$\mathscr{L}\phi = \frac{1}{s} \tag{12.40-17}$$

Also, since ϕ is a constant,

$$\dot{\phi}(t) = 0 \tag{12.40-18}$$

Equation (12.40-17) may be substituted into eqs. (12.40-9) through (12.40-14) to obtain the Laplace transform of the desired output variable. The procedure will be carried out in detail.

When the value of F_0 in (12.40-15) is substituted into (12.40-9), the result is

$$\frac{\theta}{\phi} = \frac{5(1 + 0.1s)(1 + 0.5s)(1 + 0.8s)}{5(1 + 0.1s)(1 + 0.5s)(1 + 0.8s) + s(1 + 0.02s)(1 + 2s)(1 + 0.01s)(1 + 0.2s + 0.04s^2)} \tag{12.40-19}$$

Multiplying (12.40-19) by (12.40-17) yields the Laplace transform of θ. Application of the initial value theorem gives the following initial values.

$$\theta(0^+) = 0 \tag{12.40-20}$$

$$\dot{\theta}(0^+) = 0 \tag{12.40-21}$$

$$\ddot{\theta}(0^+) = 0 \tag{12.40-22}$$

$$\dddot{\theta}(0^+) = 12500 \quad \text{units per sec}^3 \tag{12.40-23}$$

Using (12.40-1), (12.40-16), and (12.40-20), the initial value of E is

$$E(0^+) = 1 \quad \text{unit} \tag{12.40-24}$$

Likewise, from (12.40-7), (12.40-18), and (12.40-21),

$$\dot{E}(0^+) = 0 \tag{12.40-25}$$

Here W and $\dot{W}$ are found by using the above two equations, with (12.40-2) and (12.40-8), to be

$$W(0^+) = 5 \quad \text{units} \tag{12.40-26}$$

$$\dot{W}(0^+) = 0 \tag{12.40-27}$$

The initial value of X is found by multiplying (12.40-12) by (12.40-17) to obtain the Laplace transform of X. Then application of the initial value theorem yields

$$X(0^+) = 25 \quad \text{units} \qquad (12.40\text{-}28)$$

Substituting (12.40-26), (12.40-27), and (12.40-28) into (12.40-3) yields the initial value

$$\dot{X}(0^+) = -1000 \quad \text{units per sec} \qquad (12.40\text{-}29)$$

Similarly, the initial value of Y may be found by multiplying (12.40-13) by (12.40-17) and applying the initial value theorem. Thus

$$Y(0^+) = 6.25 \quad \text{units} \qquad (12.40\text{-}30)$$

Using (12.40-4), (12.40-28), (12.40-29), and (12.40-30),

$$\dot{Y}(0^+) = -240.625 \quad \text{units per sec} \qquad (12.40\text{-}31)$$

Likewise, by application of the initial value theorem,

$$Z(0^+) = 0 \qquad (12.40\text{-}32)$$

Substituting (12.40-30) and (12.40-32) into (12.40-5) gives the final initial value needed,

$$\dot{Z}(0^+) = 625 \quad \text{units per sec} \qquad (12.40\text{-}33)$$

The next step is to pick the proper time interval. The relation involving the highest frequency is the filter which has a corner frequency of 100 radians per sec. Thus the proper time interval for Method 1 is

$$\Delta T = 0.001 \text{ sec} \qquad (12.40\text{-}34)$$

For Method 2 the appropriate time interval is

$$\Delta T = 0.003 \text{ sec} \qquad (12.40\text{-}35)$$

The complete set of equations for a step-by-step numerical integration may now be written. For example, for Method 1 the equations, in the order in which they should be solved, are as follows.

$$E = 1 - \theta \tag{12.40-36}$$

$$\dot{E} = -\dot{\theta} \tag{12.40-37}$$

$$W = 5E \tag{12.40-38}$$

$$\dot{W} = 5\dot{E} \tag{12.40-39}$$

$$\dot{X} = 50(W - X) + 5\dot{W} \tag{12.40-40}$$

$$X = X_{-1} + \Delta T \dot{X}_{-1} \tag{12.40-41}$$

$$\dot{Y} = 0.5(X - Y) + 0.25\dot{X} \tag{12.40-42}$$

$$Y = Y_{-1} + \Delta T \dot{Y}_{-1} \tag{12.40-43}$$

$$\dot{Z} = 100(Y - Z) \tag{12.40-44}$$

$$Z = Z_{-1} + \Delta T \dot{Z}_{-1} \tag{12.40-45}$$

$$\dddot{\theta} = 25(Z - \dot{\theta}) + 20\dot{Z} - 5\ddot{\theta} \tag{12.40-46}$$

$$\ddot{\theta} = \ddot{\theta}_{-1} + \Delta T \dddot{\theta}_{-1} \tag{12.40-47}$$

$$\dot{\theta} = \dot{\theta}_{-1} + \Delta T \ddot{\theta}_{-1} \tag{12.40-48}$$

$$\theta = \theta_{-1} + \Delta T \dot{\theta}_{-1} \tag{12.40-49}$$

12.50 Insertion of limits

Maximum values may be placed on any variable in a numerical integration. When this is done, all the higher derivatives become zero and remain at zero, until the polarity of the variable's highest derivative is such as to reduce the limited variable. For example, suppose in the system covered in Section 12.40, that $\dot{\theta}$ had a maximum value of $+$two units per second. Then whenever $\dot{\theta}$ reached its maximum, θ would increase at 2 units per second, $\ddot{\theta}$ would become zero immediately, and $\dddot{\theta}$ would not affect the system until its polarity became negative, at which time normal operation would ensue. Usually it is desirable to use a smaller interval for a short time just after a system goes on or off limit.

In a similar fashion, limits which are gradually applied can be handled by suitable qualifications on the system equations.

If a system variable reaches a limit when a given input is applied, extra care must be taken to pick the proper initial values. As an example, if the limit on variable X in the system discussed in Section

12.40 is 15 units, the system initial values are determined in the manner that follows.

The initial values which were zero or which were not affected by X are the same as before. Thus

$$\phi(t) = 1 \text{ unit} \qquad (12.50\text{-}1)$$

$$\dot{\phi}(t) = 0 \qquad (12.50\text{-}2)$$

$$\theta(0^+) = 0 \qquad (12.50\text{-}3)$$

$$\dot{\theta}(0^+) = 0 \qquad (12.50\text{-}4)$$

$$\ddot{\theta}(0^+) = 0 \qquad (12.50\text{-}5)$$

$$E(0^+) = 1 \text{ unit} \qquad (12.50\text{-}6)$$

$$\dot{E}(0^+) = 0 \qquad (12.50\text{-}7)$$

$$W(0^+) = 5 \text{ units} \qquad (12.50\text{-}8)$$

$$\dot{W}(0^+) = 0 \qquad (12.50\text{-}9)$$

Since X is called upon to have a value which exceeds its maximum, the initial value of X is its upper limit. Thus

$$X(0^+) = 15 \quad \text{units} \qquad (12.50\text{-}10)$$

The initial value of $\dot{X}$ may be found from (12.40-3), (12.50-8), and (12.50-9) to be

$$\dot{X}(0^+) = -500 \quad \text{units per sec} \qquad (12.50\text{-}11)$$

The initial value of Y may now be found by applying the initial value theorem to the transfer relation between X and Y for X being an arbitrary constant. When this is done, it is found that the initial value of Y is one-fourth the initial value of X. Thus

$$Y(0^+) = 3.75 \quad \text{units} \qquad (12.50\text{-}12)$$

Solution of (12.40-4) with values already known yields

$$\dot{Y}(0^+) = -119.375 \quad \text{units per sec} \qquad (12.50\text{-}13)$$

Similarly, it is found that applying the initial value theorem between Y and Z,

$$Z(0^+) = 0 \qquad (12.50\text{-}14)$$

When known values are substituted into (12.40-5),

$$\dot{Z}(0^+) = 375 \quad \text{units per sec} \qquad (12.50\text{-}15)$$

Finally, $\overset{\cdots}{\theta}$ may be found, by using (12.40-6) and the previously obtained initial values, to be

$$\overset{\cdots}{\theta}\,(0^+) = 7500 \quad \text{units per sec}^3 \qquad (12.50\text{-}16)$$

12.60 Simplifying assumptions

As a numerical integration is usually used to obtain a general idea of system performance, simplifying assumptions which reduce the time required without appreciably affecting the result are often made. The major assumption is the elimination of unnecessary high-frequency factors in the system equations. Thus in the example of Section 12.40, the filter may be eliminated without serious effect by assuming that

$$Y = Z \qquad (12.60\text{-}1)$$

When this is done, the highest frequency in the system becomes 50 radians per sec. As the proper time interval was formerly based on 100 radians per sec, elimination of the filter makes possible increasing the numerical integration step interval by 2. Naturally, extreme care should be taken to make sure any simplification is legitimate.

Another simplification is the elimination of unnecessary variables by combining equations. Thus variables such as $\dot{E}$, W, and $\dot{W}$ could be easily replaced by proper values of constants and θ.

PROBLEMS

12-1. Using Method 1, find $\theta(t)$ for eq. (12.10-7) when $\Delta T = 0.05$ sec.; when $\Delta T = 0.01$ sec.

12-2. Using Method 2, find $\theta(t)$ for eq. (12.10-7) when $\Delta T = 0.04$ sec.; when $\Delta T = 0.1$ sec.

12-3. If

$$\frac{\theta}{\alpha} = \frac{1 + 0.5s}{1 + 0.1s}$$

and if α is a unit step input, find $\theta(t)$ by numerical integration using Method 2. What is a good value for ΔT? What are the initial and final values of θ, $\dot{\theta}$, $\ddot{\theta}$, and $\overset{\cdots}{\theta}$?

12-4. Repeat Problem 12-3, using

$$\frac{\theta}{\alpha} = \frac{1 + 0.5s}{(1 + 0.1s)(1 + 0.098s + 0.019s^2)}$$

12-5. Repeat Problem 12-3, using the Runge-Kutta Method described in Appendix 1 instead of Method 2.

12-6. Set up the numerical integration equations for Method 2 including all necessary initial conditions when the input is a unit step input for the system shown in Fig. 12.40-1. What is a good value for ΔT?

12-7. Repeat Problem 12-6 using the system shown in the following figures.

(a) Figure 4.20-1a

(b) Figure 4.51-2b

(c) Figure 4.53-2b

(d) Figure 4.53-2c

(e) Figure 4.54-1b

(f) Figure 5.10-1

(g) Figure 5.10-2

(h) Figure 6.40-1

(i) Figure 8.13-1

(j) Figure 9.60-1

(k) Figure 9.60-3

CHAPTER 13

AUTOMATIC COMPUTERS

13.00 Introduction

Automatic computers facilitate the solution of many control problems. The computers are of two major types, digital and analog. Digital computers deal with numbers and perform such calculations as numerical integration. Analog computers simulate the operation of a control system by using electric currents and shaft rotations to replace system variables.

Each automatic computer consists of a few basic units. In the case of digital computers, these units are:

1. Counters, which perform the numerical operations.

2. Memory units, which receive, store, transmit, and erase information.

3. Control units, which determine the sequence of the automatic operations.

4. Recording units, which record the results.

Analog computers consist of:

1. Major computing components such as integrators, summing amplifiers, and gain factor potentiometers.

2. Special computing components such as limiters, trignometric function potentiometers, and comparators.

3. Recording units.

The size of a computer determines the complexity of the problems it will handle. The basic components are essentially plug-in units. Hence several small computers are often connected together to form one large computer. Digital computers of different manufacturers differ in the speed of computation, size, circuitry techniques, and number of automatic functions. Analog computers of different manufacturers have the same differences as digital computers, except that the accuracy of the analog components is not as precise and the speed of computation is less critical.

Since digital computers deal with numbers, the results are as accurate as necessary. Their computation speed, however, is an important variable. Digital computers solve control problems by numerical integration. Computation time is therefore a function of the problem time interval, number of operations, problem time length, and operational speed of the digital computer. The reader who has solved any of the numerical integration problems in Chapter 12 will quickly recognize the merits of an automatic digital computer. Complex problems, whose solution would require hundreds of man hours by manual numerical integration, may be solved in a few hours by automatic digital computation. Automatic monitors may be incorporated so that the computer stops whenever an error or machine malfunction occurs.

Any inaccuracy in a control system solution by digital computation (other than machine malfunction) is due to the numerical integration method rather than to the computer. This is not the case when analog computers are used. Analog computers are based on an entirely different solution method. They simulate control problems by using electric and mechanical components having the same transfer function characteristics as the control circuit components. Hence computer component characteristics such as linearity, dead-spot limits, noise, voltage fluctuations, and drift have a direct effect on the solution accuracy. The same problem solved twice on a digital computer should yield answers that are identical; whereas on an analog computer, the answers usually are slightly different. This is generally a minor problem, except for very complex systems. The accuracy and reliability of present-day analog and digital computers are very high. Hence analog computer accuracy, while not exact, is usually within a very small tolerance.

Since analog computers simulate the control system characteristics, the time required for computer solution is normally the same as that required by the actual system. This, called "true-time solution," makes it possible for the analog computer to be used to simulate part of the control system, with actual system components being used for the remainder. Sometimes, however, the true time solution is either very short or very long. In these cases the whole problem may be solved on an analog computer using a more convenient time scale. This is accomplished by altering the speed of response of all the components by a convenient factor, although actual system components may not now be used in the solution.

In general, digital computers solve problems much faster than manual numerical integration, and analog computers solve problems much faster than digital computers. Problem set-up time is usually somewhat less on an analog computer than on a digital computer. There are some problems with special non-linear characteristics, however, which are more suited to one type of computer than the other.

The problem set-up time is a function of system complexity. Some very complex systems may require several weeks to set up, and only a few seconds to run. Most systems, however, can be set up in a few hours.

13.10 Binary arithmetic

Numbering systems may be based on any number. The most common numbering system is based on 10. One explanation of why the

TABLE 13.10-1

Base 10 number	Equivalent binary number	Base 10 number	Equivalent binary number	Base 10 number	Equivalent binary number
0	0	9	1001	18	10010
1	1	10	1010	19	10011
2	10	11	1011	20	10100
3	11	12	1100	21	10101
4	100	13	1101	22	10110
5	101	14	1110	23	10111
6	110	15	1111	24	11000
7	111	16	10000	25	11001
8	1000	17	10001		

base 10 came into practice is that when man first began to count, he associated objects with his fingers. The base 10 was a fortunate choice because of its convenience for most applications. However, other base numbers are used in some calculations. One often counts by dozens. The foot is divided into 12 inches, and there are 12 months in a year. Other bases are used in monetary systems. The binary system uses the base 2 and is favored for digital computer work because the number of components required is a minimum.

Approximately 50 per cent fewer components are necessary when digital computers are operated on the base 2 than when they are operated on the base 10. This is particularly important from reliability as well as economic considerations. Modern, large-scale digital computers contain thousands of electron tubes, all of which must function properly for accurate results.

The binary numerical system assigns to successive integers (reading right to left) the meanings 1, 2, 4, 8, 16, 64, etc. For example, the base 10 number 25 is 11001 in the binary system, because

$$25 = 1 \times 16 + 1 \times 8 + 0 \times 4 + 0 \times 2 + 1 \times 1 \quad (13.10\text{-}1)$$

Similarly, the other base 10 numbers in Table 13.10-1 have the binary equivalent shown for them. The binary system has only two written characters, 0 and 1.

Addition is performed by the following relations.

$$0 + 0 = 0 \quad\quad\quad (13.10\text{-}2)$$

$$1 + 1 = 10 \quad\quad\quad (13.10\text{-}3)$$

$$1 + 0 = 1 \quad\quad\quad (13.10\text{-}4)$$

Thus the sum of the base 10 numbers 4 and 5 becomes in binary notation

$$\begin{array}{r} 100 \\ 101 \\ \hline 1001 \end{array} \quad\quad\quad (13.10\text{-}5)$$

which is equal to the base 10 number 9. Multiplication is performed by the relations

$$1 \times 1 = 1 \quad\quad\quad (13.10\text{-}6)$$

$$1 \times 0 = 0 \quad\quad\quad (13.10\text{-}7)$$

$$0 \times 0 = 0 \quad\quad\quad (13.10\text{-}8)$$

As an example of multiplication, the product of 4 times 5 in binary notation is

$$\begin{array}{r} 100 \\ 101 \\ \hline 100 \\ 000 \\ 100 \\ \hline 10100 \end{array} \quad\quad\quad (13.10\text{-}9)$$

which is equal to the base 10 number 20.

Since there are only two characters in binary arithmetic, any two-position instrument could serve as a binary computer component. One instrument that is so used is the General Electric Binary Scaler Type 4SN1A3 (also called "Binary Trigger"), shown in Fig. 13.10-1. This consists of a twin-triode tube and associated circuitry.

Fig. 13.10-1. GE Binary Scaler Type 4SN1A3. (Courtesy General Electric Co.)

The sequence of operation may be followed by reference to the circuit diagram in Fig. 13.10-2. The circuit is a modification of the common bistable multivibrator. In normal operation either T_1 or T_2 is conducting, and the other is not. The system is biased so that a positive input pulse will not affect the tube operation, but a negative input pulse will cause the nonconducting tube to conduct and the conducting tube to cease conducting. A second negative input pulse will reverse the operation again. Suppose that initially T_2 is conducting. A negative trigger pulse drives the grid of the conducting tube T_2 negative beyond cutoff. The rise of plate potential of T_2 is applied across the voltage divider network in the grid circuit of T_1, causing that tube to conduct. This causes a drop of plate potential in T_1, which is applied to the grid of T_2. The drop in the grid voltage of T_2 causes the entire action to augment itself until T_2 is cut off and T_1 is conducting. Another trigger pulse would cause the same action, but would leave T_2 conducting and T_1 cut off.

By connecting the output of one binary scaler to the trigger input of another, binary counting is possible. If T_2 conducts in each binary scaler when the zero reset button is pushed, the plate voltage waveform of T_2 for four cascaded binary scalers is like that shown in Fig. 13.10-3. Special meaning is assigned to the plate voltage of T_2. The first binary scaler indicates 1 when T_2 does not conduct,

and 0 when T_2 conducts. Four cascaded binary scalers can be used
to count to 15. The first binary scaler represents 1 and 0, the second
represents 2 and 0, the third represents 4 and 0, and the fourth
represents 8 and 0.

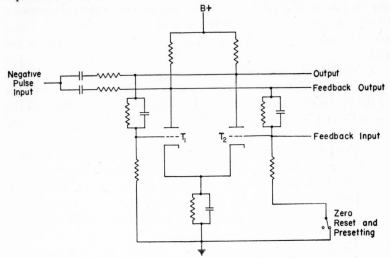

Fig. 13.10-2.   Circuit diagram of the GE Binary Scaler.

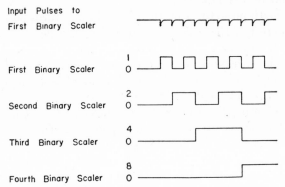

Fig. 13.10-3.   Plate voltage waveforms of T_2 and their meanings for four
cascaded binary scalers.

Sometimes little neon glow bulbs are used to indicate the condition of T_2. Thus if the light glows whenever the plate voltage on
T_2 is high (T_1 is conducting), the following counting sequence would
result for the four binary scalers represented by Fig. 13.10-3.

1. The first pulse turns on the light of the first binary scaler (No. 1 light). All other lights are out.

2. The second pulse causes the tube conduction operation in the first binary scaler to reverse. This turns off the No. 1 light. Since the output of the first binary scaler changes negatively, it causes a plate conduction reversal in the second binary scaler. This turns on the light representing 2 (No. 2 light). All other lights are out.

3. The third pulse causes a reversal of plate operation in the first scaler. This turns on the No. 1 light. Since the T_2 plate voltage of the first scaler changes in a positive direction, the operation of the second scaler is not disturbed. The count of 3 is indicated since the No. 1 and No. 2 lights are on.

4. The fourth pulse turns off the No. 1 light. Since the output of the first scaler changes negatively, the No. 2 light is also turned off. As the T_2 plate voltage of the second scaler also changes in a negative direction, it causes conduction in the third scaler to reverse. This turns on the light representing 4 (No. 4 light). All other lights are out.

5. The fifth pulse turns on the No. 1 light, and the operation of the other scalers is not affected. Since the No. 1 and No. 4 lights are on, a count of 5 is indicated.

6. The sixth pulse turns off the first light and turns on the second light. The rest of the scalers are not affected. Since the No. 2 and No. 4 lights are on, a count of 6 is indicated.

7. The seventh pulse turns on the first light. None of the other scalers is affected. Since the No. 1, No. 2, and No. 4 lights are on, a count of 7 is indicated.

8. The eighth pulse causes the conduction in all four scalers to reverse. This is because the T_2 plate potential of scalers 1, 2, and 3 changes in a negative direction, causing a negative pulse input to the scaler that follows. Since only the light representing 8 is on (No. 8 light), a count of 8 is indicated.

9. The ninth pulse turns on the No. 1 light. All other scalers are not affected. Since the No. 1 and No. 8 lights are on, a count of 9 is indicated.

10. The tenth pulse causes the No. 1 light to go out and the No. 2 light to go on. The other lights are not affected. Since the No. 2 and No. 8 lights are on, a count of 10 is indicated.

11. Succeeding pulses operate in a similar fashion. The operation may be returned to zero at any time by pushing the reset button.

Most digital computers operate on a modified-binary numbering system. The computers are composed of groups of four binary scalers. Each group counts to 10 and is called a "ten-counter." Each ten-counter represents a decimal quantity such as units, tens, hundreds, thousands, etc. In operation a ten-counter counts in the normal manner for the first 9 pulses. The tenth pulse triggers a mechanism which: (1) resets all four binary scalers in the group to zero, (2) sends an input pulse to the next highest group.

For example, 2 ten-counters cascaded together could count to 100. One ten-counter would represent units and the other, tens.

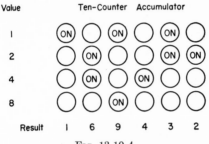

FIG. 13.10-4.

On the tenth input pulse the unit ten-counter would reset itself to zero, and send a negative pulse representing 10 to the second ten-counter. On the twentieth input pulse, the unit ten-counter again would reset itself to zero and send another input pulse representing an additional 10 to the second ten-counter. Similarly, on each tenth input pulse, the operation is repeated; until, on the one-hundredth pulse, both ten-counters are reset to zero.

Figure 13.10-4 shows a neon light arrangement for a typical ten-counter accumulator capable of counting to 1 million.

13.20 The use of digital computers

The principles of binary arithmetic, discussed in the preceding section, are utilized by most digital computers. Addition is accomplished by applying input pulses to binary scalers. Multiplication is accomplished by repeated addition; that is,

$$3 \times 4 = 4 + 4 + 4 = 12 \qquad (13.20\text{-}1)$$

Subtraction is sometimes accomplished by the addition of nine complements, and division can be achieved by repeated subtraction of the divisor from the dividend.

Automatic computing consists of some combination of addition, subtraction, multiplication, and division. In addition, certain calculating operations also require the recognition of relative numerical values such as less then, greater than, and equal to. Digital computers are capable of performing all these operations automatically.

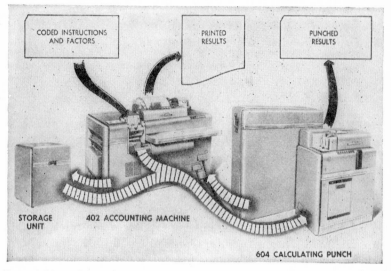

Fig. 13.20-1.   Digital computer. (Courtesy International Business Machines Corp.)

These computers are therefore valuable analysis tools, for they enable the performance of complex control system studies. Nonlinear properties such as saturations, nonlinear amplification, dead spots, and trigonometric relations can be included in a digital computer study. Thus results that are more realistic than those obtained by a linear analysis are possible.

A typical digital computer installation is shown in Fig. 13.20-1. This computer utilizes punched cards similar to those shown in Figs. 13.20-2 and 13.20-3. The cards may contain either general or specific information. The card shown in Fig. 13.20-2 contains general information. It says that Factor A, which is in Location 12, should be multiplied by Factor *B*, which is in Location 13, and the result should be stored in Location 16. A card of this type would be used to command a numerical integration procedure. The card

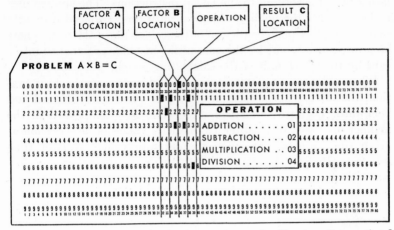

Fig. 13.20-2. General information instruction card. (Courtesy International Business Machines Corp.)

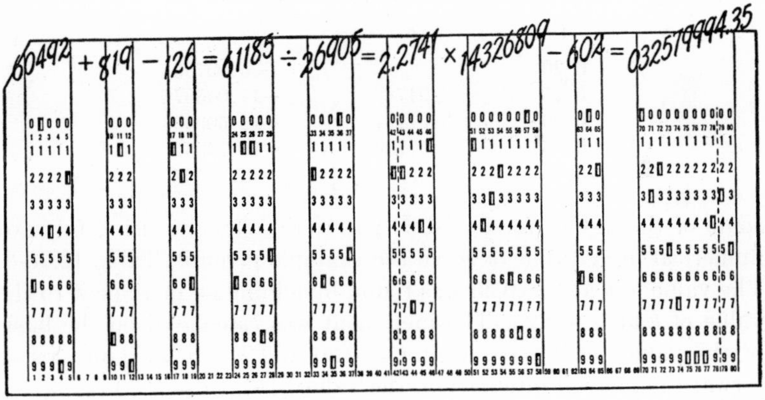

Fig. 13.20-3. Numerical data instruction card. (Courtesy International Business Machines Corp.)

shown in Fig. 13.20-3 contains specific information about a given set of numbers.

The computer shown in Fig. 13.20-1 makes use of several machine units. Cards containing coded instructions and factors are inserted in the accounting machine. This machine reads from the punched cards the factors for calculation, and the codes that instruct the machines as to what calculations are to be made. The factors are introduced into counters, and calculations are made with the calculating punch according to the coded instructions. The storage unit makes possible the holding of figures until they are needed in subsequent steps. Upon completion of the calculations, the results may be printed on a report by the accounting machine or punched into a card by the punch unit of the calculating punch, or both.

When a digital computer is used to perform a numerical integration, the integration process is often performed both forward and backward. Forward numerical integration is accomplished in the manner discussed in Chapter 12; namely, values of acceleration at given time intervals are used to find rate values at later time intervals. Backward numerical integration is the reverse of forward integration; namely, values of acceleration at given time intervals are used to find rate values at earlier time intervals.

An example will illustrate this procedure. Table 13.20-1 repeats

TABLE 13.20-1
FORWARD NUMERICAL INTEGRATION VALUES

t	$\dot{\theta}$	$\ddot{\theta}$
0.20		−5.99780
0.25	3.91787	−14.04597
0.30	3.01437	−18.50906
0.35	1.97734	−19.73231
0.40		−18.35667

some of the values for $\dot{\theta}$ and $\ddot{\theta}$ that were found by using forward numerical integration to solve the example given in Table 12.20-3. The value of $\dot{\theta}$ at $t = 0.30$ was found by adding an increment to the value of $\dot{\theta}$ at $t = 0.25$. The increment was calculated on the basis of the values of $\ddot{\theta}$ existing at $t = 0.20$ and $t = 0.25$. Thus, using forward numerical integration, the value of $\dot{\theta}$ at $t = 0.30$ is

$$\dot{\theta} = 3.91787 + \frac{0.05}{2} [3(-14.04597) - (-5.99780)] = 3.01437$$

(13.20-2)

Backward numerical integration is performed in a similar manner, except that the increment is subtracted from the previous value instead of being added to it. Thus the basic equation for $\dot{\theta}$ is

$$\dot{\theta} = \dot{\theta}_1 - (\Delta T/2)(3\ddot{\theta}_1 - \ddot{\theta}_2) \qquad (13.20\text{-}3)$$

where $\dot{\theta}$ is the value at any particular time, $\dot{\theta}_1$ is the value of $\dot{\theta}$ at a time interval of ΔT sec later, $\ddot{\theta}_1$ is the value of $\ddot{\theta}$ at a time interval of ΔT sec later, $\ddot{\theta}_2$ is the value of $\ddot{\theta}$ at a time interval of $2\Delta T$ sec later. Similarly, the basic backward numerical integration equation for θ is

$$\theta = \theta_1 - (\Delta T/2)(\dot{\theta} + \dot{\theta}_1) \qquad (13.20\text{-}4)$$

where the subscript 1 has the same meaning as it did in (13.20-3). Applying backward numerical integration to find the value of $\dot{\theta}$ at $t = 0.30$ for the system represented by Table 13.20-1, the result is

$$\dot{\theta} = 1.97734 - \frac{0.05}{2}[3(-19.73231) - (-18.35667)] = 3.17740$$

$$(13.20\text{-}5)$$

In practice, the solution to a control problem which was found by forward numerical integration is often checked by backward numerical integration. The control system values at any particular time form the starting point for a backward numerical integration. If the system response obtained by backward numerical integration is not in close agreement with that obtained by forward numerical integration, it indicates that the integration time interval is too large. If the two solutions are very close, it indicates that the time interval may be increased without appreciably affecting the results.

Another method more often used to check the accuracy of a numerical integration is that of solving the problem twice. One solution uses a time interval that is twice as large as the other. If the results of both solutions are very close, the time interval may be increased. If the results are not reasonably close, the time interval should be shortened.

13.30 Analog computers[29]

Analog computers consist of components which enable the mathematical simulation of given functions. For example, the output-to-input relation,

$$\frac{\theta_o}{\theta_i} = \frac{1}{1 + 0.098s + 0.019s^2} \qquad (13.30\text{-}1)$$

could be rewritten

$$\ddot{\theta}_o = 52.6\theta_i - 52.6\theta_o - 5.15\dot{\theta}_o \qquad (13.30\text{-}2)$$

and the operational behavior could be simulated by the arrangement shown in Fig. 13.30-1. It may be seen that this method of simulation involves only integrators, amplifiers, and summing units. More complex relations could be simulated by more integrators,

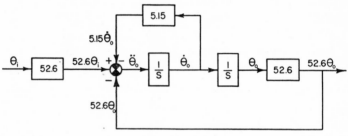

FIG. 13.30-1.   Method of simulating the relation $\dfrac{\theta_o}{\theta_i} = \dfrac{1}{1 + 0.098s + 0.019s^2}$.

amplifiers, and summing units. Subsequent discussions will show that these are the major components in most analog computers.   ·

Several typical analog computers are shown in Figs. 13.30-2, 13.30-3, 13.30-4. The Boeing Electronic Analog Computer shown in Fig. 13.30-2 is of adequate size for most control problems. The various computing components are wired together in the desired manner, and the transient results are recorded either on paper or on an oscilloscope.

A larger computer is the Reeves Electronic Analog Computer shown in Fig. 13.30-3. The two large consoles in the center of the picture consist of amplifier, integrator, gain factor, and limiter units. The large console on the right is an electronic generator which enables the realization of empirical functions. The large console on the left contains the power supply for the computer, and the smaller console on the right is a six-channel recorder. Complete problems are wired on "prepatch boards" which plug into the front of the two large consoles in the center of the picture. The use of these

Fig. 13.30-2. Boeing Electronic Analog Computer. (Courtesy Boeing Airplane Co.)

boards permits wiring a second problem at a desk while the solutions of the first are being obtained with the computer.

An extremely large analog computer is the RCA Typhoon Simulator, a portion of which is shown in Fig. 13.30-4. This equipment was built by the Radio Corporation of America under contract with the Office of Naval Research, Special Devices Center for the

Fig. 13.30-3. Reeves Electronic Analog Computer. (Courtesy Reeves Instrument Corp.)

Fig. 13.30-4. RCA Typhoon Simulator. (Courtesy Radio Corp. of America.)

Bureau of Aeronautics, and was installed at the Naval Air Development Center of the Bureau of Aeronautics, located at Johnsville, Pennsylvania.

13.40 Analog computer components

The major components in most analog computers are the following.

1. Amplifiers
2. Integrators
3. Frequency-dependent functions
4. Gain potentiometers
5. Limiters and comparators
6. Servo units
7. Recorders

The theory and operation of these units are discussed in the following sections, and the symbols representing them are given.

13.41 AMPLIFIER UNITS. Figure 13.41-1 shows the basic elements of an analog computer amplifier. It consists of input and feedback resistors and a high-gain, phase-inverting, d-c amplifier. The feed-back resistor R_F is connected between the plate of the output stage and the grid of the input stage of the d-c amplifier. The circuit is such that the grid draws practically no current. Therefore R_1 and R_F act as a voltage divider between e_i and e_o. Since the high-gain amplifier (the gain is approximately 100,000) is of the phase-invert-

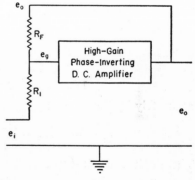

FIG. 13.41-1. Computer amplifier.

ing type, the polarity of e_o is always opposite to that of e_i, and zero voltage occurs at some point between the two. Therefore the unit operates as a small Type 0 control system with e_g acting as the error-actuating signal. If e_g has any value, the high-gain d-c amplifier changes e_o until e_g is negligibly small. Thus the relationship between e_o and e_i is determined by the magnitudes of R_F and R_1, and is

$$e_o = -\frac{R_F}{R_1} e_i \qquad (13.41\text{-}1)$$

The minus sign in (13.41-1) is due to the phase-inverting action.

Typical operating conditions of the computer amplifier are given in Table 13.41-1.

TABLE 13.41-1

TYPICAL OPERATING CONDITIONS OF A COMPUTER AMPLIFIER
(Assuming a d-c amplifier gain of 100,000)

R_F (megohms)	R_1 (megohms)	e_i (volts)	e_o (volts)	e_g (volts)
1	0.50	1	−2	0.00002
1	0.25	1	−4	0.00004
1	0.10	1	−10	0.00010

In practice, several input resistors are connected to the input grid, as shown in Fig. 13.41-2, and the output may be represented

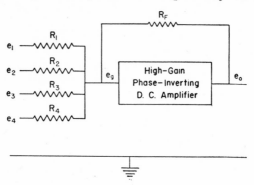

FIG. 13.41-2.   Summing amplifier.

accurately by the relation

$$e_o = -\frac{R_F}{R_1} e_1 - \frac{R_F}{R_2} e_2 - \frac{R_F}{R_3} e_3 - \frac{R_F}{R_4} e_4 \qquad (13.41\text{-}2)$$

These units are called "summing amplifiers" and are usually repre-

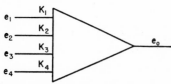

sented by the symbol shown in Fig. 13.41-3. Here K_1 is equal to the ratio R_F/R_1 and denotes the gain factor which exists for an input applied at that point.

FIG. 13.41-3.   Summing amplifier symbol.

13.42 INTEGRATOR UNITS. Analog computer integrator units are very similar to summing amplifier units. The only difference is that the feedback element is a capacitor rather than a resistor. The basic elements are shown in Fig. 13.42-1. The operation of the integrator may be seen by the following considerations. Assume a voltage e_1 is applied. Since practically no current flows through the grid of the high-gain amplifier, all the current flows through R_1 and C. Also,

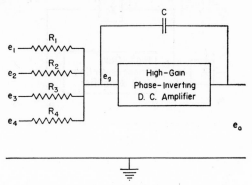

FIG. 13.42-1. Computer summing integrator.

since e_g tends to become zero,

$$e_1 = R_1 i \qquad (13.42\text{-}1)$$

and

$$e_o = -\frac{1}{C} \int i \, dt \qquad (13.42\text{-}2)$$

Solving (13.42-1) for i and inserting this value in (13.42-2) yields

$$e_o = -\frac{1}{R_1 C} \int e_1 \, dt \quad (13.42\text{-}3)$$

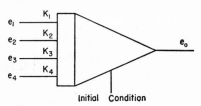

FIG. 13.42-2. Computer summing integrator symbol.

Thus e_o is the integral of the applied voltage e_1 times a constant, $1/R_1 C$. The symbol for a computer summing integrator is shown in Fig. 13.42-2. Here K_1 is a gain factor and is equal to $1/R_1 C$. The equation describing the output of the summing integrator is

$$e_o = -K_1 \int e_1 \, dt - K_2 \int e_2 \, dt - K_3 \int e_3 \, dt - K_4 \int e_4 \, dt + E_o \quad (13.42\text{-}4)$$

where E_o is the initial value of e_o. Provision is included in most computers for charging the capacitor C at the beginning of an operation to a desired magnitude so that e_o may have an initial value.

13.43 FREQUENCY-DEPENDENT FUNCTIONS. In a manner analogous to the summing amplifier and summing integrator units, frequency-dependent functions may be obtained. Figure 13.43-1 shows the

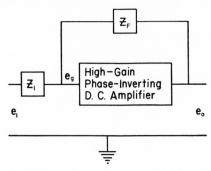

FIG. 13.43-1. Frequency-dependent function.

basic elements. The equation describing the output voltage is

$$e_o = -\frac{Z_F}{Z_1} e_1 \tag{13.43-1}$$

where Z_1 is the impedance of the input function, Z_F is the impedance

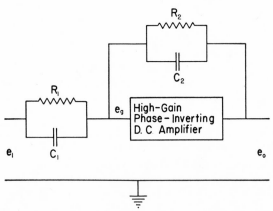

FIG. 13.43-2. Computer component having $e_o = \dfrac{-R_2(1 + R_1 C_1 s)}{R_1(1 + R_2 C_2 s)} e_1.$

of the output function. If Z_1 and Z_F are both parallel resistance-capacitance functions, as shown in Fig. 13.43-2,

$$Z_1 = \frac{R_1}{1 + R_1 C_1 s} \qquad (13.43\text{-}2)$$

$$Z_F = \frac{R_2}{1 + R_2 C_2 s} \qquad (13.43\text{-}3)$$

and $\qquad\qquad e_o = \frac{-R_2(1 + R_1 C_1 s)}{R_1(1 + R_2 C_2 s)} \, e_1 \qquad (13.43\text{-}4)$

The symbol used to represent frequency-dependent functions is shown in Fig. 13.43-3. It should be noticed that the high-gain phase-inverting amplifier in Fig. 13.43-3 is represented by a triangle similar to the amplifier symbol in Fig. 13.41-3. The only difference is that the gain value is not shown in Fig. 13.43-3. This is a common

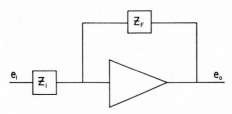

FIG. 13.43-3.   Symbol for frequency-dependent function.

convention, and therefore it should be assumed that when no gain value is given on an amplifier symbol the gain is very high.

Also it should be noted that there is no reason why the symbol in Fig. 13.43-3 (with the proper input and feedback impedances) could not be used to represent functions such as amplifiers and integrators. This is done often, particularly when using a computer such as the one described in Section 13.70 which connects in the desired resistor and capacitor values.

13.44 GAIN POTENTIOMETERS. In order to be able to set gains and coefficients at any value, potentiometers are used. Figure 13.44-1 shows the wiring schematic of a potentiometer, and Fig. 13.44-2 shows the symbol that is commonly used to represent the potentiometer. The output voltage is related to the input voltage by the equality

$$e_o = K e_1 \qquad (13.44\text{-}1)$$

where K is approximately R_1/R_2. (A small correction factor is often necessary due to other circuit impedances. Curves for the correction factor usually are supplied by the computer manufacturer.)

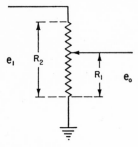

FIG. 13.44-1. Gain potentiometer.

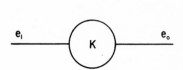

FIG. 13.44-2. Symbol for a gain potentiometer.

13.45 LIMITERS AND COMPARATORS. Units called "limiters" which limit or compare magnitudes of voltage signals are used to simulate nonlinear effects such as signal saturations. The schematic diagram

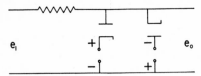

FIG. 13.45-1. Signal limiter.

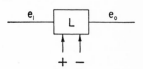

FIG. 13.45-2. Servo limiter symbol.

of a typical limiter is shown in Fig. 13.45-1. Appropriate values of bias voltages determine the limits. The symbol for a limiter is shown in Fig. 13.45-2.

The circuit shown in Fig. 13.45-1 and represented by the symbol in Fig. 13.45-2 is used to obtain the output-to-input voltage relationship shown in Fig. 13.45-3a. Output-to-input voltage relation-

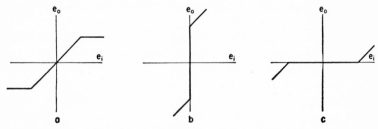

FIG. 13.45-3. Different output-to-input voltage relationships for limiters.

ships such as in b and c of Fig. 13.45-3 also are used, and may be
realized easily. Usually they are represented by a rectangular box,
as in Fig. 13.45-2, with a small sketch inside the box showing its
function.

13.46 SERVO UNITS. An analog computer servo unit is a positioning
device in which a shaft is rotated through an angle proportional to
an input signal. These units are useful in solving equations which
involve trigonometric functions, linear differential equations with

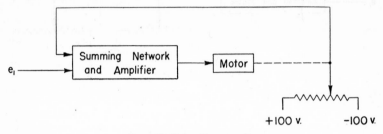

FIG. 13.46-1.   Servo unit.

variable coefficients, and the multiplication and division of two
variables. Figure 13.46-1 shows the basic elements of a servo unit.
A voltage e_1 is applied to a summing network and amplifier. This
in turn causes the operation of the motor, changing the position of
the potentiometer wiper arm until the wiper arm voltage cancels
the applied voltage. If e_1 is measured in volts, and if $+100$ and
-100 volts are applied at either end of the potentiometer, an
equilibrium point occurs when the
wiper arm has turned through
$-e_1/100$ of the total distance from
the center to one end. Figure 13.46-2
shows the symbol for a servo unit.

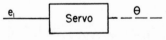

FIG. 13.46-2.   Servo unit symbol.

The solid line indicates a voltage and the broken line indicates a
shaft position.

By mounting a second potentiometer which has the same align-
ment on the shaft, multiplication is possible. This is shown in
Fig. 13.46-3, where an inverting amplifier is used to provide the e_2
voltage across the second potentiometer. The position of the second
potentiometer wiper arm is controlled by the e_1 voltage, and the
magnitude of the voltage monitored by the second wiper arm is
proportional to both e_1 and e_2.

Division is achieved by the arrangement shown in Fig. 13.46-4. This utilizes a servo unit to position two potentiometer wiper arms. One potentiometer forms a part of a conventional computer servo unit. Thus the position of both wiper arms is a function of the voltage e_1. The wiper arm of the second potentiometer is used to

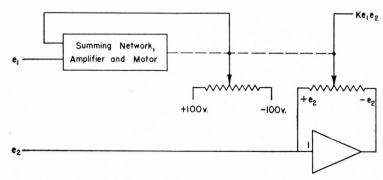

FIG. 13.46-3.   Method of multiplication.

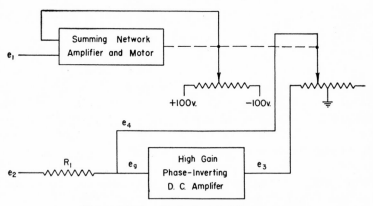

FIG. 13.46-4.   Method of division, $e_3 = -100(e_2/e_1)$.

apply the voltage e_4 to the high-gain phase-inverting amplifier. Since the wiper arm position is determined by e_1, and since the voltage applied to the potentiometer is e_3,

$$e_4 = Ke_1e_3 \qquad (13.46\text{-}1)$$

where K is a constant that depends on the voltage levels. The center tap of the second potentiometer is grounded. Therefore when $e_1 = 0$, the value of e_4 is also zero, short-circuiting the amplifier grid voltage e_g to ground potential. At other times e_g is very small due to the high-gain amplifier between e_g and e_3.

Division is accomplished in the following manner. The sum of the voltages at the grid is

$$e_2 + e_4 = e_g \tag{13.46-2}$$

However,

$$e_3 = -K_1 e_g \tag{13.46-3}$$

where K_1 is the gain of the high-gain amplifier (approximately 100,000).

Therefore (13.46-2) and (13.46-3) may be combined to yield

$$e_2 + e_4 = \frac{-e_3}{K_1} \simeq 0 \tag{13.46-4}$$

When (13.46-1) and (13.46-4) are combined, the result is

$$e_2 + K e_1 e_3 \simeq 0 \tag{13.46-5}$$

or

$$e_3 = \frac{-e_2}{K e_1} \tag{13.46-6}$$

Special functions and some trigonometric relations can be achieved by using potentiometers with special windings.

13.47 RECORDERS. System variables may be monitored in a number of ways. If the variable does not change too fast, a voltmeter indication often is an adequate monitor. If the variable changes very fast and repeats itself, a cathode ray oscilloscope may be used for monitoring. Permanent records may be obtained by positioning a direct inking pen as a function of the magnitude of a variable. The pen operates much the same as the needle of a voltmeter; namely, pen deflection is a function of signal voltage. By moving the paper at a constant speed, a permanent record of problem solution against time results. Several system variables may be recorded by using one pen for each variable. Figure 13.47-1 shows the symbol for a pen recorder.

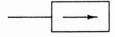

FIG. 13.47-1. Pen recorder symbol.

Usually overload protection is provided so that excessive voltages cannot damage the pen-drive mechanism. Also, each pen recorder input channel usually has an amplification switch by which the corresponding pen amplifier can be varied in discreet steps from 0.1 to 10. The unit on the right in Fig. 13.30-3 is a typical recorder of this type.

Sometimes two variables are plotted against each other. One variable controls the X-axis distance and the other variable controls the Y-axis distance. Recorders of this type are shown in the foreground of Fig. 13.30-4.

13.50 Examples of analog computation

The preliminary steps required for the solution of a problem by analog computation are very similar to that utilized in a numerical

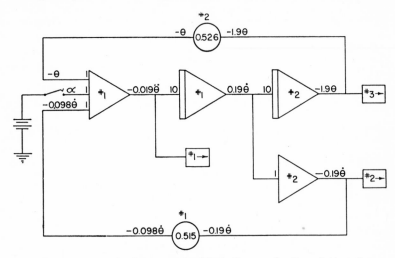

FIG. 13.50-1. Analog computer block diagram for the solution of

$$\frac{\theta}{\alpha} = \frac{1}{1 + 0.098s + 0.019s^2}.$$

integration solution. First, a control system block diagram should be drawn unless the system is very simple. Second, the transfer function equations should be solved for the highest order derivatives. Third, an analog computer block diagram should be drawn. The examples discussed in this section will illustrate these points.

As the first example, consider the second-order relation discussed in Chapter 12.

$$\frac{\theta}{\alpha} = \frac{1}{1 + 0.098s + 0.019s^2} \tag{13.50-1}$$

In differential equation form, (13.50-1) is

$$0.019\ddot{\theta} = \alpha - \theta - 0.098\dot{\theta} \tag{13.50-2}$$

Figure 13.50-1 shows an analog computer block diagram for the solution of this problem. It is assumed that the voltages representing each unit have been so chosen that the magnitude of the variables (in volts) is neither so high as to saturate computer component levels nor so low as to be lost in the signal-to-noise level. The function of each unit in Fig. 13.50-1 follows. The sum of the inputs to amplifier 1 is $0.019\ddot{\theta}$. Since inverting action takes place, the output of amplifier 1 is $-0.019\ddot{\theta}$. The $\ddot{\theta}$ signal is applied to integrator 1 at an input point which has a gain of 10. Therefore the output of

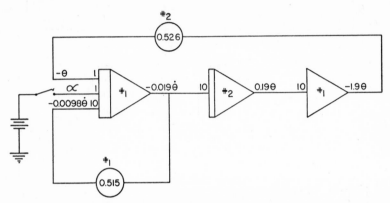

FIG. 13.50-2. Simpler method for solving the relation
$$\frac{\theta}{\alpha} = \frac{1}{1 + 0.098s + 0.019s^2}.$$

integrator 1 is $0.19\dot{\theta}$, which is the negative of 10 times the integral of the input. Since one input to amplifier 1 is $-0.098\dot{\theta}$, amplifier 2 serves to change the polarity of $0.19\dot{\theta}$, and potentiometer 1 selects the proper magnitude of $\dot{\theta}$. Integrator 2 functions in a manner similar to integrator 1. The output is 10 times the integral of the input. Potentiometer 2 selects the proper magnitude of θ to be fed back to amplifier 1. Recorders 1, 2, and 3 monitor the signals $\ddot{\theta}$, $\dot{\theta}$, and θ, respectively.

Operation of the system in Fig. 13.50-1 in response to a unit step α signal is as follows. When the switch is closed, a voltage representing α is applied to amplifier 1. This causes $\ddot{\theta}$ to have an immediate value. Integrator 1 integrates the $\ddot{\theta}$ signal, and the proper magnitude of the $\dot{\theta}$ signal is applied through amplifier 2 and potentiometer 1 to amplifier 1. Integrator 2 integrates $\dot{\theta}$ and enables the proper magnitude of θ to be applied to amplifier 1. Equilibrium is reached when the sum of the inputs to amplifier 1 is zero.

Sometimes simplifications are possible in analog computer setups. Thus the block diagram in Fig. 13.50-2 shows a simpler method of solving the same problem as that in Fig. 13.50-1. The sum of the inputs to integrator 1 is $0.019\dot{\theta}$. However, since an integrator

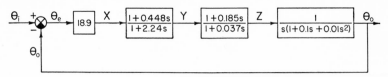

Fig. 13.50-3. Control system block diagram.

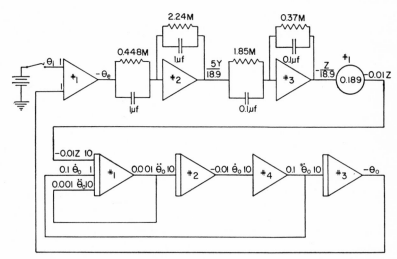

Fig. 13.50-4. Analog computer block diagram for the simulation of the control system shown in Fig. 13.50-3.

instead of an amplifier is used, the output is -0.019θ, permitting a saving of one amplifier unit. In complicated control systems considerable savings are often possible by using similar techniques.

As a second example of analog computation, consider the system shown in Fig. 13.50-3. This system is the same as the one discussed in Section 9.30. The equations which describe the operation of this control system are

$$\theta_{\text e} = \theta_{\text i} - \theta_{\text o} \tag{13.50-3}$$

$$Y = 18.9\,\frac{(1 + 0.448s)}{(1 + 2.24s)}\,\theta_{\text e} \tag{13.50-4}$$

$$Z = \frac{1 + 0.185s}{1 + 0.037s}\,Y \tag{13.50-5}$$

$$0.01\,\ddot{\theta}_{\text o} = Z - \dot{\theta}_{\text o} - 0.1\ddot{\theta}_{\text o} \tag{13.50-6}$$

Amplifier 1 in Fig. 13.50-4 solves (13.50-3). Amplifiers 2 and 3, together with their frequency-dependent input and feedback functions, solve (13.50-4) and (13.50-5). Integrator 1 solves (13.50-6), and integrators 2 and 3, together with amplifier 4, provide the other signals needed in the simulation. Potentiometer 1 provides a method of setting the system gain. If the designer chooses to observe the system operation when the gain is either higher or lower, he may do so by merely changing the potentiometer setting.

13.60 Time-scale considerations

Sometimes the transient response of a control system requires either a very long or a very short time interval. When these systems are studied by analog computer simulation, it is often advisable to scale the transient response time either up or down.

The Laplace transform time-scale theorem may be used. This theorem is

$$f(at) = \frac{F(s/a)}{a} \tag{13.60-1}$$

where a is a positive constant. If a is larger than one, the time required for an analog computer solution is less than the actual (or true) time required by the control system. Thus changing the time required for an analog computer transient response consists essentially of changing all integrating speeds and all frequency-dependent terms by a constant factor.

This may be accomplished on the computer itself, or the system equations may be changed before the problem is set up on the computer. The latter method is usually preferable. As an example, if

$$\frac{\theta_{\text o}}{\theta_{\text i}} = \frac{1}{1 + 0.1s + 0.01s^2} \tag{13.60-2}$$

the true-time Laplace transform equation which yields the system response to a unit step input is

$$\theta_o = \frac{1}{s(1 + 0.1s + 0.01s^2)} \tag{13.60-3}$$

Similarly, the true-time Laplace transform equation which yields the system response to a unit rate input is

$$\theta_o = \frac{1}{s^2(1 + 0.1s + 0.01s^2)} \tag{13.60-4}$$

If it is desired to change the time scale so that the computer transient response time is one-tenth of true-time, application of (13.60-1) to (13.60-3) yields

$$\theta_o = \frac{0.10}{(s/10)(1 + 0.1s/10 + 0.01s^2/10^2)}$$
$$= \frac{1}{s(1 + 0.01s + 0.0001s^2)} \tag{13.60-5}$$

Similarly, application of (13.60-1) to (13.60-4) for the same case yields

$$\theta_o = \frac{0.10}{(s^2/10^2)(1 + 0.1s/10 + 0.01s^2/10^2)}$$
$$= \frac{10}{s^2(1 + 0.01s + 0.0001s^2)} \tag{13.60-6}$$

The reader should find the inverse Laplace transforms of (13.60-3) and (13.60-5) and of (13.60-4) and (13.60-6). He will find that the transient responses of each pair are identical, except for the time-scale factor.

Thus in order to change the analog computer solution time for a function such as that in (13.60-2), the steps are as follows.

1. Change each s in the $(\theta_o/\theta_i)(s)$ expression to s/a, where a is the factor by which the time scale is being changed.

2. If the input is a unit step θ_i input, no additional changes are needed.

3. If the input is a unit rate θ_i input $(\theta_i = t)$, change the input to $\theta_i = at$.

4. If the input is some other input, the rapidity with which signals are applied should be changed by a factor of a. In general, the

normal Laplace transform of the input, $\theta_i(s)$, should be changed to

$$\frac{1}{a}\,\theta_i\left(\frac{s}{a}\right)$$

Time-scale changes are very common in analog computer solutions, except when partial simulation is performed. Partial simulation is the utilization of an analog computer to simulate part of the control system and actual system components to complete the control loop. True time must be used in these cases.

13.70 Operation of a typical analog computer

Figure 13.70-1 shows the front panel of an analog computer manufactured by Leonard L. Nalley, Compton, California. This is a small desk-size computer which contains in one cabinet all of the necessary power supplies; twelve high-gain phase-inverting d-c amplifiers; twenty-two resistors (each 1,000,000 ohms); six capacitors (each is 1 μf); twenty potentiometers; two pen recorder amplifiers; one voltmeter and selector switch for monitoring the output of any amplifier, recorder signal or voltage supply; balance potentiometers for nulling the output (due to drift) of the amplifiers before starting the computer; and switches for turning the equipment on and computing. Self-balancing amplifiers are also available.

The various components are wired independently of one another, and their outputs and inputs are connected to jacks on the front panel. Inter-wiring is accomplished by running wire connectors from one jack to another in the desired manner. It should be noted that some jacks are joined by black lines. This indicates that they are wired in parallel, and a voltage appearing at any jack can be picked up at any other connected to the first by a black line. In the center of the jack section there are nine bus-lines which can be used if more pick-off points are needed.

Eleven of the resistors are in the first column on the left. Each resistor has four jacks, two for each resistor terminal. In the second column there are six high-gain amplifiers, with each having two input and output jacks. Three capacitors are in the third column. Like the resistors, each capacitor has two jacks for each terminal. In addition each capacitor has two other jacks which are used to insert initial conditions. One of these jacks is grounded (this is indicated by a dot adjacent to one of the jacks), and the other is the

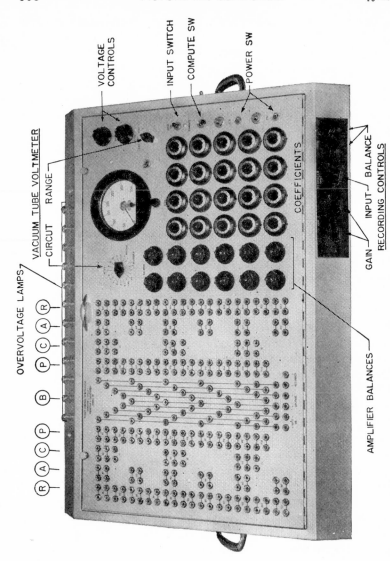

VOLTAGE CONTROLS

INPUT SWITCH

COMPUTE SW

POWER SW

VACUUM TUBE VOLTMETER

CIRCUT RANGE

OVERVOLTAGE LAMPS

R A C P B C P A C R

COEFFICIENTS

GAIN   INPUT   BALANCE

RECORDING CONTROLS

AMPLIFIER BALANCES

Fig. 13.70-1.   Nalley Electronic Analog Computer.   (Courtesy Leonard L. Nalley.)

side to which initial charges are connected. The capacitors are internally wired through relays so that their charge can not decay until the compute switch is thrown. The fourth column contains ten potentiometers, each having two input and two output jacks.

The nine bus-lines are on the right of the fourth column. Below the bus-lines there are six jacks. The first two (starting at the left) provide means for applying input signals when the input switch is operated. The next two are used to insert initial conditions (sometimes potentiometers are used to obtain proper voltages when several initial conditions or inputs are required), and the last two are the inputs to the recorder amplifiers (the output of these amplifiers is on the right side of the cabinet).

The four columns on the right of the bus-lines contain terminals for additional potentiometers, capacitors, amplifiers and resistors respectively. Each unit is identified by a number.

The amplifier balance potentiometers are on the right of the jacks. Each is identified by a number that corresponds to its amplifier. Above the balance potentiometers is the meter switch. This switch may be turned to any particular amplifier, and if the amplifier (as read on the voltmeter), is not in balance, the proper knob adjusts it. Usually the amplifiers are so stable that they need balancing only every few hours after warming-up.

The dials for each of the potentiometers whose jacks are on the right are directly below the voltmeter. Again, each is numbered to agree with its corresponding jacks.

The two knobs in the upper right corner provide means for obtaining a desired input or initial condition voltage magnitude (either positive or negative). The switch just below these sets the full-scale of the voltmeter at 3.6, 36, or 360 volts, and the switch on the left connects the meter to read either plus or minus. When the meter switch is turned to " + voltage," the voltmeter reads the voltage to which the upper-right knob is set. This voltage appears at the third jack from the left below the bus-lines. Similarly, when the meter switch is turned to " − voltage," the voltmeter reads the voltage to which the knob just below the upper-right one is set. This voltage appears at the fourth jack. The voltages are arbitrarily marked + and −, but any setting between ±50 volts can be set.

The + and − voltages are also connected to the first and second jacks on the left below the bus-lines, but the connections are made through the input switch. In the "up" switch position the voltage is that indicated by the meter for the + and − voltage positions; the + jack voltage and + voltage are in agreement as are the − jack voltage and the − voltage meter indications. When the switch is "centered" both voltages are disconnected from the + and − panel jacks. The "down" position of the input switch reverses the voltages at the + and − jacks. That is, the + voltage is connected to the − jack and the − voltage is connected to the + jack. This permits step or pulse inputs of both + and − voltages.

The compute switch is below the input switch. This switch also has three positions. The switch in the "down" position disconnects the amplifiers from the panel jacks, stops the recorder and restores the initial conditions on all capacitors. The center position of the compute switch starts the recorder. When the switch is up, the relays are operated to the compute position which reconnects the amplifiers, capacitors and resistors to the configuration patched into the panel, and the problem computation starts.

The high voltage and filament switches are below the compute switch, and each has a neon glow light to indicate its operation. Twelve neon glow lights are also on the top of the cabinet. Each is connected to one of the amplifiers, and glows when the amplifier output voltage exceeds ±65 volts.

Problems are wired into this computer in the manner discussed in the preceding sections. An analog computer diagram is drawn in the usual manner, except that the exact input and feedback impedances are marked on the diagram (using the symbolism in Fig. 13.43-3), since there is no provision for fixed amplifier and integrator input gains. If values other than 1 megohm and 1 μf are desired, they either can be wired in externally or proper parallel and series connections can be made (for example, two 1 megohm resistors in parallel are equivalent to one $\frac{1}{2}$ megohm resistor). When the system has been connected, the compute switch is thrown, and the system variables can either be monitored on the voltmeter or recorded through the recorder amplifiers.

If the system is so complex that one of these computers does not contain sufficient elements, two or more computers can be connected together. Since most analog computers contain the same basic elements, it is usually possible to connect two computers of the same or of different manufacturers together for complex problems.

In setting up a problem strict attention should be paid to the voltage levels that occur in a system. For example, the problem given in eq. (13.50-2) has its exact values given in Table 12.10-3. Thus, $\ddot{\theta}$ has a maximum value of 52.6 degrees per sec², $\dot{\theta}$ has a maximum of 4.6 degrees per sec, and θ has a maximum of 1.3 degrees when α is a unit step of 1°. If the analog computer were set up for 1 volt per unit of the variable, then $\ddot{\theta}$ would have a maximum of 52.6 volts; $\dot{\theta}$, 4.6 volts; and θ, 1.3 volts. This is not a good distribution. Low voltages may be lost in the system noise level, and high voltages may saturate the system. Therefore, we usually solve for a fraction of $\ddot{\theta}$. For example, if α in Fig. 13.50-1 is 10 volts for a unit input, then

$$-0.019\ddot{\theta} = 10 \text{ volts} \tag{13.70-1}$$

and

$$\ddot{\theta} = -526 \text{ volts} \tag{13.70-2}$$

However, since we only solve for $0.019\ddot{\theta}$, the high voltage never exists in the computer, and the maximum voltage representing $\ddot{\theta}$ is 10 volts.

Using the same value of 10 volts for α to represent a unit step, the maximum of $\dot{\theta}$ is

$$\dot{\theta} \text{ (max)} = 46 \text{ volts} \tag{13.70-3}$$

However, we only solve for $0.19\dot{\theta}$, therefore the maximum $\dot{\theta}$ voltage that would occur in this system is 8.74 volts. Similarly, the maximum θ voltage would be

$$\theta \text{ (max)} = 1.9 \times 1.3 \times 10 = 24.7 \text{ volts} \tag{13.70-4}$$

These are all reasonable values. In fact, the level of α could be increased somewhat, as most computers operate linearly up to ± 100 volts. It is advisable to check the voltage magnitudes as soon as a problem is set up. If any are much lower than the others, the system gains should be re-arranged. Similarly potentiometer setting less than 0.100 should be avoided if possible.

PROBLEMS

13-1. Perform the following operations using binary notation.

(a) 7×5
(b) $7 - 5$
(c) $7 + 5$
(d) 21×18
(e) $21/7$
(f) $21/8$
(g) $36 + 4$
(h) $3 - 15$
(i) 85×132

13-2. Draw a figure, similar to Fig. 13.10-4, representing the following numbers.

(a) 17345.89   (c) 9821.375
(b) 24312.75

13-3. Draw the analog computer block diagram arrangement for the simulation of the control systems shown in the following figures.

(a) Figure 4.20-1a   (g) Figure 5.10-2
(b) Figure 4.51-2b   (h) Figure 6.40-1
(c) Figure 4.53-2b   (i) Figure 8.13-1
(d) Figure 4.54-1b   (j) Figure 9.60-1
(e) Figure 4.53-2c   (k) Figure 9.60-3
(f) Figure 5.10-1   (l) Figure 12.40-1

13-4. Redraw each of the analog computer block diagrams in Problem 13-3 for the case when the input is a unit step and the simulator operates 10 times as fast as true time.

13-5. Repeat Problem 13-4 for the case when the input is a unit rate.

CHAPTER 14

METHODS FOR ANALYZING TRANSIENT
RESPONSE DATA

14.00 Introduction

Several methods exist for determining the frequency response that corresponds to a given transient response. These make it possible to determine the frequency response of either a complete control system or a component. The system is subjected to an arbitrary function of time input, and the output transient is analyzed by the methods discussed in this chapter.

Three methods are discussed. One method applies intuitive reasoning. The correlations between transient and frequency responses which are discussed in previous chapters are utilized. Thus factors such as time constants, overshoots, resonant frequencies, and steady-state errors often provide sufficient information, so that the designer is able to write an equation which closely approximates the actual output-to-input relation.

A second method discussed in this chapter assumes a linear differential equation with constant coefficients for the output-to-input relation. Simultaneous values for the input and output variables are obtained from the input and output transients at a sufficient number of points, so that the coefficients may be determined. Extension of this method to include curve fitting by the least-square technique is also discussed.

The third method breaks both the output and input transients into a number of discrete time-delayed contributions. The frequency characteristic is found for each of these contributions. The input frequency characteristic is the sum of its contributions, and similarly for the output. The output-to-input frequency response is obtained by dividing the output frequency characteristic by the input frequency characteristic.

14.10 Intuitive reasoning

When a system is subjected to unit step and rate inputs, the nature of the output transients is often sufficient for the designer to be able to visualize the approximate system frequency response. As an example, consider the transients for the system discussed in Section 9.30 and described by eq. (9.30-5). The output transients for unit step and rate inputs are shown in Figs. 9.10-5 and 9.10-6, respectively, and the response in Fig. 9.10-6 is repeated in Fig. 14.10-1.

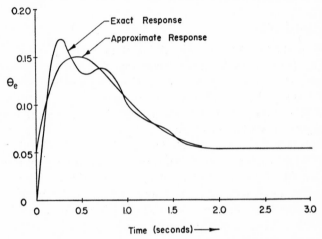

FIG. 14.10-1.   Response to a unit step input.

An approximate transient for θ_e is also shown in Fig. 14.10-1. This transient, discussed later in this section, was obtained by drawing a smooth curve which eliminated the oscillatory contribution.

The system velocity constant K_v and frequency of maximum response ω_p can be determined from these transients. The velocity constant is the reciprocal of the steady-state θ_e error for a unit rate input (see Section 4.53). Hence

$$K_v = \frac{1}{0.053} = 18.9 \qquad (14.10\text{-}1)$$

The maximum response frequency ω_p causes a resonance at approximately the same frequency in a transient response. Therefore the oscillation which is evident for both the unit step and rate input transients provides a method for determining ω_p. This frequency, measured over several cycles, shows an average period of approximately 0.53 sec per cycle. Hence

$$\omega_p \simeq \frac{2\pi}{0.53} = 11.8 \quad \text{radians per sec} \qquad (14.10\text{-}2)$$

Whenever K_v is higher than ω_p, it indicates that the open-loop Nyquist locus has the form shown in Fig. 14.10-2. Therefore in a matter of minutes the designer is able to gain a rough approximation of the open-loop frequency response locus. A closer approximation is possible by further reasoning.

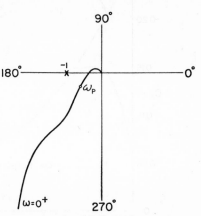

The output-to-input relation for the system represented by the transients in Fig. 14.10-1 may be approximated by determining the factors which cause transient responses. A system transient response is composed of the individual transients caused by each root in the system characteristic equation. Since the system characteristic equation is the same for both

FIG. 14.10-2. Nyquist locus for a Type 1 system with K_v greater than ω_p.

θ_o/θ_i and θ_e/θ_i, a transient response of either may be used to determine the characteristic equation roots.

The θ_e transient shown in Fig. 9.10-6 and repeated in Fig. 14.10-1 is the more informative. The approximate response shown in Fig. 14.10-1 indicates that in addition to the oscillatory transient contribution, there probably is a slowly decaying transient contribution, as shown in Fig. 14.10-3. By breaking the θ_e transient into various significant components, it appears that the transient is equal to the sum of the four factors shown in Fig. 14.10-4. Each factor is in turn due to a particular root or pair of roots in the characteristic equation.

Factor A in Fig. 14.10-4 was obtained by taking the difference between the two loci in Fig. 14.10-1. Factor B was obtained by drawing the asymptote shown in Fig. 14.10-3 and subtracting the steady-state value. Factor C is the difference between the two loci in Fig. 14.10-3. Factor D is the steady-state value.

Factor A in Fig. 14.10-4 indicates a complex pair of roots. The natural frequency is approximately ω_p, and since the transient does not decay very fast, the damping ratio is low. Letting $\zeta = 0.2$ and the natural frequency equal ω_p, this contribution indicates that one

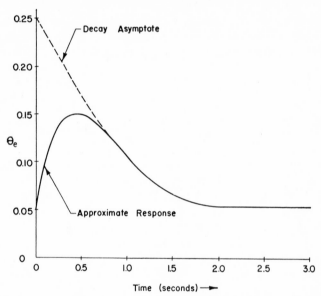

Fɪɢ. 14.10-3.   Approximate response with an asymptote for a slowly decaying transient contribution factor.

factor in the characteristic equation is

$$(1 + 0.034s + 0.0072s^2) \tag{14.10-3}$$

Contributions such as Factors B and C in Fig. 14.10-4 are caused by terms in the transient equation that have the form $K\epsilon^{-t/T}$, where T is the negative reciprocal of the root in the characteristic equation. The corresponding term in the characteristic equation has the form $(1 + Ts)$. The value of T is the same as the time (in seconds) required by these factors to reach 37% of their final value. Thus Factor B indicates that there is a $(1 + 0.8s)$ term in the characteristic equation, and Factor C indicates the presence of a $(1 + 0.24s)$ term.

Therefore an approximation of the closed-loop expression is

$$\frac{\theta_o}{\theta_i} = \frac{1 + as}{(1 + 0.034s + 0.0072s^2)(1 + 0.8s)(1 + 0.24s)} \quad (14.10\text{-}4)$$

The constant a in the numerator of (14.10-4) must be determined separately. It is necessary in order to satisfy the proper value of K_v,

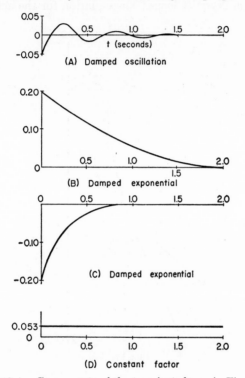

Fig. 14.10-4.   Components of the transient shown in Fig. 14.10-1.

and may be determined from the relation

$$\frac{1}{K_v} = 0.034 + 0.8 + 0.24 - a \quad (14.10\text{-}5)$$

Since $K_v = 18.9$,

$$a = 1.021 \quad (14.10\text{-}6)$$

Thus the approximate closed-loop expression is

$$\frac{\theta_o}{\theta_i} = \frac{1 + 1.021s}{(1 + 0.034s + 0.0072s^2)(1 + 0.8s)(1 + 0.24s)} \quad (14.10\text{-}7)$$

and the corresponding open-loop expression is

$$\frac{\theta_o}{\theta_e} = \frac{1 + 1.021s}{0.053s + 0.1546s^2 + 0.00113s^3 + 0.0008064s^4} \quad (14.10\text{-}8)$$

Figure 14.10-5 compares the Nyquist locus for (14.10-8) with the actual system Nyquist locus. The equation for the actual Nyquist

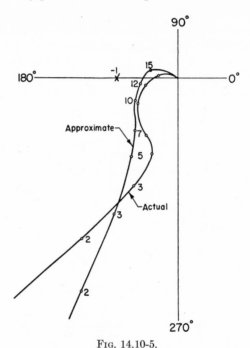

FIG. 14.10-5.

locus was given by (9.30-4). It is seen that the locus obtained by intuitive reasoning is a close approximation of the actual locus.

It is usually found, when solving a problem by intuitive reasoning, that the exact shapes and values of the transient component factors (such as those in Fig. 14.10-4) are not very critical. Hence with a little practice the designer is able to arrive at a good approximation of the system transfer function in a few minutes. This method, however, does not possess a high degree of accuracy, and is limited primarily to systems for which the transient responses to unit step and rate inputs are known.

14.20 Equation fitting

When the transient response of a linear system is known, the differential equations describing the system operation may be determined in the manner discussed in this section. The differential equation for a general output-to-input relation is

$$a_0\theta + a_1\dot\theta + a_2\ddot\theta + \ldots = \alpha + b_1\dot\alpha + b_2\ddot\alpha + \ldots \quad (14.20\text{-}1)$$

where θ is the output variable, α is the input variable. If the input and output variables (and a sufficient number of their derivatives) are known functions of time, the differential equation describing the system operation may be determined by considering the a and b coefficients in (14.20-1) as unknown quantities. At any instant of time, the equality in (14.20-1) should be satisfied. Therefore by substituting known values of θ and α and their derivatives in (14.20-1) for as many different instants of time as there are unknown a and b coefficients, a set of simultaneous equations results. These equations may be solved for the individual a and b coefficients.

As an example, let us start with the known relation,

$$\frac{\theta}{\alpha} = \frac{1}{1 + 0.098s + 0.019s^2} \quad (14.20\text{-}2)$$

or in differential equation notation,

$$\theta + 0.098\dot\theta + 0.019\ddot\theta = \alpha \quad (14.20\text{-}3)$$

This relation was also used for the numerical integration examples in Sections 12.10 and 12.20 and Appendix 1. When α is a unit step input, the equations for θ, $\dot\theta$, and $\ddot\theta$ are as follows.

$$\theta = 1 + 1.07\epsilon^{-2.58t} \sin (388t° - 110.8°) \quad (14.20\text{-}4)$$

$$\dot\theta = 7.75\epsilon^{-2.58t} \sin 388t° \quad (14.20\text{-}5)$$

$$\ddot\theta = 56.3\epsilon^{-2.58t} \sin (388t° + 110.8°) \quad (14.20\text{-}6)$$

We shall assume that the only known information is the following.

1. Here α is a unit step input. Hence $\alpha = 1$ and all derivatives of α are zero.

2. The values for θ, $\dot\theta$, and $\ddot\theta$ are known functions of time. With this information we shall find the differential equation and the transfer function expression between θ and α. The steps in the solution follow. Assume the relation between θ and α is

$$a_0\theta + a_1\dot\theta + a_2\ddot\theta = \alpha \quad (14.20\text{-}7)$$

The values for θ, $\dot{\theta}$, $\ddot{\theta}$, and α at several instants of time are shown in Table 14.20-1. At $t = \infty$, eq. (14.20-7) reduces to

$$a_0 = 1 \qquad (14.20\text{-}8)$$

Using this value for a_0, eq. (14.20-7) at $t = 0.2$ becomes

$$4.45a_1 - 4.68a_2 = 0.348 \qquad (14.20\text{-}9)$$

and when $t = 0.5$, eq. (14.20-7) is

$$-0.52a_1 - 12.70a_2 = -0.293 \qquad (14.20\text{-}10)$$

Solving (14.20-9) and (14.20-10) yields

$$a_1 = 0.098 \quad \text{and} \quad a_2 = 0.019 \qquad (14.20\text{-}11)$$

which are the correct answers.

When the order of the assumed equation is higher than necessary, an indeterminate result occurs. This indicates that the order of the assumed equation should be reduced.

For example, consider the relation

$$\frac{\theta}{\alpha} = \frac{1}{1 + 2s} \qquad (14.20\text{-}12)$$

or in differential equation notation,

$$\theta + 2\dot{\theta} = \alpha \qquad (14.20\text{-}13)$$

If α is a unit step input, the following equations describe the response for θ and the derivatives of θ.

$$\theta = 1 - \epsilon^{-0.5t} \qquad (14.20\text{-}14)$$

$$\dot{\theta} = 0.5\epsilon^{-0.5t} \qquad (14.20\text{-}15)$$

$$\ddot{\theta} = -0.25\epsilon^{-0.5t} \qquad (14.20\text{-}16)$$

$$\dddot{\theta} = 0.125\epsilon^{-0.5t} \qquad (14.20\text{-}17)$$

TABLE 14.20-1

VALUES OF VARIABLES FOR THE SYSTEM REPRESENTED BY (14.20-2) WHEN SUBJECTED TO A UNIT STEP INPUT

t	θ	$\dot{\theta}$	$\ddot{\theta}$	α
0	0	0	52.60	1
0.2	0.652	4.45	-4.68	1
0.5	1.293	-0.52	-12.70	1
∞	1.000	0	0	1

Table 14.20-2 gives the values for these variables at various instants of time.

Let us assume an equation whose order is too high for the relation between θ and α. Thus assuming

$$a_0\theta + a_1\dot\theta + a_2\ddot\theta + a_3\dddot\theta = \alpha \qquad (14.20\text{-}18)$$

substitution of the numerical values when $t = \infty$ yields $a_0 = 1$. Using this value for a_0 (and the values of the other variables when $t = 0.5$, 1.0, and 1.5,) in (14.20-18) yields

$$0.3894a_1 - 0.1947a_2 + 0.0974a_3 = 0.7788 \qquad (14.20\text{-}19)$$

$$0.3033a_1 - 0.1516a_2 + 0.0758a_3 = 0.6065 \qquad (14.20\text{-}20)$$

$$0.2362a_1 - 0.1181a_2 + 0.0590a_3 = 0.4724 \qquad (14.20\text{-}21)$$

As the solution to these equations shows them to be indeterminate, the order of the assumed eq. (14.20-18) is too high.

Reducing (14.20-18) by one order results in the assumed equation becoming

$$\theta + a_1\dot\theta + a_2\ddot\theta = 1 \qquad (14.20\text{-}22)$$

Using values of θ, $\dot\theta$, and $\ddot\theta$ when $t = 0.5$ and 1.0 in (14.20-22) yields

$$0.3894a_1 - 0.1947a_2 = 0.7788 \qquad (14.20\text{-}23)$$

$$0.3033a_1 - 0.1516a_2 = 0.6065 \qquad (14.20\text{-}24)$$

TABLE 14.20-2

VALUES OF VARIABLES FOR THE SYSTEM REPRESENTED BY (14.20-12) WHEN SUBJECTED TO A UNIT STEP INPUT

t	θ	$\dot\theta$	$\ddot\theta$	$\dddot\theta$	α
0	0	0.5000	-0.2500	0.1250	1
0.5	0.2212	0.3894	-0.1947	0.0974	1
1.0	0.3935	0.3033	-0.1516	0.0758	1
1.5	0.5276	0.2362	-0.1181	0.0590	1
2.0	0.6321	0.1839	-0.0920	0.0460	1
∞	1.0000	0	0	0	1

Again these equations are indeterminate. Hence the order of the assumed eq. (14.20-22) is still too high, and may be reduced to

$$\theta + a_1\dot\theta = 1 \qquad (14.20\text{-}25)$$

Using the values of θ and $\dot\theta$ for any finite value of time yields

$$\theta + 2\dot\theta = 1 \qquad (14.20\text{-}26)$$

which is the proper result.

It should be noted that in the two examples which have been given, the assumed equation did not include any terms for the derivatives of the input. This was because all the derivatives of the input were zero in these examples. Functions are often encountered, however, which have input derivative terms. For example, consider

$$\frac{\theta}{\alpha} = \frac{1 + .10s}{1 + 2s} \qquad (14.20\text{-}27)$$

or in differential equation form,

$$\theta + 2\dot{\theta} = \alpha + 10\dot{\alpha} \qquad (14.20\text{-}28)$$

If this system is subjected to a unit step input, the equations for the output and output rate are

$$\theta = 1 + 4\epsilon^{-0.5t} \qquad (14.20\text{-}29)$$

$$\dot{\theta} = -2\epsilon^{-0.5t} \qquad (14.20\text{-}30)$$

Numerical values for these functions at various instants of time are shown in Table 14.20-3. Again the derivatives of α are zero. Therefore including the presence of α derivative terms in the assumed equation would be useless. Thus the assumed equation should be

$$a_0\theta + a_1\dot{\theta} = \alpha \qquad (14.20\text{-}31)$$

By using known numerical values for θ, $\dot{\theta}$, and α in (14.20-31), the equation describing this system may be determined to be

$$\theta + 2\dot{\theta} = 1 \qquad (14.20\text{-}32)$$

where θ has an initial value of 5.

The only difference between the final equations given by (14.20-26) and (14.20-32) is that the latter has an initial value for θ. When the Laplace transform of (14.20-32) is written, the initial value of θ causes the appearance of the numerator s factor, noted in (14.20-27). The Laplace transform of (14.20-32) is

$$\theta + 2s\theta - 10 = \frac{1}{s} \qquad (14.20\text{-}33)$$

or

$$\theta = \frac{1 + 10s}{s(1 + 2s)} \qquad (14.20\text{-}34)$$

Since the Laplace transform of the input is

$$\alpha = \frac{1}{s} \qquad (14.20\text{-}35)$$

the combination of (14.20-34) and (14.20-35) yields

$$\frac{\theta}{\alpha} = \frac{1 + 10s}{1 + 2s} \qquad (14.20\text{-}36)$$

TABLE 14.20-3

VALUE OF VARIABLES FOR THE SYSTEM REPRESENTED BY EQ. (14.20-27) WHEN
SUBJECTED TO A UNIT STEP INPUT

t	θ	$\dot{\theta}$	α	$\dot{\alpha}$
0	5.0000	−2.0000	1	0
0.5	4.1152	−1.5576	1	0
1.0	3.4261	−1.2131	1	0
∞	1.0000	0	1	0

which is the same as the original expression given in (14.20-27).

Thus in order to obtain the complete transfer function between variables, it is essential that initial conditions be included.

14.30 Differentiation of transient data

The analysis method discussed in Section 14.20 required transient data for the input and output variables and their derivatives. Usually the designer does not have transient responses for all these variables. For example, he may have the transient response for θ, but not for the derivatives of θ. This section discusses a method for finding the derivative of a known transient.

The method is very simple. Suppose θ changes almost linearly from a value of 0.62 at $t = 0.03$ sec to a value of 0.77 at $t = 0.04$ sec. Then $\dot{\theta}$ may be calculated from this data by the formula

$$\dot{\theta} = \frac{\theta_2 - \theta_1}{t_2 - t_1} \quad \text{at } t = (t_1 + t_2)/2 \qquad (14.30\text{-}1)$$

where θ_1 is the value of θ at $t = t_1$, θ_2 is the value of θ at $t = t_2$. Thus $\dot{\theta}$ in this example is

$$\dot{\theta} = \frac{0.77 - 0.62}{0.04 - 0.03} \quad \text{at } t = (0.03 + 0.04)/2 \qquad (14.30\text{-}2)$$

$$\dot{\theta} = 15 \text{ units per sec.} \quad \text{at } t = 0.035 \qquad (14.30\text{-}3)$$

In order to illustrate the procedure, an example for a known relation will be discussed in detail. Assume that a system is represented by

$$\frac{\theta}{\alpha} = \frac{1 + 0.5s}{1 + 0.3s + 0.02s^2} \tag{14.30-4}$$

When α is a unit step input, the following output variables exist.

$$\theta = 1 - 4\epsilon^{-10t} + 3\epsilon^{-5t} \tag{14.30-5}$$

$$\dot{\theta} = 40\epsilon^{-10t} - 15\epsilon^{-5t} \tag{14.30-6}$$

$$\ddot{\theta} = -400\epsilon^{-10t} + 75\epsilon^{-5t} \tag{14.30-7}$$

We shall assume that only θ is known, and the values for the higher derivatives must be determined from the θ transient. Figure

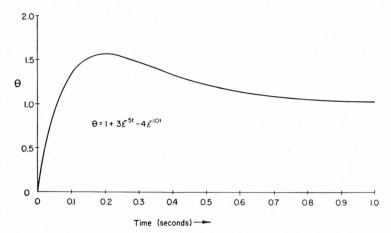

Fig. 14.30-1. θ transient for the system represented by (14.30-4) subjected to a unit step input.

14.30-1 shows the transient for θ, and columns 1 and 2 of Table 14.30-1 list the magnitude which θ has at various instants of time.

The values for time and $\dot{\theta}$ which are shown in columns 3 and 4 were calculated from the data in columns 1 and 2 by using the formula given in (14.30-1). The data in columns 3 and 4 are shown by the small circles in Fig. 14.30-2. Since $\dot{\theta}$ is a continuous, smooth function, the smooth locus drawn through the small circles shown in Fig. 14.30-2 and tabulated in columns 5 and 6 of Table 14.30-1 is a better approximation of $\dot{\theta}$ than the data in columns 3 and 4.

Therefore the formula given by (14.30-1) is applied to the data in columns 5 and 6 in order to obtain $\ddot{\theta}$. The results are shown in

TABLE 14.30-1

DIFFERENTIATION OF TRANSIENT DATA FOR THE SYSTEM REPRESENTED BY
EQ. (14.30-4) WHEN SUBJECTED TO A UNIT STEP INPUT

1 t	2 θ	3 t	4 $\dot\theta$	5 t	6 $\dot\theta$	7 t	8 $\ddot\theta$	9 t	10 $\dot\theta$
0	0			0	24.6			0	−300
0.01	0.23	0.005	23	0.01	21.8	0.005	−280	0.01	−275
0.02	0.45	0.015	22	0.02	19.0	0.015	−280	0.02	−244
0.03	0.62	0.025	17	0.03	16.4	0.025	−260	0.03	−218
0.04	0.77	0.035	15	0.04	14.2	0.035	−220	0.04	−196
0.05	0.91	0.045	14	0.05	12.3	0.045	−190	0.05	−175
0.06	1.02	0.055	11	0.06	10.5	0.055	−180	0.06	−157
0.07	1.13	0.065	11	0.07	8.9	0.065	−160	0.07	−139
0.08	1.21	0.075	8	0.08	7.6	0.075	−130	0.08	−123
0.09	1.28	0.085	7	0.09	6.5	0.085	−110	0.09	−109
0.10	1.35	0.095	7	0.10	5.5	0.095	−100	0.10	− 97
0.11	1.39	0.105	4	0.11	4.6	0.105	− 90	0.11	− 87
0.12	1.43	0.115	4	0.12	3.8	0.115	− 80	0.12	− 78
0.13	1.47	0.125	4	0.13	3.1	0.125	− 70	0.13	− 70
0.14	1.50	0.135	3	0.14	2.5	0.135	− 60	0.14	− 63
0.15	1.52	0.145	2	0.15	1.9	0.145	− 60	0.15	− 56
0.16	1.54	0.155	2	0.16	1.4	0.155	− 50	0.16	− 49
0.17	1.55	0.165	1	0.17	0.9	0.165	− 50	0.17	− 43
0.18	1.55	0.175	0	0.18	0.5	0.175	− 40	0.18	− 39
0.19	1.56	0.185	1	0.19	0.1	0.185	− 40	0.19	− 33
0.20	1.56	0.195	0	0.20	−0.2	0.195	− 30	0.20	− 29
0.22	1.55	0.21	−0.5	0.22	−0.7	0.21	− 25	0.22	− 21
0.24	1.54	0.23	−0.5	0.24	−1.1	0.23	− 20	0.24	− 14
0.26	1.51	0.25	−1.5	0.26	−1.3	0.25	− 10	0.26	− 10
0.28	1.49	0.27	−1.0	0.28	−1.5	0.27	− 10	0.28	− 4
0.30	1.47	0.29	−1.0	0.30	−1.6	0.29	− 5	0.30	0
0.35	1.40	0.325	−1.4	0.35	−1.4	0.325	+ 4	0.35	+ 5
0.40	1.33	0.375	−1.4	0.40	−1.2	0.375	4	0.40	6
0.45	1.27	0.425	−1.2	0.45	−0.95	0.425	5	0.45	5
0.50	1.22	0.475	−1.0	0.50	−0.75	0.475	4	0.50	4
0.55	1.17	0.525	−1.0	0.55	−0.60	0.525	3	0.55	3
0.60	1.14	0.575	−0.6	0.60	−0.45	0.575	3	0.60	2
0.65	1.11	0.625	−0.6	0.65	−0.35	0.625	2	0.65	1.5
0.70	1.09	0.675	−0.4	0.70	−0.30	0.675	1	0.70	1
0.75	1.07	0.725	−0.4	0.75	−0.25	0.725	1	0.75	0.5
0.80	1.05	0.775	−0.4	0.80	−0.20	0.775	1	0.80	0
0.85	1.04	0.825	−0.2	0.85	−0.20	0.825	0	0.85	0
0.90	1.03	0.875	−0.2	0.90	−0.20	0.875	0	0.90	0
0.95	1.02	0.925	−0.2	0.95	−0.20	0.925	0	0.95	0
1.00	1.02	0.975	0	1.00	−0.15	0.975	1	1.00	0

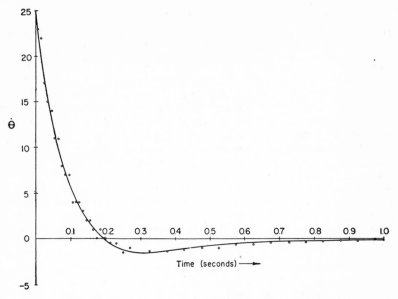

Fig. 14.30-2.   Magnitude of $\dot{\theta}$ calculated from θ data.

columns 7 and 8 of Table 14.30-1 and by the small circles in Fig. 14.30-3. Again a smooth locus representing a more accurate approximation of $\ddot{\theta}$ is drawn through the circles, and the result is tabulated in columns 9 and 10.

The same procedure could be repeated for as many higher order derivatives as necessary. However, the accuracy decreases with every additional derivative. The reader should compare the actual values for $\dot{\theta}$ and $\ddot{\theta}$, as given by (14.30-6) and (14.30-7), with the approximate values shown in columns 6 and 10 of Table 14.30-1. The deviation is not large for either case, but it is much larger for $\ddot{\theta}$ than it is for $\dot{\theta}$.

In order to complete this example, let us assume that the output and input are related by an equation of the form

$$a_0\theta + a_1\dot{\theta} + a_2\ddot{\theta} = 1 \qquad (14.30\text{-}8)$$

where $a_0 = 1$ because $\dot{\theta}$ and $\ddot{\theta}$ both decay to zero. The values for a_1 and a_2 may be determined by substituting values for θ, $\dot{\theta}$, and $\ddot{\theta}$ at two different instants of time in (14.30-8), and solving the result-

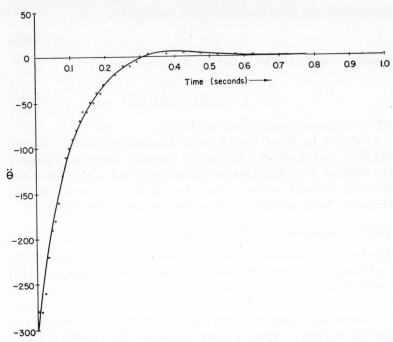

FIG. 14.30-3.   Magnitude of $\ddot{\theta}$ calculated from θ data.

ing equations. Thus using the values of θ, $\dot{\theta}$, and $\ddot{\theta}$ at $t = 0.1$ and 0.3 in (14.30-8), the following equations result.

$$5.5a_1 - 97a_2 = -0.35 \qquad (14.30\text{-}9)$$

$$-1.6a_1 + 0 = -0.47 \qquad (14.30\text{-}10)$$

Hence $a_1 = 0.294$ and $a_2 = 0.0203$ (14.30-11)

and the differential equation representing the system is

$$\theta + 0.294\dot{\theta} + 0.0203\ddot{\theta} = 1 \qquad (14.30\text{-}12)$$

where $\dot{\theta}$ has an initial value of 24.6.

In order to compare the result obtained by the method discussed in this section with the original transfer expression, we can express (14.30-12) in Laplace transform notation as

$$\theta + 0.294s\theta + 0.0203(s^2\theta - 24.6) = 1/s \qquad (14.30\text{-}13)$$

Then, since the Laplace transform of the input is

$$\alpha = 1/s \qquad (14.30\text{-}14)$$

combination of (14.30-13) and (14.30-14) yields

$$\frac{\theta}{\alpha} = \frac{1 + 0.499s}{1 + 0.294s + 0.0203s^2} \qquad (14.30\text{-}15)$$

which compares favorably with (14.30-4).

It should be noted that if other values of time were used in (14.30-9) and (14.30-10), the results might be different. Therefore the designer often averages the values for a_1 and a_2 that are found by using different values of time. In addition, he sometimes uses the least-square method, which is discussed in Section 14.40.

14.40 Least-square method

The least-square method provides a technique for determining the coefficients of a linear differential or any type of equation which would best fit a series of simultaneous values of the equation's variables. Thus an analytic expression best representing some experimentally determined data can be found. The form of the analytic expression must be assumed before this method is applicable, and the number of sets of values available must be greater than the number of unknown coefficients.

Assume that the equation describing the relation is of the form

$$-A + XB + YC + ZD = 0 \qquad (14.40\text{-}1)$$

where A, B, C, and D are known functions of time, X, Y, and Z are unknown coefficients. For example, if the relation is

$$-\alpha - b_1\dot{\alpha} + a_0\theta + a_1\dot{\theta} = 0, \qquad (14.40\text{-}2)$$

where α, $\dot{\alpha}$, θ, and $\dot{\theta}$ are known functions of time, a_1, a_0, and b_1 are unknown coefficients, then equating like coefficients in (14.40-1) and (14.40-2) yields the following equalities.

$$A = \alpha, \qquad B = \dot{\alpha}, \qquad C = \theta, \qquad D = \dot{\theta} \qquad (14.40\text{-}3)$$
$$X = -b_1, \qquad Y = a_0, \qquad Z = a_1$$

The number of terms in (14.40-1) could be increased or decreased (depending on the particular case) without altering the procedure.

While it would be ideal if the sum of all terms in (14.40-1) were equal to zero for every instant of time, this may not be the case. It is difficult to measure each known variable accurately, and also,

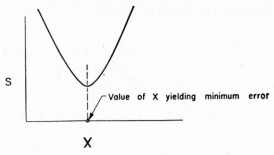

FIG. 14.40-1.

it may be difficult (if not impossible) to determine a set of coefficients which satisfies (14.40-1) for all instants of time. Let the left-hand side of (14.40-1) be squared, and the result at each observed point be represented by the constant S_n. Thus (14.40-1) becomes

$$(-A_n + XB_n + YC_n + ZD_n)^2 = S_n \qquad (14.40\text{-}5)$$

where the subscript n refers to a particular instant of time. If readings are taken at a number of instants of time, the result is

$$S = (-A_1 + XB_1 + YC_1 + ZD_1)^2 + (-A_2 + XB_2 + YC_2 + ZD_2)^2 + \cdots \qquad (14.40\text{-}6)$$

$$= \Sigma(-A_n + XB_n + YC_n + ZD_n)^2 \qquad (14.40\text{-}7)$$

where $S = S_1 + S_2 + S_3 + \cdots$.

The least-square method endeavors to minimize the value of S. It is based on the usually valid assumption that with all coefficients except one having the proper value, a plot of S versus the remaining coefficient (such as X) has the shape shown in Fig. 14.40-1. Thus taking the partial derivative of (14.40-7) with respect to each of the unknown coefficients provides a method for determining the set of coefficients which minimizes the error. If the function shown in Fig. 14.40-1 does not have a well-defined null, this method will not yield accurate results. Usually, however, the results are very accurate.

The partial derivative of S with respect to X is

$$\frac{\partial S}{\partial X} = 0 = 2[B_1(-A_1+XB_1+YC_1+ZD_1)+B_2(-A_2+XB_2+YC_2+ZD_2)+\ldots]$$

(14.40-8)

$$= -\Sigma A_n B_n + X\Sigma B_n^2 + Y\Sigma B_n C_n + Z\Sigma B_n D_n$$

(14.40-9)

where

$$\Sigma A_n B_n = A_1 B_1 + A_2 B_2 + A_3 B_3 + \ldots$$
$$\Sigma B_n^2 = B_1^2 + B_2^2 + B_3^2 + \ldots$$
$$\Sigma B_n C_n = B_1 C_1 + B_2 C_2 + B_3 C_3 + \ldots$$
$$\Sigma B_n D_n = B_1 D_1 + B_2 D_2 + B_3 D_3 + \ldots$$

Similarly,

$$\frac{\partial S}{\partial Y} = 0 = -\Sigma A_n C_n + X\Sigma B_n C_n + Y\Sigma C_n^2 + Z\Sigma C_n D_n$$

(14.40-10)

$$\frac{\partial S}{\partial Z} = 0 = -\Sigma A_n D_n + X\Sigma B_n D_n + Y\Sigma C_n D_n + Z\Sigma D_n^2$$

(14.40-11)

The coefficients X, Y, and Z are determined by solving (14.40-9), (14.40-10), and (14.40-11) simultaneously. Using determinant notation, the results are

$$X = \frac{\begin{vmatrix} \Sigma A_n B_n & \Sigma B_n C_n & \Sigma B_n D_n \\ \Sigma A_n C_n & \Sigma C_n^2 & \Sigma C_n D_n \\ \Sigma A_n D_n & \Sigma C_n D_n & \Sigma D_n^2 \end{vmatrix}}{\Delta}$$

(14.40-12)

$$Y = \frac{\begin{vmatrix} \Sigma B_n^2 & \Sigma A_n B_n & \Sigma B_n D_n \\ \Sigma B_n C_n & \Sigma A_n C_n & \Sigma C_n D_n \\ \Sigma B_n D_n & \Sigma A_n D_n & \Sigma D_n^2 \end{vmatrix}}{\Delta}$$

(14.40-13)

$$Z = \frac{\begin{vmatrix} \Sigma B_n^2 & \Sigma B_n C_n & \Sigma A_n B_n \\ \Sigma B_n C_n & \Sigma C_n^2 & \Sigma A_n C_n \\ \Sigma B_n D_n & \Sigma C_n D_n & \Sigma A_n D_n \end{vmatrix}}{\Delta}$$

(14.40-14)

where

$$\Delta = \begin{vmatrix} \Sigma B_n^2 & \Sigma B_n C_n & \Sigma B_n D_n \\ \Sigma B_n C_n & \Sigma C_n^2 & \Sigma C_n D_n \\ \Sigma B_n D_n & \Sigma C_n D_n & \Sigma D_n^2 \end{vmatrix}$$

Experience has shown that, if the transients being analyzed are oscillatory, twenty points evenly distributed throughout one oscillation usually yield highly accurate results.

14.50 Slope method

The basic principle of the Laplace transform for a delayed function, which was discussed in Section 3.14 and illustrated in Fig. 3.10-1,

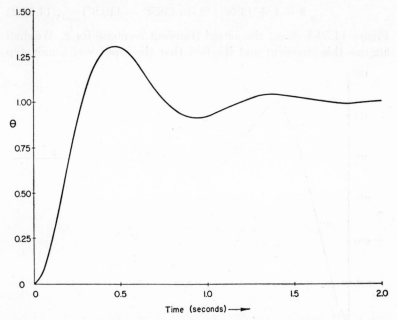

Fig. 14.50-1. $\theta = 1 + 1.07\epsilon^{-2.58t} \sin (388t° - 110.8°)$.

may be used to find the approximate frequency response of a function. The method divides the input and output transients into straight-line segments. The Laplace transforms of these segments are shown in parts a, e, f, and g of Fig. 3.10-1. The Laplace transform of the complete transient is the sum of all the transforms due to each factor. The output-to-input frequency response is found by dividing the Laplace transform of the output by the Laplace transform of the input, substituting $j\omega$ for s, and calculating the resulting function for various values of ω. The examples given in this section will illustrate the procedure.

For the first example, consider a system which is represented by the transfer function

$$\frac{\theta}{\alpha} = \frac{1}{1 + 0.098s + 0.019s^2} \qquad (14.50\text{-}1)$$

This relation was also used as an example in Sections 12.10, 12.20, and 14.20. When α is a unit step input, the output is

$$\theta = 1 + 1.07\epsilon^{-2.58t} \sin (388t^\circ - 110.8^\circ) \qquad (14.50\text{-}2)$$

Figure 14.50-1 shows the actual transient response for θ. We shall assume this transient and the fact that the input was a unit step

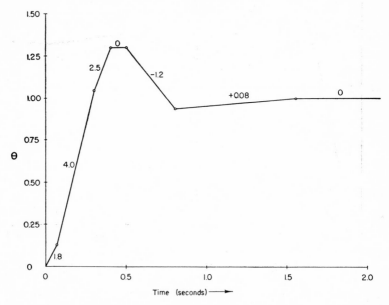

FIG. 14.50-2. Straight-line approximation of the transient in Fig. 14.50-1. The slope in units per second is shown for each segment.

are all that is known about the system. With this information we shall determine the system frequency response characteristic and compare the result with the actual characteristic.

Figure 14.50-2 shows the straight-line segment approximation to the θ transient response. The segments have a slope of 1.8 units per second between $t = 0$ and $t = 0.07$; 4.0 units per second between $t = 0.07$ and $t = 0.30$; 2.5 units per second between $t = 0.30$ and

$t = 0.40$; 0 unit per second between $t = 0.40$ and $t = 0.50$; -1.2 units per second between $t = 0.50$ and $t = 0.80$; 0.08 unit per second between $t = 0.80$ and $t = 1.55$; and 0 unit per second above $t = 1.55$. This straight-line transient approximation can be broken into the components shown in Fig. 14.50-3. Each component starts

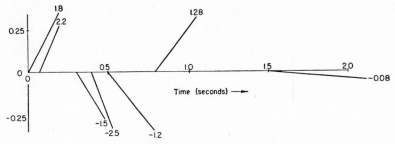

FIG. 14.50-3.   Components of the transient in Fig. 14.50-2. The slope in units per second is shown for each component.

at the time indicated and is of infinite duration. Thus the Laplace transform of the approximate output transient may be written

$$\theta = \frac{1.8}{s^2} + \frac{2.2}{s^2}\, \epsilon^{-0.07s} - \frac{1.5}{s^2}\, \epsilon^{-0.3s} - \frac{2.5}{s^2}\, \epsilon^{-0.4s}$$

$$- \frac{1.2}{s^2}\, \epsilon^{-0.5s} + \frac{1.28}{s^2}\, \epsilon^{-0.8s} - \frac{0.08}{s^2}\, \epsilon^{-1.55s} \quad (14.50\text{-}3)$$

Since the Laplace transform of the input is

$$\alpha = 1/s \quad\quad\quad\quad (14.50\text{-}4)$$

(14.50-3) and (14.50-4) can be combined to yield the transfer expression

$$\frac{\theta}{\alpha} = \frac{1}{s}\, (1.8 + 2.2\epsilon^{-0.07s} - 1.5\epsilon^{-0.3s} - 2.5\epsilon^{-0.4s}$$

$$- 1.2\epsilon^{-0.5s} + 1.28\epsilon^{-0.8s} - 0.08\epsilon^{-1.55s}) \quad (14.50\text{-}5)$$

The frequency response is found by substituting $j\omega$ for s in (14.50-5) and calculating the result for various values of ω. Table 14.50-1 compares the frequency response results obtained by (14.50-5) with those obtained by using the actual expression in (14.50-1). Since (14.50-5) is indeterminate at $\omega = 0$, its value may be found by applying L'Hospital's rule. This rule says that if the quotient $F_1(s)/F_2(s)$ assumes the indeterminate form $0/0$ or ∞/∞ when $s = a$, then

TABLE 14.50-1

FREQUENCY RESPONSE RESULTS USING THE SLOPE METHOD FOR THE EXAMPLE
SHOWN IN FIG. 14.50-1

ω	θ/α			
	Slope method		Actual	
	Amplitude	Phase	Amplitude	Phase
0	0.996	0°	1.000	0°
2	1.06	−12.9	1.06	−12.0°
5	1.38	−45.6	1.39	−43.0°
10	0.81	−131.2	0.75	−132.6°

$$\lim_{s \to a} \frac{F_1(s)}{F_2(s)} = \lim_{s \to a} \frac{dF_1(s)/ds}{dF_2(s)/ds} \qquad (14.50\text{-}6)$$

provided the latter limit exists.

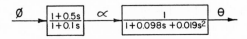

FIG. 14.50-4.

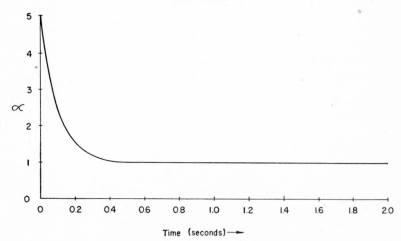

FIG. 14.50-5. $\alpha = 1 + 4\epsilon^{-10t}$.

As a second example of the slope method, consider that the system shown in Fig. 14.50-4 is subject to a unit step ϕ input. The transient responses for α and θ are

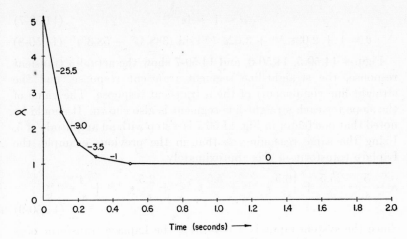

FIG. 14.50-6.   Straight-line approximation of the transient in Fig. 14.50-5. The slope in units per second is shown for each segment.

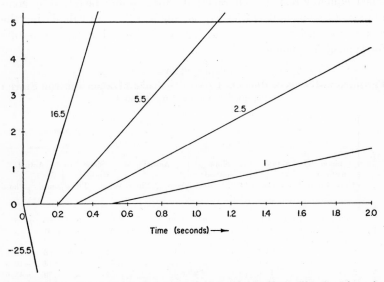

FIG. 14.50-7.   Components of the transient in Fig. 14.50-6. The slope in units per second is shown for each component.

$$\alpha = 1 + 4\epsilon^{-10t} \qquad (14.50\text{-}7)$$

$$\theta = 1 + 2.08\epsilon^{-10t} + 3.62\epsilon^{-2.57t} \sin(388.4t° - 58.3°) \qquad (14.50\text{-}8)$$

Figures 14.50-5, 14.50-6, and 14.50-7 show the actual α transient response, the straight-line segment transient response, and the straight-line components of the α transient response. The value of the slope for each straight-line segment is also shown. It should be noted that one factor in Fig. 14.50-7 is a step with an amplitude of 5. Using the same reasoning as that in the previous example, the Laplace transform of α is approximately

$$\alpha = \frac{5}{s} - \frac{25.5}{s^2} + \frac{16.5}{s^2}\,\epsilon^{-0.1s} + \frac{5.5}{s^2}\,\epsilon^{-0.2s} + \frac{2.5}{s^2}\,\epsilon^{-0.3s} + \frac{1}{s^2}\,\epsilon^{-0.5s}$$

$$(14.50\text{-}9)$$

Since the system input is a unit step, the Laplace transform of ϕ is

$$\phi = 1/s \qquad (14.50\text{-}10)$$

The frequency response characteristic for α/ϕ may be found by combining (14.50-9) and (14.50-10), letting $s = j\omega$, and calculating the results for various values of ω. Table 14.50-2 tabulates the results for typical frequencies.

TABLE 14.50-2

FREQUENCY RESPONSE RESULTS USING THE SLOPE METHOD FOR THE SYSTEM REPRESENTED BY FIG. 14.50-4

ω	α/ϕ				θ/ϕ				θ/α			
	Slope method		Actual		Slope method		Actual		Slope method		Actual	
	Amp.	Phase	Amp.	Phase	Amp.	Phase	Amp.	Phase	Amp.	Phase	Amp.	Phase
0	1.00	0°	1.00	0°	1.05	0°	1.00	0°	1.05	0°	1.00	0°
1	1.12	22.2°	1.11	20.9°	1.18	12.0°	1.13	15.2°	1.05	−10.2°	1.01	−5.7°
1.5	1.26	30.1°	1.24	28.4°	1.24	17.4°	1.28	19.7°	0.98	−12.7°	1.03	−8.7°
2	1.43	35.7°	1.39	33.7°	1.46	19.7°	1.47	21.7°	1.03	−16.0°	1.06	−12.0°
3	1.80	41.4°	1.73	39.6°	1.37	15.2°	1.96	20.1°	1.31	−26.2°	1.14	−19.5°
5	2.55	42.9°	2.41	41.6°	3.65	−2.9°	3.35	−1.4°	1.43	−45.8°	1.39	−43.0°
8	3.29	39.5°	3.22	37.3°	3.88	−65.5°	3.96	−68.1°	1.18	−105.0°	1.23	−105.4°
10	3.81	33.6°	3.60	33.7°	2.67	−100.3°	2.71	−98.9°	0.70	−133.9°	0.75	−132.6°
15	4.43	26.8°	4.19	26.1°	1.08	−125.7°	1.17	−129.7°	0.24	−152.5°	0.28	−155.8°
20	4.84	20.8°	4.49	20.9°	0.16	−189.6°	0.65	−142.4°	0.03	−210.4°	0.14	−163.5°
30	5.09	15.0°	4.75	14.6°	0.12	−52.3°	0.29	−155.1°	0.02	−67.3°	0.06	−169.7°
50	5.37	5.6°	4.91	9.0°	0.03	−179.9°	0.10	−165.0°	0.01	−185.5°	0.02	−174.0°

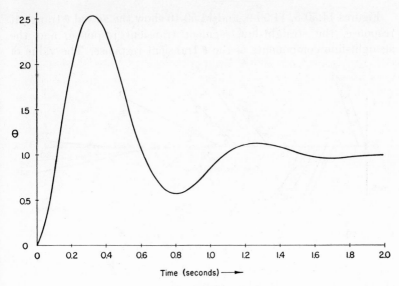

Fig. 14.50-8.

$$\theta = 1 + 2.08\epsilon^{-10t} + 3.62\epsilon^{-2.57t} \sin (388.4t° - 58.3°).$$

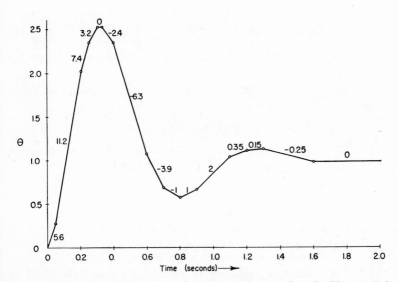

Fig. 14.50-9. Straight-line approximation of the transient in Fig. 14.50-8. The slope in units per second is shown for each component.

Figures 14.50-8, 14.50-9, and 14.50-10 show the actual θ transient response, the straight-line segment transient response, and the straight-line components of the θ transient response. The value of

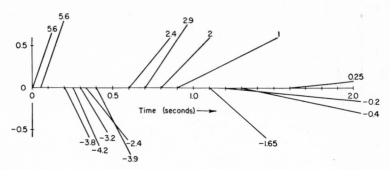

FIG. 14.50-10.   Components of the transients in Fig. 14.50-9. The slope in units per second is shown for each component.

the slope for each segment is also shown. The Laplace transform of the approximate transient response is

$$\theta = \frac{1}{s^2} (5.6 + 5.6\epsilon^{-0.05s} - 3.8\epsilon^{-0.2s} - 4.2\epsilon^{-0.25s} - 3.2\epsilon^{-0.3s}$$
$$- 2.4\epsilon^{-0.33s} - 3.9\epsilon^{-0.4s} + 2.4\epsilon^{-0.6s} + 2.9\epsilon^{-0.7s} + 2\epsilon^{-0.8s} + \epsilon^{-0.9s}$$
$$- 1.65\epsilon^{-1.1s} - 0.2\epsilon^{-1.2s} - 0.4\epsilon^{-1.3s} + 0.25\epsilon^{-1.6s} \quad (14.50\text{-}11)$$

This equation for θ may be combined with either (14.50-9) or (14.50-10) in order to find the relations θ/α and θ/ϕ. The frequency response characteristics for these functions are tabulated in Table 14.50-2.

PROBLEMS

14-1. The major portion of the calculations for the systems described by the equations listed below are contained in the text of this book. These systems may be used to illustrate the methods discussed in this chapter. For each of these systems, find and plot $\theta_o(t)$ when θ_i is a unit step input and when θ_i is a unit rate input. Also find $F_o(j\omega)$.

    (a) The system described by eq. (4.20-14).
    (b) The system described by eq. (7.40-5).
    (c) The system described by eq. (8.13-4).
    (d) The system described by eq. (9.10-12).

14-2. Apply intuitive reasoning to each of the transients found in Problem 14-1, and determine how accurately you can guess the open-loop function.

14-3. Find $\dot{\theta}_o(t)$, $\ddot{\theta}_o(t)$, $\dddot{\theta}_o(t)$, and $\ddddot{\theta}_o(t)$ for the system in Problem 14-1a when subjected to a unit step input. (Note: Taking the derivative of a function whose initial value is zero is a relatively simple task. The equations fall into a pattern which is evident from inspection of similar equations in Appendix 6.) Evaluate the equations at a sufficient number of points, and use these values in (14.20-1) to find a set of simultaneous equations from which the original coefficients can be determined by the equation fitting method.

14-4. Find $\dot{\theta}_o(t)$, $\ddot{\theta}_o(t)$, and $\dddot{\theta}_o(t)$ for the system in Problem 14-1b when subjected to a unit step input. Evaluate the equations at a sufficient number of points, and use these values in eq. (14.20-1) to find a set of simultaneous equations from which the original coefficients can be determined by the equation fitting method.

14-5. Repeat Problem 14-4, using the system in Problem 14-1c.

14-6. Repeat Problem 14-3, using the system in Problem 14-1d.

14-7. Use the method in Section 14.30 to obtain the derivatives found in Problems 14-3, 14-4; 14-5, and 14-6. How do the results compare?

14-8. Apply the least-square method to the data in Table 12.20-3. Find θ/α.

14-9. Repeat Problem 14-8 for the data in Table 14.30-1.

14-10. Apply the slope method to the transients found in Problem 14-1. How does $(\theta_o/\theta_i)(j\omega)$ determined by this method compare with the actual values?

CHAPTER 15

NONLINEAR SYSTEMS

15.00 Introduction[10,27,28,32,37,40]

The speed of response and the accuracy of automatic control systems may be greatly improved when linear analysis techniques are used in the system design, and linear components are used in the system. However, the designer should not consider a linear system as the ultimate in control system design. Nonlinear elements are sometimes beneficial. If nonlinear elements are properly used in a control system, performance can be improved without requiring any improvement in the characteristics of the system components.

This possibility is often neglected because of the extreme difficulty encountered in handling and solving nonlinear differential equations. Fortunately, the advent of automatic computing equipment provides one method of circumventing this problem.

Since a thorough discussion of nonlinear techniques is a separate study in itself, this chapter is intended only as a brief discussion of some avenues which the designer may utilize. Linear analysis techniques, combined with intuitive reasoning, provide the basis for understanding the effect of most nonlinear properties.

Nonlinear components need not increase the complexity of a control system. In fact, the opposite may be true. Complexity in a control system is not an indication of good design. Often, an ingenious designer is able to solve a difficult problem in a simple manner by utilizing nonlinear elements.

15.10 Variable open-loop gain systems

If the open-loop gain of a system is varied as a function of the error amplitude, significant improvement in the system response to step inputs can be achieved. Figure 15.10-1 shows a typical possibility. The block diagram in Fig. 15.10-2 may be used to describe the

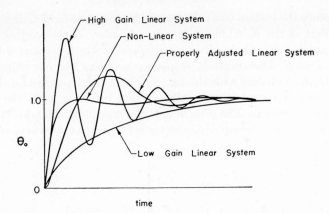

FIG. 15.10-1.   Transient responses of a linear system compared with a possible transient response of a non-linear system.

operation of a variable-gain system. A linear system is one in which the magnitude of Z is directly proportional to θ_e, or

$$Z = K_1\theta_e \qquad (15.10\text{-}1)$$

A variable-gain system is exemplified by (15.10-1) becoming

$$Z = (K_1 + K_2|\theta_e|)\theta_e \qquad (15.10\text{-}2)$$

The reader probably can suggest different methods by which the $K_2|\theta_e|$ factor in (15.10-2) can be achieved. Some possibilities exist in the following.

(1) Plate current and other characteristics of vacuum tubes

(2) Saturation effects

(3) Rectifying and summing circuits

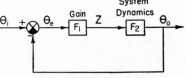

FIG. 15.10-2.

Usually the designer first proves that a particular departure from a linear system is beneficial. Then he searches for a simple method of achieving the signal. Often in different control systems, the type and purpose of signals which are used are similar, but the methods by which the signals are achieved are wholly unrelated.

The beneficial effect of the $K_2|\theta_e|$ portion of (15.10-2) may be seen by considering the case when the system is subjected to a unit step input. With the $K_2|\theta_e|$ factor, the magnitude of Z is larger, and hence the system reacts faster. As the magnitude of θ_e decreases the effect of the $K_2|\theta_e|$ factor becomes smaller. Therefore this type of signal is particularly effective in systems which encounter large error signals. The transient responses (such as the one shown in Fig. 15.10-1) change with the magnitude of the input, and a single curve cannot completely describe system behavior, as is the case for a linear system. The principle, however, can be extended by the designer so that a variable-gain factor is an effective system element.

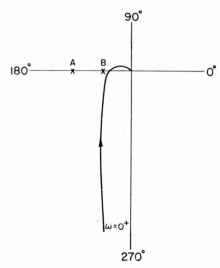

Fig. 15.10-3.   Nyquist locus for a variable-gain system.

Figure 15.10-3 shows the Nyquist locus for this system. The -1 point is normally at A, but when the effect of the $K_2|\theta_e|$ factor is included, the -1 point location varies between A and B. Either numerical integration techniques or automatic computer simulation may be used to design systems with variable gains.

15.20 Variable coefficients

Sometimes coefficients in a transfer function vary (usually unintentionally) under different operating conditions. For example, consider the open-loop expression

$$\frac{\theta_o}{\theta_e} = \frac{5}{s(1 + as + 0.01s^2)} \qquad (15.20\text{-}1)$$

As long as the coefficient a is larger than 0.05, the Nyquist locus for (15.20-1) is stable. Stability in a variable-coefficient system, such as (15.20-1), can be achieved by adjusting the open-loop function so that the Nyquist locus is stable under all significant operating conditions. Coefficients may be intentionally varied to optimize system performance under different operating conditions. For example, compensator changes may be made as a function of altitude in an autopilot for an aircraft which must perform at sea level or extreme altitudes.

15.30 Saturation effects

System saturations usually limit the capability of a system because they prevent sufficient control strength. The most common effect of a saturation is that it causes a persistent oscillation in the system when the input signal is large. Thus the output oscillates or hunts around the desired value.

Sometimes this is advantageous, for it permits a simple control system. For example, suppose that the gain in a control system were increased far beyond the normal linear-analysis value. Then if a limit were placed on the error signal, the output would oscillate about the desired value. A system of this type possesses both a very fast speed of response (due to the high gain) and simplicity. It has the disadvantages of a steady-state oscillatory output and the accompanying equipment wear and waste of power.

15.40 Time-delay elements

Some systems contain elements which delay but do not appreciably alter the control signals. An example of this is a data-sampling

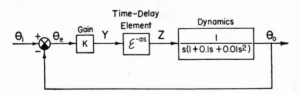

Fig. 15.40-1.   Control system with a time-delay element.

device which monitors the data, but does not immediately forward the data to the next element in the system. The Laplace transform theorem for a delayed function expresses the operation of these elements.

For the system shown in Fig. 15.40-1, the operation of the delay element is described by

$$\frac{Z}{Y} = \epsilon^{-as} \qquad (15.40\text{-}1)$$

where a is the time delay of the element in seconds. The open-loop expression for the system is

$$\frac{\theta_o}{\theta_e} = \frac{K\epsilon^{-as}}{s(1 + 0.1s + 0.01s^2)} \qquad (15.40\text{-}2)$$

If the time-delay element delays the signals 0.1 sec, the open-loop frequency response function shown in Fig. 15.40-2 is

$$\frac{\theta_o}{\theta_e} = \frac{K\epsilon^{-0.1j\omega}}{j\omega(1 - 0.01\omega^2 + 0.1j\omega)} \qquad (15.40\text{-}3)$$

Table 15.40-1 contains the amplitude and phase values for various frequencies.

TABLE 15.40-1

TRANSFER FUNCTION VALUES

ω	$Z/Y = \epsilon^{-0.1j\omega}$		θ_0/Z		$(1/K)(\theta_0/\theta_e)$	
	A	ϕ	A	ϕ	A	ϕ
0	1	$0°$	∞	$-90°$	∞	$-90.0°$
1	1	$-5.7°$	1.006	$-95.8°$	1.006	$-101.5°$
2	1	$-11.5°$	0.510	$-101.8°$	0.510	$-113.3°$
3	1	$-17.2°$	0.348	$-108.2°$	0.348	$-125.4°$
5	1	$-28.7°$	0.223	$-123.7°$	0.223	$-152.4°$
7	1	$-40.1°$	0.166	$-143.8°$	0.166	$-183.9°$
10	1	$-57.3°$	0.100	$-180.0°$	0.100	$-237.3°$
12	1	$-68.8°$	0.065	$-200.0°$	0.065	$-268.8°$
15	1	$-86.0°$	0.034	$-219.8°$	0.034	$-305.8°$
20	1	$-114.6°$	0.014	$-236.3°$	0.014	$-350.9°$

The normal linear analysis techniques may be applied to many nonlinear problems. This may be demonstrated by selecting the gain for the system shown in Fig. 15.40-1 on the basis of its open-loop frequency response locus. Thus $K = 3.1$ when $M_p = 1.5$, and $K = 5.6$ when the system is neutrally stable.

Two output transient responses for a unit step input are shown in Fig. 15.40-3. These were obtained by numerical integration, using

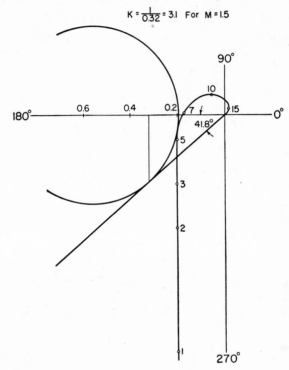

$$K = \frac{1}{0.32} = 3.1 \text{ For } M = 1.5$$

Fig. 15.40-2.   Nyquist locus of $(1/K)(\theta_o/\theta_e)$ for the system shown in Fig. 15.40-1.

the method described in Section 12.20 with $\Delta T = 0.02$. The system is properly adjusted when the gain is 3.1; however, when the gain is increased to 5.6, the output is too oscillatory.

Thus linear techniques are fully applicable to many nonlinear problems. Some nonlinear elements, such as relays, cause constant phase shifts or amplitude variations. Linear analysis can be applied to these systems by including the amplitude and phase effects in the open-loop frequency response calculations.

If the designer would like to achieve a constant delay element such as Z/Y in Fig. 15.40-1, he may do so in a number of ways. For example, if Y is an electric signal, it may be recorded on a magnetic tape and monitored a sec later.

The frequency response characteristic of Z/Y is

$$Z/Y = 1\angle -57.3a\omega° \qquad (15.40\text{-}4)$$

The amplitude is unity for all frequencies from 0 to ∞, and the phase lag increases linearly with frequency. The reason for the

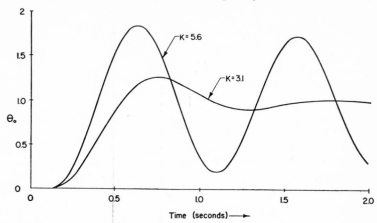

FIG. 15.40-3. Transient response of the system shown in Fig. 15.40-1 with $a = 0.1$ sec.

phase lag may be seen by referring to Fig. 1.30-2, where it was shown that the phase angle is determined by

$$\text{phase angle} = \phi = \frac{360\omega(T_1 - T_2)}{2\pi} \quad \text{degrees} \quad (15.40\text{-}5)$$

where $T_1 - T_2$ is the time difference between two sinusoidal signals, $2\pi/\omega = T_1$, ω is the signal frequency. If the delay is a constant amount,

$$\phi = -57.3a\omega \quad \text{degrees} \qquad (15.40\text{-}6)$$

where $a = T_2 - T_1$. This is the same phase result as was obtained in (15.40-4). A linear relation which has this phase characteristic in the low-frequency zone (those frequencies less than $\omega = 1/a$), and whose amplitude ratio is also approximately unity in this zone is

$$F(s) = \frac{1}{1 + aj\omega} \qquad (15.40\text{-}7)$$

The designer might find that the characteristic in (15.40-7) is fully adequate for some of his delay-element requirements. Some other delay relations are given in the problems at the end of this chapter.

PROBLEMS

15-1. Select a control system whose output transient for a unit step input is given in this book. Alter the system so that a variable open-loop gain (such as that in eq. 15.10-2) exists. Select values for the variable-gain factor. Find $\theta_o(t)$ when the input is a step whose magnitude is:

(a) 1　　　　　　　　　　　　　(c) 2

(b) 1/2

15-2. Select the gain so that the following systems are always stable and M_p is never excessive.

(a) $F_o = \dfrac{K_o}{s(1 + as)(1 + s + s^2)}$

where a varies between 0.1 and 1.

(b) $F_o = \dfrac{K_o}{s(1 + as + 0.01s^2)(1 + 0.05s)}$

where a varies between 0.02 and 0.05.

(c) $F_o = \dfrac{K(1 + 5s)}{s(s + a)(s + 20)}$

where a varies between -0.5 and 2.

15-3. Select a lead compensator for each case in Problem 15-2.

15-4. Select a combined feedback and cascaded compensator for each case in Problem 15-2. Use K_v and ω_u as criteria of the amount the selected compensator improves the system.

15-5. Find $\theta(t)$ for the system represented by equation 12.10-1 when α is a unit step input and the maximum value of $\dot{\theta}$ is ± 4 units per sec.

15-6. The following function has been suggested as a time-delay element. Compare its merits and limitations with the function given in eq. (15.40-7).

$$F = \frac{1 - 0.5aj\omega}{1 + 0.5aj\omega}$$

where a is the time-delay in seconds. How could this function be achieved?

15-7. Select values for A, B, C, D, and E so that the following function follows $\epsilon^{-aj\omega}$ to as high a frequency as possible.

$$F = \frac{(1 - Aaj\omega)(1 - Baj\omega)}{(1 + Caj\omega)(1 + Daj\omega)(1 + Eaj\omega)}$$

15-8. Find the output if the function in Problem 15-7 is subjected to a pulse of unit height and 0.10 sec duration, where A, B, C, D, and E have the values found in Problem 15-7 and $a = 0.05$ sec. Repeat for $a = 0.20$ sec.

15-9. The following function has been suggested as a time-delay element:

$$F = \frac{1}{(1 + as/n)^n}$$

where a is the time-delay in seconds. Find the output when the input is a unit step, $a = 0.1$, and $n = 3$. Repeat for $n = 1, 2, 5$ and 10.

APPENDIX 1

RUNGE-KUTTA NUMERICAL INTEGRATION
METHOD

The Runge-Kutta numerical integration method yields accurate results, using larger intervals of the independent variable (time) than either of the methods in Chapter 12. It has the disadvantage of requiring more computation for each of the intervals; however, the computation is a repetitive type, so that once one becomes familiar with the computation procedure he is able to progress rapidly. Hence the method is recommended for those who often have occasion to perform numerical integrations.

The approximate maximum time interval which may be used to obtain reasonably accurate results with a minimum of computation time is

$$\Delta T = \frac{4}{3\omega_1} \quad \text{sec} \tag{1-1}$$

This is 4 times as large as in Method 2 in Chapter 12 and about 11 times as large as in Method 1. The same example used in Chapter 12 is presented in this Appendix, and the results using the recommended time interval (0.2 second) and other intervals are shown.

Calculating form for the Runge-Kutta numerical integration method

Procedure:

1. Solve the equation for the highest derivative. If that derivative is of the second order, use the form below. If it is of higher or lower order, add or subtract columns so that there are as many columns as needed. Calculations in each column (except the highest derivative) are similar, as can be seen by comparing θ and $\dot{\theta}$.

2. Select ΔT to be approximately $4/3\omega_1$ sec, where ω_1 is as defined in Section 12.10.

3. After finding the values at t_1, repeat the procedure to find them at t_2, where $t_2 = t_1 + \Delta T_1$, using t_1 as the starting point rather than t_0

t	θ	$\dot{\theta}$	$\ddot{\theta}$
t_0	$\theta_0 = $ initial val.	$\dot{\theta}_0 = $ initial val.	$\ddot{\theta}_0 = $ use θ_0 and $\dot{\theta}_0$ in eq.
t_{01}	$\theta_{01} = \theta_0 + (\Delta T/2)\dot{\theta}_0$	$\dot{\theta}_{01} = \dot{\theta}_0 + (\Delta T/2)\ddot{\theta}_0$	$\ddot{\theta}_{01} = $ use θ_{01} and $\dot{\theta}_{01}$ in eq.
t_{02}	$\theta_{02} = \theta_0 + (\Delta T/2)\dot{\theta}_{01}$	$\dot{\theta}_{02} = \dot{\theta}_0 + (\Delta T/2)\ddot{\theta}_{01}$	$\ddot{\theta}_{02} = $ use θ_{02} and $\dot{\theta}_{02}$ in eq.
t_{03}	$\theta_{03} = \theta_0 + \dot{\theta}_{02}\Delta T$	$\dot{\theta}_{03} = \dot{\theta}_0 + \ddot{\theta}_{02}\Delta T$	$\ddot{\theta}_{03} = $ use θ_{03} and $\dot{\theta}_{03}$ in eq.
$t_1 = t_0 + \Delta T$	$\theta_1 = \theta_0 + \Delta\theta_0$	$\dot{\theta}_1 = \dot{\theta}_0 + \Delta\dot{\theta}_0$	$\ddot{\theta}_1 = $ use θ_1 and $\dot{\theta}_1$ in eq.

where $\Delta\theta_0 = (\Delta T/6)(\dot{\theta}_0 + 2\dot{\theta}_{01} + 2\dot{\theta}_{02} + \dot{\theta}_{03})$, and $\Delta\dot{\theta}_0 = (\Delta T/6)(\ddot{\theta}_0 + 2\ddot{\theta}_{01} + 2\ddot{\theta}_{02} + \ddot{\theta}_{03})$.

RESULTS USING THE RUNGE-KUTTA METHOD

Differential equation; $\ddot{\theta} = 52.63 - 52.63\theta - 5.158\dot{\theta}$, $\omega_1 = 7.25$ radians per sec.

t	θ			
	Exact	Runge-Kutta result		
		$\Delta T = 0.1$	$\Delta T = 0.2$	$\Delta T = 0.3$
0	0	0	0	0
0.1	0.215	0.212		
0.2	0.652	0.649	0.599	
0.3	1.048	1.059		0.684
0.4	1.267	1.301	1.258	
0.5	1.292	1.334		
0.6	1.193	1.231	1.188	1.305
0.7	1.058	1.070		
0.8	0.954	0.967	0.959	
0.9	0.911	0.914		1.190
1.0	0.920	0.934	0.912	
1.1	0.957	0.958		
1.2	0.996	0.989	0.986	0.916

t	θ			
	Exact	Runge-Kutta result		
		$\Delta T = 0.1$	$\Delta T = 0.2$	$\Delta T = 0.3$
0	0	0	0	0
0.1	3.751	3.766		
0.2	4.446	4.544	4.693	
0.3	3.216	3.337		4.613
0.4	1.160	1.153	1.604	
0.5	−0.518	−0.550		
0.6	−1.312	−1.572	−1.307	1.075
0.7	−1.272	−1.528		
0.8	−0.753	−0.833	−0.806	
0.9	−0.270	−0.224		−1.555
1.0	0.276	0.147	0.241	
1.1	0.417	0.311		
1.2	0.337	0.273	0.401	−0.678

t	θ			
	Exact	Runge-Kutta result		
		$\Delta T = 0.1$	$\Delta T = 0.2$	$\Delta T = 0.3$
0	52.60	52.60	52.60	52.60
0.1	21.89	22.09		
0.2	− 4.68	− 4.97	− 3.12	
0.3	−19.13	−20.31		− 7.19
0.4	−20.03	−21.80	−21.86	
0.5	−12.70	−14.75		
0.6	− 3.35	− 4.07	− 3.17	−21.59
0.7	3.53	4.21		
0.8	6.29	6.04	6.32	
0.9	5.53	5.67		− 2.01
1.0	2.80	2.73	3.41	
1.1	0.13	0.59		
1.2	− 1.51	− 0.85	− 1.33	7.92

APPENDIX 2

METHODS FOR FINDING ROOTS OF EQUATIONS

Quadratic equation

General form:

$$as^2 + bs + c = 0$$

Roots:

$$s = \frac{-b \pm \sqrt{b^2 - 4ac}}{2a}$$

Cubic equation

General form:

$$s^3 + as^2 + bs + c = 0$$

To find the roots, solve the following.

$$d = \frac{3b - a^2}{9}$$

$$e = \frac{2a^3 - 9ab + 27c}{54}$$

$$f = \sqrt{e^2 + d^3} \qquad \text{(see Note)}$$

$$g = \sqrt[3]{f - e}$$

$$h = \sqrt[3]{-f - e}$$

The roots are as follows.

$$s_1 = g + h - \frac{a}{3}$$

$$s_2 = \frac{-(g + h) + (g - h)\sqrt{-3}}{2} - \frac{a}{3}$$

$$s_3 = \frac{-(g + h) - (g - h)\sqrt{-3}}{2} - \frac{a}{3}$$

Note: If f is an imaginary number, the roots are all real and unequal. In this case, find ϕ, where

$$\cos \phi = \frac{e}{\sqrt{-d^3}}$$

Then the roots are

$$s_1 = \mp 2 \sqrt{-d} \cos \frac{\phi}{3} - \frac{a}{3}$$

$$s_2 = \mp 2 \sqrt{-d} \cos \left(\frac{\phi}{3} + 120° \right) - \frac{a}{3}$$

$$s_3 = \mp 2 \sqrt{-d} \cos \left(\frac{\phi}{3} + 240° \right) - \frac{a}{3}$$

Real roots

If the order of an equation is an odd number, it has at least one real root. This may be determined by dividing the equation by different assumed real root values until the remainder is zero. A good initial value to assume is a root based on the two lower-order terms. Thus if the equation is

$$s^3 + 2.5s^2 + 3.5s + 3 = 0$$

assume $s = -3/3.5 = -0.86$, and then

$$
\begin{array}{r}
s^2 + 1.64s + 2.09 \\
s + 0.86 \overline{\smash{\big)}\ s^3 + 2.50s^2 + 3.50s + 3.00} \\
\underline{s^3 + 0.86s^2} \\
1.64s^2 + 3.50s \\
\underline{1.64s^2 + 1.41s} \\
2.09s + 3.00 \\
\underline{2.09s + 1.80} \\
+ 1.20
\end{array}
$$

The remainder of the next to last step is used to find the next trial root. Assume $s = -3.00/2.09 = -1.44$; then

$$
\begin{array}{r}
s^2 + 1.06s + 1.97 \\
s + 1.44 \overline{\smash{\big)}\ s^3 + 2.50s^2 + 3.50s + 3.00} \\
\underline{s^3 + 1.44s^2} \\
1.06s^2 + 3.50s \\
\underline{1.06s^2 + 1.53s} \\
1.97s + 3.00 \\
\underline{1.97s + 2.84} \\
0.16
\end{array}
$$

The next assumption is

$$s = -3.00/1.97 = -1.52.$$

Additional assumptions are made until the remainder is negligible. The final factors are

$$(s + 1.5)(s^2 + s + 2)$$

The roots of the quadratic may be found using the quadratic formula.

Higher order equations

A method developed by S. Lin[33] enables one to determine both real and complex higher order equation roots simply and accurately. It factors quadratic expressions rather than single roots from the original equation, and has the only limitation that the natural frequencies of the quadratic factors should be several octaves apart. A description of the method follows. Express the original equation in the form

$$s^n + a_{n-1}s^{n-1} + a_{n-2}s^{n-2} + \ldots + a_2s^2 + a_1s + a_0 = 0$$

Then the first trial divisor is

$$s^2 + \frac{a_1}{a_2}s + \frac{a_0}{a_2}$$

The original equation is divided by the trial divisor, giving

$$s^2 + \frac{a_1}{a_2}s + \frac{a_0}{a_2} \overline{\left) s^n + a_{n-1}s^{n-1} + a_{n-2}s^{n-2} + \ldots + a_2s^2 + a_1s + a_0 \right.}$$

$$
\begin{array}{c}
b_2s^2 + b_1s + a_0 \\
b_2s^2 + c_1s + c_0 \\
\hline
\text{Remainder}
\end{array}
$$

If the remainder is appreciable, the process is repeated, using as the next trial divisor

$$s^2 + \frac{b_1}{b_2}s + \frac{a_0}{b_2}$$

Usually the remainder will be negligible after three or four times. As an example, consider a case of known roots,

$$(s^2 + s + 1)(s^2 + 10s + 100) = s^4 + 11s^3 + 111s^2 + 110s + 100$$

The first trial divisor is

$$s^2 + \tfrac{110}{111}s + \tfrac{100}{111} = s^2 + 0.99s + 0.9$$

and the long division step are as follows.

$$\begin{array}{r} s^2 + 10.01s \; + 100.2 \\ \hline \end{array}$$

$$s^2 + 0.99s + 0.9\overline{\smash{\big)}\; s^4 + 11.00s^3 + 111.0s^2 + 110.0s + 100.0}$$
$$\underline{s^4 + 0.99s^3 + 0.9s^2}$$
$$10.01s^3 + 110.1s^2 + 110.0s$$
$$\underline{10.01s^3 + 9.9s^2 + 9.0s}$$
$$100.2s^2 + 101.0s + 100.0$$
$$\underline{100.2s^2 + 99.2s + 90.2}$$
$$1.8s + 9.8$$

The second trial divisor is

$$s^2 + \frac{101}{100.2}\, s + \frac{100}{100.2} = s^2 + 1.008s + 0.998$$

and the remainder after division is negligible.

Root locus method

The root locus method discussed in Chapter 8 can be used to find the roots of an equation by expressing the equation in the form shown in eq. (5.60-3) and applying the root locus method techniques.

APPENDIX 3

DESIGN DATA FOR CASCADED FUNCTIONS

When calculating the transfer relation of a single lead, lag, rate, or filter compensating function, it is always assumed that the input impedance is zero and the output impedance is infinite. As long as a compensating function is inserted in the system between a low-impedance source (such as a cathode follower) and a high-impedance output (such as the grid of a tube), the actual transfer relation should approximate the theoretical transfer relation.

If two or more compensating functions are cascaded together, the assumed input and output impedances no longer hold. The output impedance of the first function is not infinite, and the input of the second function is not zero. Therefore either buffer stages are needed, or the interaction effects must be taken into account.

The following design data include these interactions. They were obtained by equating the actual voltage output-to-input relation to the desired cascaded compensator relation. In each case, the selection of the proper resistor and capacitor value calls for assuming one or more values and solving in the order given for the other values.

Sometimes the solution calls for circuit components with imaginary parts or negative values. When this occurs, the fault may be either of the following:

1. The original assumption was too high or too low.
2. The case is impossible to handle by cascaded functions.

When the former occurs, try a different assumption or rearrange the terms. When the latter happens, it is usually because two compensators are peaked too close together. If this is not necessary, changing the desired compensator will avoid the necessity of a buffer stage.

A lead circuit is by definition one in which the output amplitude at the high frequencies is greater than the input, and the phase angle has an appreciable positive magnitude over a limited frequency band. Its general equation is of the form

$$\frac{E_o}{E_1} = \frac{1 + \alpha Ts}{1 + Ts} \tag{3-1}$$

where T is any positive value, α is any positive value greater than 1.

A lag circuit is the inverse of a lead circuit. The output amplitude at the higher frequencies is lower (but always of finite value) than the input, and the phase angle is negative over a limited frequency band. Its general equation form is

$$\frac{E_o}{E_1} = \frac{1 + Ts}{1 + \alpha Ts} \tag{3-2}$$

A rate circuit is by definition one in which the output is the derivative of the input over a limited low-frequency band. The general equation is

$$\frac{E_o}{E_1} = \frac{s}{1 + Ts} \tag{3-3}$$

A filter circuit is by definition one in which the output amplitude decreases to zero as the frequency increases. The general equation is

$$\frac{E_o}{E_1} = \frac{1}{1 + Ts} \tag{3-4}$$

The following design data are included.

1. Lag-filter
2. Lead-filter
3. Lead-lag (α lead $= \alpha$ lag)
4. Lead-lag (α lead $< \alpha$ lag)
5. Lead-lag (α lead $> \alpha$ lag)
6. Lead-lead

7. Lead-lead-lag
8. Lead-rate
9. Rate-filter
10. Rate-rate
11. Filter-filter

1. Lag-filter design

General relation:

$$\frac{E_o}{E_1} = \frac{1 + T_1 s}{(1 + \alpha T_1 s)(1 + T_2 s)}$$

Actual relation:

$$\frac{E_o}{E_1} = \frac{1 + R_3 C_1 s}{1 + [(R_1 + R_3)C_1 + (R_1 + R_2)C_2]s + (R_1 R_2 + R_2 R_3 + R_1 R_3)C_1 C_2 s^2}$$

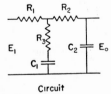

Circuit   Frequency Response   Response to
                                              Unit Step Input

Fig. 3-1.   Lag-filter.

Given T_1, T_2, and α; to solve, assume C_1 and C_2, then solve in the following order.

(1) $\quad R_3 = \dfrac{T_1}{C_1}$

(2) $\quad a = \dfrac{T_1 C_2(\alpha - 1)(T_2 - T_1) + \alpha T_1 T_2 C_1}{C_1 C_2}$

(select constants so a is positive)

(3) $\quad R_2 = \dfrac{\alpha T_1 + T_2 \pm \sqrt{(\alpha T_1 + T_2)^2 - 4aC_2}}{2C_2}$

(see Note 1)

(4) $\quad R_1 = \dfrac{T_1(\alpha - 1) + T_2 - R_2 C_2}{C_1 + C_2}$

Note 1: R_2 should not be too high as it can cause R_1 in (4) to be negative. Therefore, in order for the numerator of (4) to be positive,

$$R_2 \quad \text{must be less than} \quad [T_1(\alpha - 1) + T_2]/C_2$$

Note 2: If $R_1 C_2$ is appreciably smaller than either $(R_1 + R_3)C_1$ or $R_2 C_2$ and if $R_1 R_3$ is appreciably smaller than either $R_1 R_2$ or $R_2 R_3$, then $T_1 = R_3 C_1$, $\alpha = 1 + R_1/R_3$, $T_2 = R_2 C_2$.

2. Lead-filter design

General relation:
$$\frac{E_o}{E_1} = \frac{K(1 + \alpha T_1 s)}{(1 + T_1 s)(1 + T_2 s)}$$

Actual relation:
$$\frac{E_o}{E_1} = \frac{R_3(1 + R_1 C_1 s)}{R_1 + R_3 + (R_3 R_1 C_1 + R_1 R_2 C_2 + R_1 R_3 C_2 + R_3 R_2 C_2)s + R_3 R_1 C_1 R_2 C_2 s^2}$$

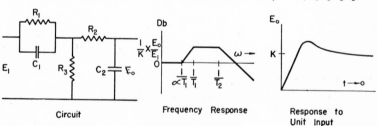

Circuit   Frequency Response   Response to Unit Input

FIG. 3-2. Lead-filter.

Given α, T_1, and T_2; to solve, assume R_1, and $\alpha K =$ some value less than one (in general a good value is $\alpha K = 0.9$). Then solve in order:

$$(1) \quad K = \frac{\text{(selected value)}}{\alpha}$$

$$(2) \quad R_2 = \frac{T_2 R_1}{(1 - \alpha K)(\alpha T_1 - T_2/K)}$$

$$(3) \quad R_3 = \frac{R_1 K}{1 - K}$$

$$(4) \quad C_1 = \frac{\alpha T_1}{R_1}$$

$$(5) \quad C_2 = \frac{T_2}{\alpha K R_2}$$

$$(6) \quad K = \frac{R_3}{R_1 + R_3}$$

Note: If C_2 is appreciably smaller than C_1 and if R_2 is appreciably larger than either R_1 or R_3, then $\alpha T_1 = R_1 C_1$, $\alpha = 1 + R_1/R_3$, $T_2 = R_2 C_2$.

3. Lead-lag (with α lead $= \alpha$ lag) design

(Good only when lag circuit is peaked at a lower frequency than the lead circuit.) General relation:

$$\frac{E_o}{E_i} = \frac{(1 + \alpha T_1 s)(1 + T_2 s)}{(1 + T_1 s)(1 + \alpha T_2 s)}$$

Actual relation:

$$\frac{E_o}{E_i} = \frac{(1 + R_1 C_1 s)(1 + R_2 C_2 s)}{1 + (R_1 C_1 + R_2 C_2 + R_1 C_2)s + R_1 R_2 C_1 C_2 s^2}$$

To solve; assume C_1 then $R_1 = \alpha T_1/C_1$,

$$C_2 = \frac{(\alpha - 1)(T_2 - T_1)}{\alpha T_1} C_1$$

$$R_2 = \frac{T_2}{C_2}$$

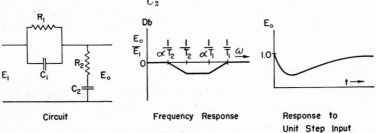

Circuit   Frequency Response   Response to
                                             Unit Step Input

FIG. 3-3.   Lead-lag (α lead $= \alpha$ lag).

4. Lead-lag (with α lead $<$ α lag) design

(Good only when lag circuit is peaked at a lower frequency than the lead circuit.) General relation:

$$\frac{E_o}{E_1} = \frac{(1 + \alpha_1 T_1 s)(1 + T_2 s)}{(1 + T_1 s)(1 + \alpha_2 T_2 s)}$$

Actual relation:

$$\frac{E_o}{E_1} = \frac{1 + (R_1 C_1 + R_3 C_1 + R_2 C_2)s + R_2 C_2(R_1 + R_3)C_1 s^2}{1 + (R_1 C_1 + R_3 C_1 + R_2 C_2 + R_1 C_2)s + [R_2 C_2(R_1 + R_3)C_1 + R_1 C_1 R_3 C_2]s^2}$$

Given α_1, α_2, T_1 and T_2; to solve, assume C_1, then solve for

$$a = T_2(\alpha_2 - 1) - T_1(\alpha_1 - 1)$$
$$b = (\alpha_1 - 1)(\alpha_2 T_2 - \alpha_1 T_1)$$

Then

$$R_1 = \frac{bT_1}{aC_1}$$

$$R_2 = \frac{R_1 T_2}{a}$$

$$R_3 = \frac{(\alpha_2 - \alpha_1)T_1 T_2}{aC_1}$$

$$C_2 = \frac{a^2 C_1}{bT_1}$$

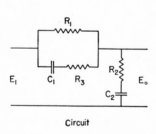

Circuit

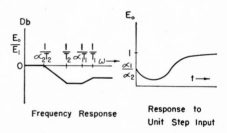

Frequency Response

Response to Unit Step Input

FIG. 3-4. Lead-lag (α lead $<$ α lag).

5. Lead-lag (with α lead $>$ α lag) design

(Good only when lag circuit is peaked at a lower frequency than the lead circuit.) General relation:

$$\frac{E_o}{E_1} = K \times \frac{(1 + \alpha_1 T_1 s)(1 + T_2 s)}{(1 + T_1 s)(1 + \alpha_2 T_2 s)}$$

Actual relation:

$$\frac{E_o}{E_1} = \frac{R_2 + R_3 + (R_1 R_3 C_1 + R_2 R_3 C_2 + R_1 R_2 C_1)s + R_1 R_2 R_3 C_1 C_2 s^2}{R_1 + R_2 + R_3 + (R_1 R_2 C_1 + R_1 R_3 C_1 + R_1 R_2 C_2 + R_2 R_3 C_2)s + R_1 R_2 R_3 C_1 C_2 s^2}$$

To solve, assume C_1; then

$$R_1 = \frac{\alpha_1 T_1}{C_1}$$

$$a = \alpha_2 T_2(\alpha_1 - 1) - \alpha_1 T_1(\alpha_2 - 1)$$

$$b = \alpha_2 \alpha_1{}^2 T_1(\alpha_2 - 1)(T_2 - T_1)$$

$$R_2 = \frac{b}{a(\alpha_1 - \alpha_2)C_1}$$

$$R_3 = \frac{\alpha_1 T_1 \alpha_2 T_2}{aC_1}$$

$$C_2 = \frac{a^2 C_1}{b}$$

$$K = \frac{R_2 + R_3}{R_1 + R_2 + R_3}$$

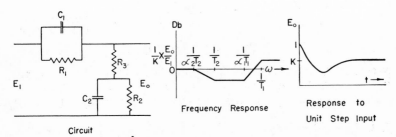

FIG. 3-5.   Lead-lag (α lead $>$ α lag).

6. Lead-lead design

General relation:

$$\frac{E_o}{E_1} = K \times \frac{(1 + \alpha_1 T_1 s)(1 + \alpha_2 T_2 s)}{(1 + T_1 s)(1 + T_2 s)}$$

Actual relation:

$$\frac{E_o}{E_1} = \frac{R_3 R_4(1 + R_1 C_1 s)(1 + R_2 C_2 s)}{\begin{aligned} & R_1 R_2 + R_1 R_3 + R_1 R_4 + R_2 R_3 + R_3 R_4 \\ & \quad + [(R_2 R_3 + R_3 R_4)R_1 C_1 + (R_1 R_3 + R_1 R_4 + R_3 R_4)R_2 C_2]s \\ & \quad\quad\quad\quad\quad\quad\quad\quad\quad\quad\quad + R_1 R_2 R_3 R_4 C_1 C_2 s^2 \end{aligned}}$$

Given α_1, α_2, T_1, and T_2; to solve, assume C_1; then $R_1 = \alpha_1 T_1/C_1$; assume C_2, then $R_2 = \alpha_2 T_2/C_2$; then solve in order.

$$a = R_1\alpha_1(\alpha_2 T_2 - T_1)(\alpha_2 - 1) + R_2\alpha_2(\alpha_1 T_1 - T_2)(\alpha_1 - 1)$$
$$b = R_1 R_2\alpha_2(2T_2 - \alpha_1 T_1 - \alpha_1 T_2)$$
$$c = R_1{}^2 R_2\alpha_2 T_2$$

Note 1. a and b may be negative.

$$R_3 = \frac{-b \pm \sqrt{b^2 - 4ac}}{2a}$$

$$R_4 = \frac{R_1\alpha_2 T_2 + R_2\alpha_1 T_1}{\alpha_1 T_1(\alpha_2 - 1) + \alpha_2 T_2(\alpha_1 - 1) - R_1\alpha_2 T_2/R_3}$$

$$K = \frac{1}{\alpha_1\alpha_2}$$

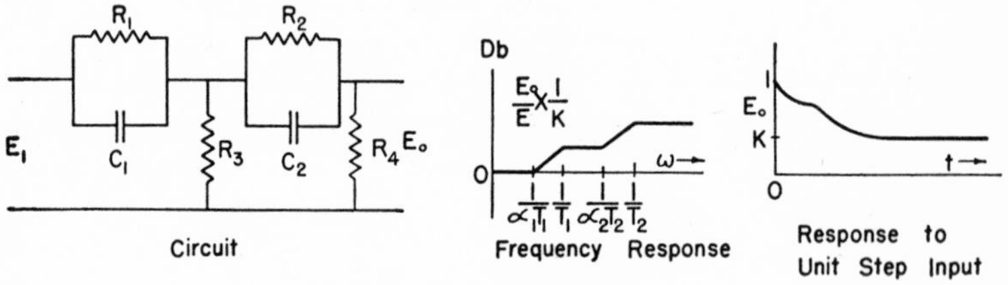

Circuit   Frequency Response   Response to Unit Step Input

Fig. 3-6.   Lead-lead.

Note 2. If R_1 and R_3 are both appreciably larger than either R_2 or R_4, if C_2 is appreciably larger than C_1, and if $R_2 C_2$ is appreciably larger than $R_4 C_1$, then $\alpha_1 T_1 = R_1 C_1$, $\alpha_1 = 1 + R_1/R_3$, $\alpha_2 T_2 = R_2 C_2$, $\alpha_2 = 1 + R_2/R_4$.

7. Lead-lead-lag design

(Good only when the lag circuit is peaked at a lower frequency than either lead circuit, and when α_3 is between α_1 and α_2.) General relation:

$$\frac{E_o}{E_1} = K\frac{(1 + \alpha_1 T_1 s)(1 + \alpha_2 T_2 s)(1 + T_3 s)}{(1 + T_1 s)(1 + T_2 s)(1 + \alpha_3 T_3 s)}$$

Actual relation:

$$\frac{E_o}{E_1} = \frac{R_3(1 + R_1 C_1 s)(1 + R_2 C_2 s)(1 + R_4 C_4 s)}{\begin{aligned}&R_1+R_3+[(R_1 R_2+R_2 R_3)(C_2+C_4)+R_1 R_3(C_1+C_4)+(R_1+R_3)R_4 C_4]s\\&+[R_1 R_2 R_3(C_1 C_2+C_1 C_4+C_2 C_4)+R_4 C_4(R_1 R_2 C_2+R_1 R_3 C_1+R_2 R_3 C_2)]s^2\\&+R_1 C_1 R_2 C_2 R_3 R_4 C_4 s^3\end{aligned}}$$

Given α_1, α_2, α_3, T_1, T_2, and T_3; to solve, assume C_1, then solve the following.

$$R_1 = \frac{\alpha_1 T_1}{C_1}$$

$$K = \frac{\alpha_3}{\alpha_1 \alpha_2} = \frac{R_3}{R_1 + R_2}$$

$$R_3 = \frac{\alpha_3}{\alpha_1 \alpha_2 - \alpha_3} R_1$$

$$a = T_1 T_2 + \alpha_3 T_3 (T_1 + T_2)$$

$$b = T_1(1 - K\alpha_1) + T_2(1 - \alpha_2) + T_3(\alpha_3 - 1)$$

$$c = \alpha_2 T_2 T_3 + K\alpha_1 T_1 (T_3 + \alpha_2 T_2)$$

$$R_2 = \frac{K(b\alpha_2 T_2 + c - a)}{a - bK\alpha_1 T_1 - c}$$

$$C_2 = \frac{\alpha_2 T_2}{R_2} \qquad C_4 = \frac{b}{R_2 + KR_1} \qquad R_4 = \frac{T_3}{C_4}$$

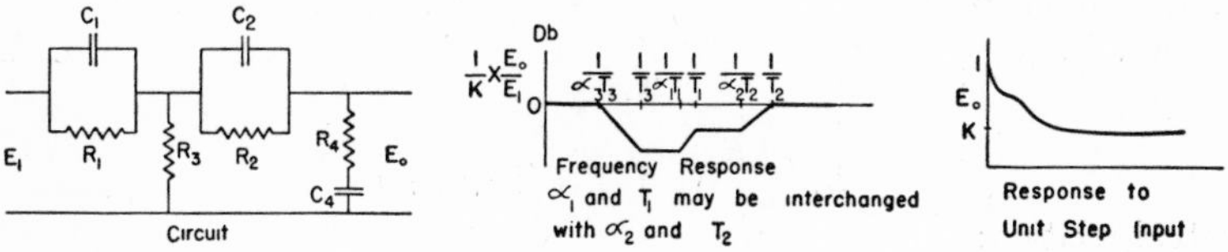

Circuit

Frequency Response
α_1 and T_1 may be interchanged
with α_2 and T_2

Response to
Unit Step Input

FIG. 3-7.   Lead-lead-lag.

8. Lead-rate design

General relation:

$$\frac{E_o}{E_1} = K \times \frac{s(1 + \alpha_1 T_1 s)}{(1 + T_1 s)(1 + T_2 s)}$$

Actual relation:

$$\frac{E_o}{E_1} = \frac{R_3 R_4 C_2 s (1 + R_1 C_1 s)}{R_1 + R_3 + (R_1 R_3 C_1 + R_1 R_3 C_2 + R_1 R_4 C_2 + R_3 R_4 C_2)s + R_1 R_3 R_4 C_1 C_2 s^2}$$

Given α, T_1, and T_2; to solve assume values for C_1 and C_2; then solve

$$R_1 = \frac{\alpha T_1}{C_1}$$

$$R_4 = \frac{T_1 + T_2 \pm \sqrt{(T_1 - T_2)^2 - 4C_2 T_1 T_2 / C_1}}{2C_2}$$

$$R_3 = \frac{\alpha T_1 T_2}{C_1(\alpha R_4 C_2 - T_2)}$$

$$K = \frac{R_3 R_4 C_2}{R_1 + R_3}$$

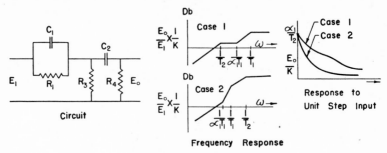

FIG. 3-8.   Lead-rate.

Note: If R_1 and R_3 are both appreciably smaller than R_4 and if C_2 is appreciably smaller than C_1, then $\alpha T_1 = R_1 C_1$, $\alpha = 1 + R_1/R_3$, $T_2 = R_4 C_2$, $K = R_3 R_4 C_2/(R_1 + R_3)$.

9. Rate-filter design

General relation:

$$\frac{E_o}{E_i} = K \frac{s}{(1 + T_1 s)(1 + T_2 s)}$$

Actual relation:

$$\frac{E_o}{E_i} = \frac{R_1 C_1 s}{1 + (R_1 C_1 + R_1 C_2 + R_2 C_2)s + R_1 R_2 C_1 C_2 s^2}$$

Given T_1 and T_2; to solve, assume C_1 and C_2; then solve the following.

$$R_2 = \frac{T_1 + T_2 \pm \sqrt{(T_1 - T_2)^2 - 4T_1 T_2 C_2/C_1}}{2C_2}$$

$$R_1 = \frac{T_1 T_2}{R_2 C_1 C_2}$$

$$K = R_1 C_1$$

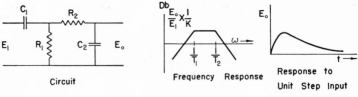

FIG. 3-9.   Rate-filter.

Note: If $R_1 C_2$ is appreciably smaller than either $R_1 C_1$ or $R_2 C_2$, then $T_1 = R_1 C_1$, $T_2 = R_2 C_2$.

10. Rate-rate design

(Good only when T_1 and T_2 have not the same value.) General relation:

$$\frac{E_o}{E_1} = \frac{Ks^2}{(1 + T_1s)(1 + T_2s)}$$

Actual relation:

$$\frac{E_o}{E_1} = \frac{R_1C_1R_2C_2s^2}{1 + (R_1C_2 + R_1C_1 + R_2C_2)s + R_1C_1R_2C_2s^2}$$

Given T_1 and T_2; to solve, assume values for C_1 and C_2; then solve the following.

$$R_1 = \frac{T_1 + T_2 \pm \sqrt{(T_1 + T_2)^2 - 4T_1T_2(1 + C_2/C_1)}}{2(C_1 + C_2)}$$

$$R_2 = \frac{T_1T_2}{R_1C_1C_2}$$

$$K = T_1T_2$$

Note: If R_1C_2 is appreciably smaller than either R_1C_1 or R_2C_2, then $T_1 = R_1C_1$, $T_2 = R_2C_2$.

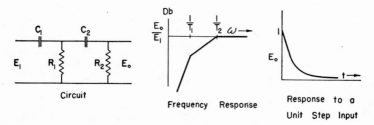

Fig. 3-10.　Rate-rate.

11. Filter-filter design

(Good only when T_1 and T_2 have not the same value.) General relation:

$$\frac{E_o}{E_1} = \frac{1}{(1 + T_1s)(1 + T_2s)}$$

Actual relation:

$$\frac{E_o}{E_1} = \frac{1}{1 + (R_1C_1 + R_1C_2 + R_2C_2)s + R_1C_1R_2C_2s^2}$$

Given T_1 and T_2; to solve, assume values for R_1 and R_2; then solve the following.

$$C_2 = \frac{T_1 + T_2 \pm \sqrt{(T_1 + T_2)^2 - 4T_1T_2(R_1 + R_2)/R_2}}{2(R_1 + R_2)}$$

$$C_1 = \frac{T_1 T_2}{R_1 R_2 C_2}$$

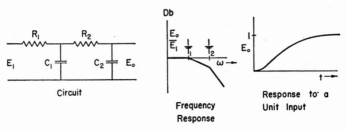

Circuit   Frequency Response   Response to a Unit Input

FIG. 3-11.   Filter-filter.

Note: If R_1C_2 is appreciably smaller than either R_1C_1 or R_2C_2, then $T_1 = R_1C_1$, $T_2 = R_2C_2$.

APPENDIX 4

COMPLEX NUMBERS

Forms

An imaginary number occurs in taking the square root of a negative real number. Thus $\sqrt{-4}$ is an imaginary number, and is usually written as $2\sqrt{-1}$ or $2j$, where $j = \sqrt{-1}$.

A complex number is one containing both real and imaginary parts. An example is $3 + j4$. Complex numbers may be expressed in the following forms:

1. Rectangular form, $a + jb$ (example is $3 + j4$).

2. Polar form, $A\angle\phi$, (the same example is $5\angle53.1°$).

3. Exponential form, $A\epsilon^{j\phi}$, (the same example is $5\epsilon^{j0.93}$), where the angle ϕ is measured in radians.

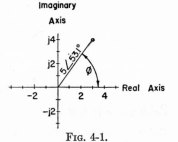

FIG. 4-1.

The polar and rectangular forms are shown graphically in Fig. 4-1. The exponential form may be shown by comparing Maclaurin series expansions for $\epsilon^{j\phi}$ with those for $\cos\phi$ and $j\sin\phi$. In summary,

$$a \pm jb = A\angle\pm\phi = A\epsilon^{\pm j\phi} = A(\cos\phi \pm j\sin\phi),$$

where $A = \sqrt{a^2 + b^2}$.

Addition and subtraction

Addition and subtraction are performed by expressing the complex numbers in the rectangular form and adding or subtracting the real and imaginary parts. Examples:

$$5\angle53.1° + 10\angle36.9° = 3 + j4 + 8 + j6 = 11 + j10 = 14.9\angle42.3°$$

$$5\angle-53.1° + 10\angle36.9° = 3 - j4 + 8 + j6 = 11 + j2 = 11.2\angle10.3°$$

$$5\angle53.1° - 10\angle36.9° = 3 + j4 - 8 - j6 = -5 - j2 = 5.4\angle201.8°$$

$$A_1\angle\phi_1 + A_2\angle\phi_2 = a_1 + jb_1 + a_2 + jb_2 = (a_1 + a_2) + j(b_1 + b_2)$$

Multiplication

Multiplication of complex numbers may be done rather simply by expressing the numbers in either the exponential or polar form. The result is the
product of the amplitudes and the sum of the phase angles. Examples:

$$(5\angle 53.1°)(10\angle 36.9°) = 50\angle 90°$$
$$(5\angle -53.1°)(10\angle 36.9°) = 50\angle -16.2°$$
$$(3\epsilon^{j2})(2\epsilon^{-j}) = 6\epsilon^{j}$$
$$A_1\angle \phi_1 A_2\angle \phi_2 = A_1 A_2\angle \phi_1 + \phi_2$$

Division

Division is similar to multiplication. The amplitudes are divided, and the
denominator phase angle is subtracted from the numerator phase angle
when the numbers are expressed in either the polar or exponential form.
Examples:

$$\frac{5\angle 53.1°}{10\angle 36.9°} = 0.5\angle 16.2°$$
$$\frac{5\epsilon^{j2}}{2\epsilon^{-j3}} = 2.5\epsilon^{j5}$$
$$\frac{A_1\angle \phi_1}{A_2\angle \phi_2} = \frac{A_1}{A_2}\angle \phi_1 - \phi_2$$

Raising to a power

Raising a complex number to a power is a special form of multiplication.
The amplitude is raised to the desired power and the phase is multiplied
by the power. Examples:

$$(5\angle 53.1°)^2 = 25\angle 106.2°$$
$$(5\angle -53.1°)^3 = 125\angle -159.3°$$
$$(5\angle -53.1°)^{\frac{1}{2}} = 2.24\angle -26.55° \text{ and } 2.24\angle -206.55°$$
$$(A_1\angle \phi_1)^n = A_1{}^n\angle n\phi_1$$

Logarithm

The logarithm to the base ϵ of a complex number is found by expressing
the number in the exponential form. The result is a complex number, the
real part being the logarithm of the amplitude, and the imaginary part
being the phase angle in radians. Examples:

$$\ln 5\epsilon^{j2} = \ln 5 + \ln \epsilon^{j2} = \ln 5 + j2$$
$$\ln 5\epsilon^{-j2} = \ln 5 + \ln \epsilon^{-j2} = \ln 5 - j2$$
$$\ln A_1\epsilon^{j\phi_1} = \ln A_1 + j\phi_1$$

APPENDIX 5

DERIVATION OF THE NYQUIST CRITERION

The Nyquist stability criterion was developed in 1932 by H. Nyquist at the Bell Laboratories. It originally was an application of one of Cauchy's mathematical theorems to feedback amplifier design, but it is ideally suited to many other related problems, one of which is automatic control design.

Given any $F(s)$ which has no singularities other than poles within a particular closed contour, the poles and zeros of $F(s)$ inside the contour are related by the theorem.

$$\oint \frac{F'(s)}{F(s)}\, ds = 2\pi j (P - Z) \tag{5-1}$$

where $\oint$ indicates integration about the particular closed contour, $F'(s)$ is the derivative of $F(s)$ with respect to s, $j = \sqrt{-1}$, P = number of poles of $F(s)$ inside the contour, Z = number of zeros of $F(s)$ inside the contour.

Since the foregoing statement involved a number of terms which have special mathematical meaning, they will be defined. A singularity is a value that s may have so that $F(s)$ is not analytic; $F(s)$ is analytic if it satisfies the Cauchy-Riemann equations,

$$\frac{\partial u}{\partial \sigma} = \frac{\partial v}{\partial \omega}, \qquad \frac{\partial u}{\partial \omega} = \frac{-\partial v}{\partial \sigma} \tag{5-2}$$

where u is the real part of $F(s)$ with $s = \sigma + j\omega$, v is the imaginary part of $F(s)$ with $s = \sigma + j\omega$. For example, if

$$F(s) = \frac{s + 5}{s + 4} \tag{5-3}$$

then

$$F(\sigma + j\omega) = \frac{\sigma + j\omega + 5}{\sigma + j\omega + 4} = u + jv \tag{5-4}$$

where

$$u = \frac{\sigma^2 + \omega^2 + 20 + 9\sigma}{(\sigma + 4)^2 + \omega^2}$$

$$v = \frac{-\omega}{(\sigma + 4)^2 + \omega^2}$$

The Cauchy-Riemann equations are satisfied, since

367

$$\frac{\partial u}{\partial \sigma} = \frac{\partial v}{\partial \omega} = \frac{\omega^2 - \sigma^2 - 8\sigma - 16}{[(\sigma + 4)^2 + \omega^2]^2} \tag{5-5}$$

$$\frac{\partial u}{\partial \sigma} = \frac{-\partial v}{\partial \omega} = \frac{-2\omega(\sigma + 4)}{[(\sigma + 4)^2 + \omega^2]^2} \tag{5-6}$$

However, at the point $s = -4$ ($\sigma = -4$ and $\omega = 0$) both (5-5) and (5-6) are indeterminate, and therefore (5-3) is analytic at all points except $s = -4$. A pole is any denominator root of $F(s)$. If s is equal to a pole, which would be $s = -4$ in (5-3), then $F(s) = \infty$. In this particular application all poles are singularities. This is true in any application that involves rational functions. A zero is any numerator root of $F(s)$. If s is equal to a zero, which would be $s = -5$ in (5-3), then $F(s) = 0$. The closed contour may be any completely enclosed contour in the s-plane. The particular contour which is used for the Nyquist criterion is shown in Fig. 5.30-2.

A simplified proof of (5-1) can be shown by the following considerations. Let $F(s)$ have a zero of nth order at $s = a$, where a is inside the contour of integration, and let there be no other zeros or poles inside the contour. Then

$$F(s) = (s - a)^n G(s) \tag{5-7}$$

$$F'(s) = n(s - a)^{n-1}G(s) + (s - a)^n G'(s) \tag{5-8}$$

$$\frac{F'(s)}{F(s)} = \frac{n}{s - a} + \frac{G'(s)}{G(s)} \tag{5-9}$$

$$\oint \frac{F'(s)}{F(s)} \, ds = \oint \frac{n}{s - a} \, ds + \oint \frac{G'(s)}{G(s)} \, ds \tag{5-10}$$

where $G(s)$ is the factor of $F(s)$ which has neither poles nor zeros inside the contour of integration. By the calculus of residues,

$$\oint \frac{n}{s - a} \, ds = -2\pi n j \tag{5-11}$$

when a is inside the contour. Similarly, $G'(s)/G(s)$ can be factored into partial fractions so that

$$\frac{G'(s)}{G(s)} = \frac{G'(s)}{(s + b_1)(s + b_2)(s + b_3) \ldots} \tag{5-12}$$

$$= \frac{A_1}{s + b_1} + \frac{A_2}{s + b_2} + \ldots \tag{5-13}$$

Again, by the calculus of residues,

$$\oint \frac{A_1}{s + b_1} \, ds = \oint \frac{A_2}{s + b_2} \, ds = \ldots = 0 \tag{5-14}$$

when b_1, b_2, etc. are not inside the contour of integration. Substituting (5-14) and (5-11) in (5-10) gives (5-1) for $P = 0$ and $Z = n$.

If both zeros and poles are present inside the contour of integration, so that the form is

$$F(s) = \frac{(s - a)^{n_1}(s - b)^{n_2}}{(s - c)^{n_3}(s - d)^{n_4}} \, G(s) \tag{5-15}$$

where a is a zero inside the contour of order n_1, b is a zero inside the contour of order n_2, c is a pole inside the contour of order n_3, d is a pole inside the contour of order n_4, $G(s)$ is the remaining factor which has neither poles nor zeros inside the contour, and the ratio to be integrated is

$$\frac{F'(s)}{F(s)} = \frac{n_1}{s - a} + \frac{n_2}{s - b} - \frac{n_3}{s - c} - \frac{n_4}{s - d} + \frac{G'(s)}{G(s)} \tag{5-16}$$

The result is

$$\oint \frac{F'(s)}{F(s)} ds = -2\pi j(n_1 + n_2 - n_3 - n_4) \tag{5-17}$$

which is the same as (5-1) where P is the total number of poles ($n_3 + n_4$) inside the contour, and Z is the total number of zeros ($n_1 + n_2$) inside the contour.

The preceding results may be interpreted by utilizing the properties of complex numbers. First, let

$$H(s) = \ln F(s) \tag{5-18}$$

where ln denotes the logarithm to the base ϵ. Then

$$\frac{dH(s)}{ds} = \frac{1}{F(s)} \frac{dF(s)}{ds} = \frac{F'(s)}{F(s)} \tag{5-19}$$

and (5-1) can be written

$$\oint \frac{F'(s)}{F(s)} ds = \oint \frac{d[\ln F(s)]}{ds} \, ds = 2\pi j(P - Z) \tag{5-20}$$

Since the logarithm of a complex number (see Appendix 4) is

$$\ln F(s) = \ln |F(s)| + j\phi = A + j\phi \tag{5-21}$$

(5-20) becomes

$$\oint dA + \oint j \, d\phi = 2\pi j(P - Z) \tag{5-22}$$

The first integral is zero since the amplitude of $\ln F(s)$ is the same at the beginning and end of the contour. Equation (5-22) then reduces to

$$\phi_2 - \phi_1 = 2\pi(P - Z) \quad \text{radians} \tag{5-23}$$

where ϕ_1 and ϕ_2 are the initial and final values of ϕ, and ϕ is the phase angle of $F(s)$ as s assumes the span of values over the contour of integration.

Since one revolution is 2π radians, and since P and Z are always integers, the relation in its final form is

$$N = P - Z \qquad (5\text{-}24)$$

where N is the number of encirclements of the origin which the $F(s)$ locus makes as it assumes values of s along the s-plane contour of integration (N is positive when encirclement is counterclockwise as s assumes clockwise values of the s-plane contour), P is the number of poles inside the s-plane contour of integration, Z is the number of zeros inside the s-plane contour of integration.

Thus (5-24) provides a valuable relation betwen the poles, zeros, and phase of $F(s)$. Knowing any two, the third may be found. The result is rigorous, and applies to all rational fractions in s, which are of the type used in control analysis. Chapter 5 discusses the application of (5-24) to analysis problems.

APPENDIX 6

LAPLACE TRANSFORM OPERATIONS AND PAIRS

OPERATIONS

No.	Name	$f(t)$	$F(s)$
1	Linearity Multiplication by a constant Addition	$Kf(t)$ $f_1(t) + f_2(t)$	$KF(s)$ $F_1(s) + F_2(s)$
2	Differentiation	$\dfrac{d}{dt}f(t)$	$sF(s) - f(0^+)$
3	Integration	$\int f(t)\,dt$	$\dfrac{F(s)}{s} + \dfrac{f^{(-1)}(0^+)}{s}$
4	Delayed function	$f(t-a)$ where $f(t-a) = 0$ for $0 < t < a$	$\epsilon^{-as}F(s)$ where $F(s) = \mathcal{L}f(t)$
5	Time scale change	$f(at)$	$\dfrac{F(s/a)}{a}$
6	Initial value	$\lim_{t\to 0} f(t) = \lim_{s\to\infty} sF(s)$	
7	Final value	$\lim_{t\to\infty} f(t) = \lim_{s\to 0} sF(s)$	

$$\to \int_{t=0}^{} \iota\, dt$$
$$\frac{}{s}$$

$$E = \frac{1}{C}\int \iota\, dt$$
$$E = L\frac{di}{dt}$$

$$q = \frac{di}{dt}$$
$$E = q/c$$
$$E = qL$$

371

LAPLACE TRANSFORM PAIRS

Eq. No.*	$F(s)$	$f(t)$ $0 \leq t$
00.000	1	unit impulse at $t = 0$
00.001	$\dfrac{1}{1 + 2\zeta s/\omega_1 + s^2/\omega_1^2}$	$\dfrac{\omega_1}{\sqrt{1-\zeta^2}}\,\epsilon^{-\zeta\omega_1 t}\sin\omega_1\sqrt{1-\zeta^2}\,t$
00.001	$\dfrac{1}{1 + s^2/\omega_1^2}$	$\omega_1 \sin\omega_1 t$
00.002	$\dfrac{1}{(1 + 2\zeta_1 s/\omega_1 + s^2/\omega_1^2)(1 + 2\zeta_2 s/\omega_2 + s^2/\omega_2^2)}$	$\dfrac{\omega_1\omega_2^2\,\epsilon^{-\zeta_1\omega_1 t}\sin(\omega_1\sqrt{1-\zeta_1^2}\,t - \psi_1)}{\sqrt{1-\zeta_1^2}\,(A^2 + 4AB\zeta_1\omega_1 + 4B^2\omega_1^2)^{1/2}}$ $+\dfrac{\omega_1^2\omega_2\,\epsilon^{-\zeta_2\omega_2 t}\sin(\omega_2\sqrt{1-\zeta_2^2}\,t - \psi_2)}{\sqrt{1-\zeta_2^2}\,(A^2 + 4AB\zeta_2\omega_2 + 4B^2\omega_2^2)^{1/2}}$ where $A = \omega_1^2 - \omega_2^2$, $B = \zeta_2\omega_2 - \zeta_1\omega_1$ $\psi_1 = \tan^{-1}\dfrac{2B\omega_1\sqrt{1-\zeta_1^2}}{-A - 2B\zeta_1\omega_1}$, $\psi_2 = -\tan^{-1}\dfrac{2B\omega_2\sqrt{1-\zeta_2^2}}{A + 2B\zeta_2\omega_2}$
00.002	$\dfrac{1}{(1 + s^2/\omega_1^2)(1 + 2\zeta s/\omega_2 + s^2/\omega_2^2)}$	$\dfrac{\omega_1^2\omega_2^2}{[(\omega_2^2 - \omega_1^2)^2 + 4\zeta^2\omega_1^2\omega_2^2]^{1/2}}\left[\dfrac{1}{\omega_1}\sin(\omega_1 t - \psi_1)\right.$ $\left.+\dfrac{1}{\omega_2\sqrt{1-\zeta^2}}\,\epsilon^{-\zeta\omega_2 t}\sin(\omega_2\sqrt{1-\zeta^2}\,t - \psi_2)\right]$ where $\psi_1 = \tan^{-1}\dfrac{2\zeta\omega_1\omega_2}{\omega_2^2 - \omega_1^2}$, $\psi_2 = \tan^{-1}\dfrac{-2\zeta\omega_2^2\sqrt{1-\zeta^2}}{\omega_1^2 - \omega_2^2(1 - 2\zeta^2)}$
00.002	$\dfrac{1}{(1 + s^2/\omega_1^2)(1 + s^2/\omega_2^2)}$	$\dfrac{\omega_1\omega_2}{\omega_1^2 - \omega_2^2}(\omega_1\sin\omega_2 t - \omega_2\sin\omega_1 t)$
00.002	$\dfrac{1}{(1 + 2\zeta s/\omega_1 + s^2/\omega_1^2)^2}$	$\dfrac{\omega_1}{2(1-\zeta^2)^{3/2}}\,\epsilon^{-\zeta\omega_1 t}(\sin\omega_1\sqrt{1-\zeta^2}\,t - \omega_1\sqrt{1-\zeta^2}\,t\cos\omega_1\sqrt{1-\zeta^2}\,t)$

00.002	$1/(1 + s^2/\omega_1^2)^2$	$(\omega_1/2)(\sin \omega_1 t - \omega_1 t \cos \omega_1 t)$
00.0n0	$\dfrac{1}{(1 + Ts)^n}$	$\dfrac{1}{T^n(n-1)!}\, t^{n-1}\epsilon^{-t/T}$
00.010	$1/(1 + Ts)$	$(1/T)\,\epsilon^{-t/T}$
00.011	$\dfrac{1}{(1 + Ts)(1 + 2\zeta s/\omega_1 + s^2/\omega_1^2)}$	$\dfrac{T\omega_1^2\epsilon^{-t/T}}{1 - 2\zeta T\omega_1 + T^2\omega_1^2} + \dfrac{\omega_1\epsilon^{-\zeta\omega_1 t}\sin(\omega_1\sqrt{1 - \zeta^2}\,t - \psi)}{[(1 - \zeta^2)(1 - 2\zeta T\omega_1 + T^2\omega_1^2)]^{1/2}}$ where $\psi = \tan^{-1}\dfrac{T\omega_1\sqrt{1 - \zeta^2}}{1 - T\zeta\omega_1}$
00.011	$\dfrac{1}{(1 + Ts)(1 + s^2/\omega_1^2)}$	$\dfrac{T\omega_1^2}{1 + T^2\omega_1^2}\,\epsilon^{-t/T} + \dfrac{\omega_1\sin(\omega_1 t - \psi)}{(1 + T^2\omega_1^2)^{1/2}}$ where $\psi = \tan^{-1} T\omega_1$
00.020	$\dfrac{1}{(1 + T_1 s)(1 + T_2 s)}$	$\dfrac{1}{T_1 - T_2}(\epsilon^{-t/T_1} - \epsilon^{-t/T_2})$
00.020	$\dfrac{1}{(1 + Ts)^2}$	$\left(\dfrac{1}{T^2}\right) t\epsilon^{-t/T}$
00.020	$1/(1 - s^2/\omega_1^2)$	$-\omega_1 \sinh \omega_1 t$
00.021	$\dfrac{1}{(1 + T_1 s)(1 + T_2 s)}$ $(1 + 2\zeta s/\omega_1 + s^2/\omega_1^2)$	$\dfrac{T_1^2\omega_1^2}{(T_1 - T_2)(1 - 2\zeta T_1\omega_1 + T_1^2\omega_1^2)}\,\epsilon^{-t/T_1}$ $+\ \dfrac{T_2^2\omega_1^2}{(T_2 - T_1)(1 - 2\zeta T_2\omega_1 + T_2^2\omega_1^2)}\,\epsilon^{-t/T_2}$ $+\ \dfrac{\omega_1\epsilon^{-\zeta\omega_1 t}\sin(\omega_1\sqrt{1 - \zeta^2}\,t - \psi)}{[(1 - 2\zeta T_1\omega_1 + T_1^2\omega_1^2)(1 - 2\zeta T_2\omega_1 + T_2^2\omega_1^2)]^{1/2}}$ where $\psi = \tan^{-1}\dfrac{T_1\omega_1\sqrt{1 - \zeta^2}}{1 - T_1\zeta\omega_1} + \tan^{-1}\dfrac{T_2\omega_1\sqrt{1 - \zeta^2}}{1 - T_2\zeta\omega_1}$

* See Section 3.30.

LAPLACE TRANSFORM PAIRS (*Continued*)

Eq. No.*	$F(s)$	$f(t)$	$0 \leq t$
00.021	$\dfrac{1}{(1+T_1 s)(1+T_2 s)(1+s^2/\omega_1^2)}$	$\dfrac{T_1^2\omega_1^2\epsilon^{-t/T_1}}{(T_1-T_2)(1+T_1^2\omega_1^2)} + \dfrac{T_2^2\omega_1^2\epsilon^{-t/T_2}}{(T_2-T_1)(1+T_2^2\omega_1^2)} + \dfrac{\omega_1\sin(\omega_1 t-\psi)}{[(1+T_1^2\omega_1^2)(1+T_2^2\omega_1^2)]^{1/2}}$ where $\psi = \tan^{-1}T_1\omega_1 + \tan^{-1}T_2\omega_1$	
00.021	$\dfrac{1}{(1+Ts)^2(1+2\zeta s/\omega_1 + s^2/\omega_1^2)}$	$\dfrac{\omega_1^2}{1-2T\zeta\omega_1+T^2\omega_1^2}\left[t\epsilon^{-t/T} + \dfrac{2T(1-T\zeta\omega_1)}{1-2T_1\zeta\omega_1+T^2\omega_1^2}\epsilon^{-t/T} + \dfrac{1}{\omega_1\sqrt{1-\zeta^2}}\epsilon^{-\zeta\omega_1 t}\sin(\omega_1\sqrt{1-\zeta^2}\,t-\psi) \right]$ where $\psi = 2\tan^{-1}\dfrac{T\omega_1\sqrt{1-\zeta^2}}{1-T\zeta\omega_1}$	
00.021	$\dfrac{1}{(1+Ts)^2(1+s^2/\omega_1^2)}$	$\dfrac{\omega_1}{1+T^2\omega_1^2}\sin(\omega_1 t-\psi) + \left[\dfrac{\omega_1^2}{1+T^2\omega_1^2}t + \dfrac{2T\omega_1^2}{(1+T^2\omega_1^2)^2}\right]\epsilon^{-t/T}$ where $\psi = 2\tan^{-1}T\omega_1$	
00.030	$\dfrac{1}{(1+T_1 s)(1+T_2 s)(1+T_3 s)}$	$\dfrac{T_1}{(T_1-T_2)(T_1-T_3)}\epsilon^{-t/T_1} + \dfrac{T_2}{(T_2-T_1)(T_2-T_3)}\epsilon^{-t/T_2} + \dfrac{T_3}{(T_3-T_1)(T_3-T_2)}\epsilon^{-t/T_3}$	
00.030	$\dfrac{1}{(1+T_1 s)(1+T_2 s)^2}$	$\dfrac{T_1}{(T_2-T_1)^2}\epsilon^{-t/T_1} + \dfrac{(T_2-T_1)t - T_1T_2}{T_2(T_2-T_1)^2}\epsilon^{-t/T_2}$	
00.030	$\dfrac{1}{(1+Ts)^3}$	$\dfrac{1}{2T^3}t^2\epsilon^{-t/T}$	

00.031	$$\frac{1}{(1 + T_1 s)(1 + T_2 s)(1 + T_3 s)(1 + s^2/\omega_1^2)}$$	$$\frac{T_1^3\omega_1^2\epsilon^{-t/T_1}}{(T_1 - T_2)(T_1 - T_3)(1 + T_1^2\omega_1^2)} + \frac{T_2^3\omega_1^2\epsilon^{-t/T_2}}{(T_2 - T_1)(T_2 - T_3)(1 + T_2^2\omega_1^2)}$$ $$+ \frac{T_3^3\omega_1^2\epsilon^{-t/T_3}}{(T_3 - T_1)(T_3 - T_2)(1 + T_3^2\omega_1^2)}$$ $$+ \frac{\omega_1 \sin(\omega_1 t - \psi)}{[(1 + T_1^2\omega_1^2)(1 + T_2^2\omega_2^2)(1 + T_3^2\omega_1^2)]^{1/2}}$$ where $\psi = \tan^{-1}T_1\omega_1 + \tan^{-1}T_2\omega_1 + \tan^{-1}T_3\omega_1$

00.n00	$$\frac{1}{s^n}$$	$\dfrac{1}{(n-1)!}\,t^{n-1}$ when n is a positive integer
00.100	$$\frac{1}{s}$$	1
00.101	$$\frac{1}{s(1 + 2\zeta s/\omega_1 + s^2/\omega_1^2)}$$	$1 + \dfrac{1}{\sqrt{1 - \zeta^2}}\,\epsilon^{\zeta\omega_1 t}\sin(\omega_1\sqrt{1-\zeta^2}\,t - \psi)$ where $\psi = \tan^{-1}\dfrac{\sqrt{1-\zeta^2}}{-\zeta}$
00.101	$$\frac{1}{s(1 + s^2/\omega_1^2)}$$	$1 - \cos\omega_1 t$
00.102	$$\frac{1}{s(1 + 2\zeta_1 s/\omega_1 + s^2/\omega_1^2)(1 + 2\zeta_2 s/\omega_2 + s^2/\omega_2^2)}$$	$$1 + \frac{\omega_2^2\epsilon^{-\zeta_1\omega_1 t}\sin(\omega_1\sqrt{1-\zeta_1^2}\,t - \psi_1)}{\sqrt{1-\zeta_1^2}(A^2 + 4AB\zeta_1\omega_1 + 4B^2\omega_1^2)^{1/2}}$$ $$+ \frac{\omega_1^2\epsilon^{-\zeta_2\omega_2 t}\sin(\omega_2\sqrt{1-\zeta_2^2}\,t - \psi_2)}{\sqrt{1-\zeta_2^2}(A^2 + 4AB\zeta_2\omega_2 + 4B^2\omega_2^2)^{1/2}}$$ where $A = \omega_1^2 - \omega_2^2,\quad B = \zeta_2\omega_2 - \zeta_1\omega_1$ $$\psi_1 = \tan^{-1}\frac{\sqrt{1-\zeta_1^2}}{-\zeta_1} + \tan^{-1}\frac{2B\omega_1\sqrt{1-\zeta_1^2}}{-A - 2B\zeta_1\omega_1}$$ $$\psi_2 = \tan^{-1}\frac{\sqrt{1-\zeta_2^2}}{-\zeta_2} - \tan^{-1}\frac{2B\omega_2\sqrt{1-\zeta_2^2}}{A + 2B\zeta_2\omega_2}$$

* See Section 3.30.

LAPLACE TRANSFORM PAIRS (*Continued*)

Eq. No.*	$F(s)$	$f(t)$ $0 \leq t$
00.102	$\dfrac{1}{s(1 + s^2/\omega_1^2)(1 + 2\zeta s/\omega_2 + s^2/\omega_2^2)}$	$1 + \dfrac{1}{[(\omega_1^2 - \omega_2^2)^2 + 4\zeta^2\omega_1^2\omega_2^2]^{1/2}}\left[\dfrac{\omega_1^2\epsilon^{-\zeta\omega_2 t}\sin(\omega_2\sqrt{1-\zeta^2}\,t - \psi_2)}{\sqrt{1-\zeta^2}} - \omega_2^2\cos(\omega_1 t - \psi_1)\right]$ where $\psi_1 = \tan^{-1}\dfrac{2\zeta\omega_1\omega_2}{\omega_2^2 - \omega_1^2}$ $\psi_2 = \tan^{-1}\dfrac{\sqrt{1-\zeta^2}}{-\zeta} - \tan^{-1}\dfrac{2\zeta\omega_2^2\sqrt{1-\zeta^2}}{\omega_1^2 + 2\zeta^2\omega_2^2 - \omega_2^2}$
00.102	$\dfrac{1}{s(1 + s^2/\omega_1^2)(1 + s^2/\omega_2^2)}$	$1 + \dfrac{1}{\omega_1^2 - \omega_2^2}(\omega_2^2\cos\omega_1 t - \omega_1^2\cos\omega_2 t)$
00.102	$\dfrac{1}{s(1 + s^2/\omega_1^2)^2}$	$1 - \cos\omega_1 t - \dfrac{\omega_1}{2}t\sin\omega_1 t$
00.110	$\dfrac{1}{s(1 + Ts)}$	$1 - \epsilon^{-t/T}$
00.111	$\dfrac{1}{s(1 + Ts)(1 + 2\zeta s/\omega_1 + s^2/\omega_1^2)}$	$1 - \dfrac{T^2\omega_1^2}{1 - 2T\zeta\omega_1 + T^2\omega_1^2}\epsilon^{-t/T} + \dfrac{\epsilon^{-\zeta\omega_1 t}\sin(\omega_1\sqrt{1-\zeta^2}\,t - \psi)}{\sqrt{1-\zeta^2}\,(1 - 2\zeta T\omega_1 + T^2\omega_1^2)^{1/2}}$ where $\psi = \tan^{-1}\dfrac{\sqrt{1-\zeta^2}}{-\zeta} + \tan^{-1}\dfrac{T\omega_1\sqrt{1-\zeta^2}}{1 - T\zeta\omega_1}$
00.111	$\dfrac{1}{s(1 + Ts)(1 + s^2/\omega_1^2)}$	$1 - \dfrac{T^2\omega_1^2}{1 + T^2\omega_1^2}\epsilon^{-t/T} - \dfrac{\cos(\omega_1 t - \psi)}{(1 + T^2\omega_1^2)^{1/2}}$ where $\psi = \tan^{-1}T\omega_1$

00.120	$\dfrac{1}{s(1+T_1 s)(1+T_2 s)}$	$1 + \dfrac{1}{T_2 - T_1}(T_1\epsilon^{-t/T_1} - T_2\epsilon^{-t/T_2})$
00.120	$\dfrac{1}{s(1+Ts)^2}$	$1 - \dfrac{(T+t)}{T}\,\epsilon^{-t/T}$
00.121	$\dfrac{1}{s(1+T_1 s)\left(1+\dfrac{2\zeta s}{\omega_1}+\dfrac{s^2}{\omega_1^2}\right)}$	$1 + \dfrac{T_1^3\omega_1^2}{(T_2-T_1)(1-2T_1\zeta\omega_1+T_1^2\omega_1^2)}\,\epsilon^{-t/T_1}$ $+ \dfrac{T_2^3\omega_1^2}{(T_1-T_2)(1-2\zeta T_2\omega_1+T_2^2\omega_1^2)}\,\epsilon^{-t/T_2}$ $+ \dfrac{\epsilon^{-\zeta\omega_1 t}\sin\left(\omega_1\sqrt{1-\zeta^2}\,t-\psi\right)}{[(1-\zeta^2)(1-2T_1\zeta\omega_1+T_1^2\omega_1^2)(1-2T_2\zeta\omega_1+T_2^2\omega_1^2)]^{1/2}}$ where $\psi = \tan^{-1}\dfrac{T_1\omega_1\sqrt{1-\zeta^2}}{1-T_1\zeta\omega_1} + \tan^{-1}\dfrac{T_2\omega_1\sqrt{1-\zeta^2}}{1-T_2\zeta\omega_1} + \tan^{-1}\dfrac{\sqrt{1-\zeta^2}}{-\zeta}$
00.121	$\dfrac{1}{s(1+T_1 s)(1+T_2 s)(1+s^2/\omega_1^2)}$	$1 + \dfrac{T_1^3\omega_1^2}{(T_2-T_1)(1+T_1^2\omega_1^2)}\,\epsilon^{-t/T_1} + \dfrac{T_2^3\omega_1^2}{(T_1-T_2)(1+T_2^2\omega_1^2)}\,\epsilon^{-t/T_2}$ $- \dfrac{\cos\,(\omega_1 t - \psi)}{[(1+T_1^2\omega_1^2)(1+T_2^2\omega_1^2)]^{1/2}}$ where $\psi = \tan^{-1}T_1\omega_1 + \tan^{-1}T_2\omega_1$
00.130	$\dfrac{1}{s(1+T_1 s)(1+T_2 s)(1+T_3 s)}$	$1 - \dfrac{T_1^2}{(T_1-T_2)(T_1-T_3)}\,\epsilon^{-t/T_1} - \dfrac{T_2^2}{(T_2-T_1)(T_2-T_3)}\,\epsilon^{-t/T_2}$ $- \dfrac{T_3^2}{(T_3-T_1)(T_3-T_2)}\,\epsilon^{-t/T_3}$
00.130	$\dfrac{1}{s(1+T_1 s)(1+T_2 s)^2}$	$1 - \dfrac{T_1^2}{(T_1-T_2)^2}\,\epsilon^{-t/T_1} + \left[\dfrac{t}{T_1-T_2} + \dfrac{T_2(2T_1-T_2)}{(T_1-T_2)^2}\right]\epsilon^{-t/T_2}$
00.130	$\dfrac{1}{s(1+Ts)^3}$	$1 - \left(1+\dfrac{t}{T}+\dfrac{t^2}{2T^2}\right)\epsilon^{-t/T}$

* See Section 3.30.

LAPLACE TRANSFORM PAIRS (Continued)

Eq. No.*	$F(s)$	$f(t)$ $0 \leq t$
00.131	$\dfrac{1}{s(1 + T_1 s)(1 + T_2 s)(1 + T_3 s)(1 + s^2/\omega_1^2)}$	$1 - \dfrac{T_1^4 \omega_1^2 \epsilon^{-t/T_1}}{(T_2 - T_1)(T_1 - T_3)(1 + T_1^2 \omega_1^2)} - \dfrac{T_2^4 \omega_1^2 \epsilon^{-t/T_2}}{(T_2 - T_1)(T_2 - T_3)(1 + T_2^2 \omega_1^2)} - \dfrac{T_3^4 \omega_1^2 \epsilon^{-t/T_2}}{(T_3 - T_1)(T_3 - T_2)(1 + T_3^2 \omega_1^2)} - \dfrac{\cos(\omega_1 t - \psi)}{[(1 + T_1^2 \omega_1^2)(1 + T_2^2 \omega_1^2)(1 + T_3^2 \omega_1^2)]^{1/2}}$ where $\psi = \tan^{-1} T_1 \omega_1 + \tan^{-1} T_2 \omega_1 + \tan^{-1} T_3 \omega_1$
00.200	$\dfrac{1}{s^2}$	t
00.201	$\dfrac{1}{s^2(1 + 2\zeta s/\omega_1 + s^2/\omega_1^2)}$	$t - \dfrac{2\zeta}{\omega_1} + \dfrac{1}{\omega_1 \sqrt{1 - \zeta^2}} \epsilon^{-\zeta \omega_1 t} \sin\left(\omega_1 \sqrt{1 - \zeta^2}\, t - \psi\right)$ where $\psi = 2 \tan^{-1}(\sqrt{1 - \zeta^2})/ - \zeta$
00.201	$\dfrac{1}{s^2(1 + s^2/\omega_1^2)}$	$t - \dfrac{1}{\omega_1} \sin \omega_1 t$
00.202	$\dfrac{1}{s^2(1 + 2\zeta_1 s/\omega_1 + s^2/\omega_1^2)(1 + 2\zeta_2 s/\omega_2 + s^2/\omega_2^2)}$	$t - \dfrac{2\zeta_1}{\omega_1} - \dfrac{2\zeta_2}{\omega_2} + \dfrac{\omega_2^2 \epsilon^{-\zeta_1 \omega_1 t} \sin\left(\omega_1 \sqrt{1 - \zeta_1^2}\, t - \psi_1\right)}{\omega_1 \sqrt{1 - \zeta_1^2}\,(A^2 + 4AB\zeta_1 \omega_1 + 4B^2 \omega_1^2)^{1/2}}$ $+ \dfrac{\omega_1^2 \epsilon^{-\zeta_2 \omega_2 t} \sin\left(\omega_2 \sqrt{1 - \zeta_2^2}\, t - \psi_2\right)}{\omega_2 \sqrt{1 - \zeta_2^2}\,(A^2 + 4AB\zeta_2 \omega_2 + 4B^2 \omega_2^2)^{1/2}}$ where $A = \omega_1^2 - \omega_2^2$, $B = \zeta_2 \omega_2 - \zeta_1 \omega_1$ $\psi_1 = 2 \tan^{-1} \dfrac{\sqrt{1 - \zeta_1^2}}{-\zeta_1} + \tan^{-1} \dfrac{2B\omega_1 \sqrt{1 - \zeta_1^2}}{-A - 2B\zeta_1 \omega_1}$ $\psi_2 = 2 \tan^{-1} \dfrac{\sqrt{1 - \zeta_2^2}}{-\zeta_2} - \tan^{-1} \dfrac{2B\omega_2 \sqrt{1 - \zeta_2^2}}{A + 2B\zeta_2 \omega_2}$

00.202	$\dfrac{1}{s^2(1 + s^2/\omega_1^2)(1 + 2\zeta s/\omega_2 + s^2/\omega_2^2)}$	$t - \dfrac{2\zeta}{\omega_2} + \dfrac{1}{[(\omega_1^2 - \omega_2^2)^2 + 4\zeta^2\omega_1^2\omega_2^2]^{1/2}}\left[\dfrac{\omega_1^2}{\omega_2^2\sqrt{1-\zeta^2}}\,\epsilon^{-\zeta\omega_2 t}\sin(\omega_2\sqrt{1-\zeta^2}\,t - \psi_2) - \dfrac{\omega_2^2}{\omega_1}\sin(\omega_1 t - \psi_1)\right]$ where $\psi_1 = \tan^{-1}\dfrac{2\zeta\omega_1\omega_2}{\omega_2^2 - \omega_1^2}$ $\psi_2 = 2\tan^{-1}\dfrac{\sqrt{1-\zeta^2}}{-\zeta} - \tan^{-1}\dfrac{2\zeta\omega_2^2\sqrt{1-\zeta^2}}{\omega_1^2 + 2\zeta^2\omega_2^2 - \omega_2^2}$
00.202	$\dfrac{1}{s^2(1 + s^2/\omega_1^2)(1 + s^2/\omega_2^2)}$	$t + \dfrac{1}{\omega_1^2 - \omega_2^2}\left(\dfrac{\omega_2^2}{\omega_1}\sin\omega_1 t - \dfrac{\omega_1^2}{\omega_2}\sin\omega_2 t\right)$
00.210	$\dfrac{1}{s^2(1 + Ts)}$	$T\left(\epsilon^{-t/T} + \dfrac{t}{T} - 1\right)$
00.211	$\dfrac{1}{s^2(1 + Ts)(1 + 2\zeta s/\omega_1 + s^2/\omega_1^2)}$	$t - T - \dfrac{2\zeta}{\omega_1} + \dfrac{T^3\omega_1^2}{1 - 2\zeta T\omega_1 + T^2\omega_1^2}\,\epsilon^{-t/T}$ $+ \dfrac{\epsilon^{-\zeta\omega_1 t}\sin(\omega_1\sqrt{1 - \zeta^2}\,t - \psi)}{\omega_1[(1-\zeta^2)(1 - 2\zeta T\omega_1 + T^2\omega_1^2)]^{1/2}}$ where $\psi = 2\tan^{-1}\dfrac{\sqrt{1-\zeta^2}}{-\zeta} + \tan^{-1}\dfrac{T\omega_1\sqrt{1-\zeta^2}}{1 - T\zeta\omega_1}$
00.211	$\dfrac{1}{s^2(1 + Ts)(1 + s^2/\omega_1^2)}$	$t - T + \dfrac{T^3\omega_1^2}{1 + T^2\omega_1^2}\,\epsilon^{-t/T} - \dfrac{\sin(\omega_1 t - \psi)}{\omega_1(1 + T^2\omega_1^2)^{1/2}}$ where $\psi = \tan^{-1}T\omega_1$
00.220	$\dfrac{1}{s^2(1 + T_1 s)(1 + T_2 s)}$	$t - T_1 - T_2 - \dfrac{1}{T_1 - T_2}[T_2^2\epsilon^{-t/T_2} - T_1^2\epsilon^{-t/T_1}]$

* See Section 3.30.

LAPLACE TRANSFORM PAIRS (Continued)

Eq. No.*	$F(s)$	$f(t)$, $0 \leq t$
00.220	$\dfrac{1}{s^2(1 - s^2/\omega_1^2)}$	$t - \dfrac{1}{\omega_1}\sinh \omega_1 t$
00.220	$\dfrac{1}{s^2(1 + Ts)^2}$	$t - 2T + (t + 2T)\epsilon^{-t/T}$
00.221	$\dfrac{1}{s^2(1 + T_1 s)(1 + 2\zeta s/\omega_1 + s^2/\omega_1^2)}$	$t - T_1 - T_2 - \dfrac{2\zeta}{\omega_1} - \dfrac{(T_2 - T_1)(1 - 2T_1\zeta\omega_1 + T_1^2\omega_1^2)}{T_1^4\omega_1^2}\epsilon^{-t/T_1}$
		$- \dfrac{(T_1 - T_2)(1 - 2T_2\zeta\omega_1 + T_2^2\omega_1^2)}{T_2^4\omega_1^2}\epsilon^{-t/T_2}$
		$+ \dfrac{\epsilon^{-\zeta\omega_1 t}\sin\left(\omega_1\sqrt{1 - \zeta^2}\,t - \psi\right)}{\omega_1[(1 - \zeta^2)(1 - 2T_1\zeta\omega_1 + T_1^2\omega_1^2)(1 - 2T_2\zeta\omega_1 + T_2^2\omega_1^2)]^{1/2}}$
		where $\psi = 2\tan^{-1}\dfrac{\sqrt{1 - \zeta^2}}{-\zeta} + \tan^{-1}\dfrac{T_1\omega_1\sqrt{1 - \zeta^2}}{1 - T_1\zeta\omega_1} + \tan^{-1}\dfrac{T_2\omega_1\sqrt{1 - \zeta^2}}{1 - T_2\zeta\omega_1}$
00.221	$\dfrac{1}{s^2(1 + T_1 s)(1 + s^2/\omega_1^2)}$	$t - T_1 - T_2 + \dfrac{T_1^4\omega_1^2}{(T_1 - T_2)(1 + T_1^2\omega_1^2)}\epsilon^{-t/T_1}$
		$+ \dfrac{T_2^4\omega_1^2}{(T_2 - T_1)(1 + T_2^2\omega_1^2)}\epsilon^{-t/T_2} - \dfrac{\sin(\omega_1 t - \psi)}{\omega_1[(1 + T_1^2\omega_1^2)(1 + T_2^2\omega_1^2)]^{1/2}}$
		where $\psi = \tan^{-1}T_1\omega_1 + \tan^{-1}T_2\omega_2$
00.230	$\dfrac{1}{s^2(1 + T_1 s)(1 + T_2 s)(1 + T_3 s)}$	$t - (T_1 + T_2 + T_3) - \dfrac{1}{(T_1 - T_2)(T_2 - T_3)(T_3 - T_1)}[T_1^3(T_2 - T_3)\epsilon^{-t/T_1}$
		$+ T_2^3(T_3 - T_1)\epsilon^{-t/T_2} + T_3^3(T_1 - T_2)\epsilon^{-t/T_3}]$
00.230	$\dfrac{1}{s^2(1 + Ts)^3}$	$t - 3T + [3T + 2t + t^2/2T]\epsilon^{-t/T}$

00.231	$\dfrac{1}{s^2(1+T_1 s)(1+T_2 s)(1+T_3 s)(1+s^2/\omega_1^2)}$	$t - T_1 - T_2 - T_3 + \dfrac{T_1^5\omega_1^2\epsilon^{-t/T_1}}{(T_2-T_1)(T_1-T_2)(T_1-T_3)(1+T_1^2\omega_1^2)}$ $+ \dfrac{T_2^5\omega_1^2\epsilon^{-t/T_2}}{(T_2-T_1)(T_2-T_3)(1+T_2^2\omega_1^2)} + \dfrac{T_3^5\omega_1^2\epsilon^{-t/T_3}}{(T_3-T_1)(T_3-T_2)(1+T_3^2\omega_1^2)}$ $- \dfrac{\sin(\omega_1 t - \psi)}{\omega_1[(1+T_1^2\omega_1^2)(1+T_2^2\omega_1^2)(1+T_3^2\omega_1^2)]^{1/2}}$ where $\psi = \tan^{-1}T_1\omega_1 + \tan^{-1}T_2\omega_1 + \tan^{-1}T_3\omega_1$
00.301	$\dfrac{1}{s^3(1+s^2/\omega_1^2)}$	$\dfrac{1}{\omega_1^2}(\cos\omega_1 t - 1) + \dfrac{1}{2}t^2$
00.320	$\dfrac{1}{s^3(1+T_1 s)(1+T_2 s)}$	$\dfrac{1}{2}t^2 - (T_1+T_2)t - \dfrac{1}{T_1-T_2}[T_2^3(1-\epsilon^{-t/T_2}) - T_1^3(1-\epsilon^{-t/T_1})]$
00.320	$\dfrac{1}{s^3(1-s^2/\omega_1^2)}$	$\dfrac{1}{2}t^2 - \dfrac{1}{\omega_1^2}(\cosh\omega_1 t - 1)$
01.001	$\dfrac{1+as}{1+2\zeta s/\omega_1 + s^2/\omega_1^2}$	$\omega_1\left[\dfrac{1-2a\zeta\omega_1 + a^2\omega_1^2}{1-\zeta^2}\right]^{1/2}\epsilon^{-\zeta\omega_1 t}\sin\left(\omega_1\sqrt{1-\zeta^2}\,t + \psi\right)$ where $\psi = \tan^{-1}\dfrac{a\omega_1\sqrt{1-\zeta^2}}{1-a\zeta\omega_1}$
01.001	$\dfrac{1+as}{(1+s^2/\omega_1^2)}$	$\omega_1(1+a^2\omega_1^2)^{1/2}\sin(\omega_1 t + \psi)$ where $\psi = \tan^{-1}a\omega_1$
01.002	$\dfrac{1+as}{(1+2\zeta s/\omega_1 + s^2/\omega_1^2)(1+s^2/\omega_2^2)}$	$\dfrac{\omega_1\omega_2}{[(\omega_1^2 - \omega_2^2)^2 + 4\zeta^2\omega_1^2\omega_2^2]^{1/2}}\left[\omega_1(1+a^2\omega_2^2)^{1/2}\sin(\omega_2 t + \psi_1)\right.$ $\left. + \dfrac{\omega_2}{\sqrt{1-\zeta^2}}(1 - 2a\zeta\omega_1 + a^2\omega_1^2)^{1/2}\epsilon^{-\zeta\omega_1 t}\sin\left(\omega_1\sqrt{1-\zeta^2}\,t + \psi_2\right)\right]$ where $\psi_1 = \tan^{-1}a\omega_2 - \tan^{-1}\dfrac{2\zeta\omega_1\omega_2}{\omega_1^2 - \omega_2^2}$ $\psi_2 = \tan^{-1}\dfrac{a\omega_1\sqrt{1-\zeta^2}}{1-a\zeta\omega_1} - \tan^{-1}\dfrac{2\zeta\omega_1^2\sqrt{1-\zeta^2}}{2\zeta^2\omega_1^2 + \omega_2^2 - \omega_1^2}$

* See Section 3.30.

LAPLACE TRANSFORM PAIRS (*Continued*)

Eq. No.*	$F(s)$	$f(t)$ $\qquad 0 \leq t$
01.011	$\dfrac{1 + as}{(1 + Ts)(1 + 2\zeta s/\omega_1 + s^2/\omega_1^2)}$	$\dfrac{\omega_1}{\sqrt{1 - \zeta^2}} \left(\dfrac{1 - 2a\zeta\omega_1 + a^2\omega_1^2}{1 - 2T\zeta\omega_1 + T^2\omega_1^2} \right)^{1/2} \epsilon^{-\zeta\omega_1 t} \sin\left(\omega_1\sqrt{1 - \zeta^2}\, t + \psi\right)$ $+ \dfrac{(T - a)\omega_1^2}{1 - 2T\zeta\omega_1 + T^2\omega_1^2}\, \epsilon^{-t/T}$ where $\psi = \tan^{-1}\dfrac{a\omega_1\sqrt{1 - \zeta^2}}{1 - a\zeta\omega_1} - \tan^{-1}\dfrac{T\omega_1\sqrt{1 - \zeta^2}}{1 - T\zeta\omega_1}$
01.011	$\dfrac{1 + as}{(1 + Ts)(1 + s^2/\omega_1^2)}$	$\dfrac{\omega_1^2(T - a)}{1 + T^2\omega_1^2}\, \epsilon^{-t/T} + \omega_1\left(\dfrac{1 + a^2\omega_1^2}{1 + T^2\omega_1^2}\right)^{1/2} \sin(\omega_1 t + \psi)$ where $\psi = \tan^{-1} a\omega_1 - \tan^{-1} T\omega_1$
01.012	$\dfrac{1 + as}{(1 + Ts)(1 + 2\zeta s/\omega_2 + s^2/\omega_2^2)}$	$\dfrac{T^2(T - a)\omega_1^2\omega_2^2}{(1 + T^2\omega_1^2)(1 - 2T\zeta\omega_2 + T^2\omega_2^2)}\, \epsilon^{-t/T}$ $+ \omega_1\omega_2^2\left\{ \dfrac{1 + a^2\omega_1^2}{(1 + T^2\omega_1^2)[(\omega_2^2 - \omega_1^2)^2 + 4\zeta^2\omega_1^2\omega_2^2]} \right\}^{1/2} \sin(\omega_1 t + \psi_1)$ $+ \dfrac{\omega_1^2\omega_2^2}{\sqrt{1 - \zeta^2}}\left\{ \dfrac{1 - 2a\zeta\omega_2 + a^2\omega_2^2}{(1 - 2T\zeta\omega_2 + T^2\omega_2^2)[(\omega_2^2 - \omega_1^2)^2 + 4\zeta^2\omega_1^2\omega_2^2]} \right\}^{1/2}$ $\epsilon^{-\zeta\omega_2 t} \sin\left(\omega_2\sqrt{1 - \zeta^2}\, t + \psi_2\right)$ where $\psi_1 = \tan^{-1} a\omega_1 - \tan^{-1} T\omega_1 - \tan^{-1}\dfrac{2\zeta\omega_1\omega_2}{\omega_2^2 - \omega_1^2}$ $\psi_2 = \tan^{-1}\dfrac{a\omega_2\sqrt{1 - \zeta^2}}{1 - a\zeta\omega_2} - \tan^{-1}\dfrac{T\omega_2\sqrt{1 - \zeta^2}}{1 - T\zeta\omega_2}$ $- \tan^{-1}\dfrac{2\zeta\omega_2^2\sqrt{1 - \zeta^2}}{\omega_1^2 - \omega_2^2 + 2\zeta^2\omega_2^2}$
01.020	$\dfrac{1 + as}{(1 + T_1 s)(1 + T_2 s)}$	$\dfrac{T_1 - a}{T_1(T_1 - T_2)}\, \epsilon^{-t/T_1} - \dfrac{T_2 - a}{T_2(T_1 - T_2)}\, \epsilon^{-t/T_2}$

01.020	$\dfrac{1+as}{(1+T_s)^2}$	$\left[\dfrac{T-a}{T^3}t + \dfrac{a}{T^2}\right]\epsilon^{-t/T}$
01.021	$\dfrac{1+as}{(1+T_s)^2(1+s^2/\omega_1^2)}$	$\dfrac{\omega_1(1+a^2\omega_1^2)^{1/2}}{1+T^2\omega_1^2}\sin(\omega_1 t + \psi) + \left[\dfrac{\omega_1^2(T-a)}{T(1+T^2\omega_1^2)}t + \dfrac{\omega_1^2(2T+aT^2\omega_1^2-a)}{(1+T^2\omega_1^2)^2}\right]\epsilon^{-t/T}$ where $\psi = \tan^{-1}a\omega_1 - 2\tan^{-1}T\omega_1$
01.021	$\dfrac{1+as}{(1+T_1 s)(1+T_2 s)(1+s^2/\omega_1^2)}$	$\dfrac{T_1\omega_1^2(T_1-a)}{(T_1-T_2)(1+T_1^2\omega_1^2)}\epsilon^{-t/T_1} + \dfrac{T_2\omega_1^2(T_2-a)}{(T_2-T_1)(1+T_2^2\omega_1^2)}\epsilon^{-t/T_2} + \dfrac{\omega_1(1+a^2\omega_1^2)^{1/2}\sin(\omega_1 t - \psi)}{[(1+T_1^2\omega_1^2)(1+T_2^2\omega_1^2)]^{1/2}}$ where $\psi = \tan^{-1}T_1\omega_1 + \tan^{-1}T_2\omega_1 - \tan^{-1}a\omega_1$
01.030	$\dfrac{1+as}{(1+T_1 s)(1+T_2 s)(1+T_3 s)}$	$\dfrac{T_1-a}{(T_1-T_2)(T_1-T_3)}\epsilon^{-t/T_1} + \dfrac{T_2-a}{(T_2-T_1)(T_2-T_3)}\epsilon^{-t/T_2} + \dfrac{T_3-a}{(T_3-T_1)(T_3-T_2)}\epsilon^{-t/T_3}$
01.030	$\dfrac{1+as}{(1+T_1 s)(1+T_2 s)^2}$	$\dfrac{T_1-a}{(T_1-T_2)^2}\epsilon^{-t/T_1} + \left[\dfrac{T_2-a}{T_2^2(T_2-T_1)}t + \dfrac{a-T_1}{(T_2-T_1)^2}\right]\epsilon^{-t/T_2}$
01.040	$\dfrac{1+as}{(1+T_1 s)(1+T_2 s)(1+T_3 s)^2}$	$\dfrac{T_1(T_1-a)}{(T_1-T_2)(T_1-T_3)^2}\epsilon^{-t/T_1} + \dfrac{T_2(T_2-a)}{(T_2-T_1)(T_2-T_3)^2}\epsilon^{-t/T_2}$ $+ \left[\dfrac{T_3-a}{T_3(T_3-T_1)(T_3-T_2)}t + \dfrac{2T_1T_2T_3 - aT_1T_2 + (a - T_1 - T_2)T_3^2}{(T_3-T_1)^2(T_3-T_2)^2}\right]\epsilon^{-t/T_3}$

* See Section 3.30.

LAPLACE TRANSFORM PAIRS (*Continued*)

Eq. No.*	$F(s)$	$f(t)$ $0 \le t$
01.040	$\dfrac{1+as}{(1+T_1 s)(1+T_2 s)^3}$	$\dfrac{T_1(T_1-a)}{(T_1-T_2)^3}\epsilon^{-t/T_1} + \left[\dfrac{(a-T_1)}{2T_1 T_2^2(T_1-T_2)}t^2 + \dfrac{(a-T_1)}{T_2(T_1-T_2)^2}t + \dfrac{T_1(a-T_1)}{(T_1-T_2)^3}\right]\epsilon^{-t/T_2}$
01.040	$\dfrac{1+as}{(1+T_1 s)^2(1+T_2 s)^2}$	$\left[\dfrac{T_1-a}{T_1(T_1-T_2)^2}t + \dfrac{aT_1+aT_2-2T_1 T_2}{(T_1-T_2)^3}\right]\epsilon^{-t/T_1} + \left[\dfrac{T_2-a}{T_2^2(T_2-T_1)^2}t + \dfrac{aT_1+aT_2-2T_1 T_2}{(T_2-T_1)^3}\right]\epsilon^{-t/T_2}$
01.101	$\dfrac{1+as}{s(1+2\zeta s/\omega_1 + s^2/\omega_1^2)}$	$1 + \dfrac{1}{\sqrt{1-\zeta^2}}[1-2a\zeta\omega_1 + a^2\omega_1^2]^{1/2}\epsilon^{-\zeta\omega_1 t}\sin(\omega_1\sqrt{1-\zeta^2}\,t+\psi)$ where $\psi = \tan^{-1}\dfrac{a\omega_1\sqrt{1-\zeta^2}}{1-a\zeta\omega_1} - \tan^{-1}\dfrac{\sqrt{1-\zeta^2}}{-\zeta}$
01.101	$\dfrac{1+as}{s(1+s^2/\omega_1^2)}$	$1 - (1+a^2\omega_1^2)^{1/2}\cos(\omega_1 t+\psi)$ where $\psi = \tan^{-1}a\omega_1$
01.110	$\dfrac{1+as}{s(1+Ts)}$	$1+\dfrac{a-T}{T}\epsilon^{-t/T}$
01.111	$\dfrac{1+as}{s(1+Ts)(1+s^2/\omega_1^2)}$	$1+\dfrac{T\omega_1^2(a-T)}{1+T^2\omega_1^2}\epsilon^{-t/T} - \left[\dfrac{1+a^2\omega_1^2}{1+T^2\omega_1^2}\right]^{1/2}\cos(\omega_1 t+\psi)$ where $\psi = \tan^{-1}a\omega_1 - \tan^{-1}T\omega_1$
01.111	$\dfrac{1+as}{s(1+Ts)(1+2\zeta s/\omega_1 + s^2/\omega_1^2)}$	$1+\dfrac{1}{\sqrt{1-\zeta^2}}\left[\dfrac{1-2a\zeta\omega_1+a^2\omega_1^2}{1-2T\zeta\omega_1+T^2\omega_1^2}\right]^{1/2}\epsilon^{-\zeta\omega_1 t}\sin(\omega_1\sqrt{1-\zeta^2}\,t + \psi) + \dfrac{T\omega_1^2(a-T)}{1-2T\zeta\omega_1+T^2\omega_1^2}\epsilon^{-t/T}$ where $\psi = \tan^{-1}\dfrac{a\omega_1\sqrt{1-\zeta^2}}{1-a\zeta\omega_1} - \tan^{-1}\dfrac{T\omega_1\sqrt{1-\zeta^2}}{1-T\zeta\omega_1} - \tan^{-1}\dfrac{\sqrt{1-\zeta^2}}{-\zeta}$

01.120	$\dfrac{1+as}{s(1+T_1s)(1+T_2s)}$	$1 + \dfrac{T_1-a}{T_2-T_1}\,\epsilon^{-t/T_1} - \dfrac{T_2-a}{T_2-T_1}\,\epsilon^{-t/T_2}$
01.120	$\dfrac{1+as}{s(1+Ts)^2}$	$1 + \left[\dfrac{a-T}{T^2}\,t - 1\right]\epsilon^{-t/T}$
01.121	$\dfrac{1+as}{s(1+T_1s)(1+T_2s)(1+s^2/\omega_1^2)}$	$1 - \dfrac{T_1^2\omega_1^2(T_1-a)}{(T_1-T_2)(1+T_1^2\omega_1^2)}\,\epsilon^{-t/T_1} - \dfrac{T_2^2\omega_1^2(T_2-a)}{(T_2-T_1)(1+T_2^2\omega_1^2)}\,\epsilon^{-t/T_2}$ $-\dfrac{(1+a^2\omega_1^2)^{1/2}\cos(\omega_1 t - \psi)}{[(1+T_1^2\omega_1^2)(1+T_2^2\omega_1^2)]^{1/2}}$ where $\psi = \tan^{-1}T_1\omega_1 + \tan^{-1}T_2\omega_1 - \tan^{-1}a\omega_1$
01.121	$\dfrac{1+as}{s(1+Ts)^2(1+s^2/\omega_1^2)}$	$1 - \left[\dfrac{1+a^2\omega_1^2}{1+T^2\omega_1^2}\right]^{1/2}\cos(\omega_1 t + \psi) + \left[\dfrac{\omega_1^2(a-T)}{(1+T^2\omega_1^2)}\,t + \dfrac{T\omega_1^2(2a-3T-T^3\omega_1^2)}{(1+T^2\omega_1^2)^2}\right]\epsilon^{-t/T}$ where $\psi = \tan^{-1}a\omega_1 - 2\tan^{-1}T\omega_1$
01.130	$\dfrac{1+as}{s(1+T_1s)(1+T_2s)(1+T_3s)}$	$1 - \dfrac{T_1(T_1-a)}{(T_1-T_2)(T_1-T_3)}\,\epsilon^{-t/T_1} - \dfrac{T_2(T_2-a)}{(T_2-T_1)(T_2-T_3)}\,\epsilon^{-t/T_2}$ $-\dfrac{T_3(T_3-a)}{(T_3-T_1)(T_3-T_2)}\,\epsilon^{-t/T_3}$
01.130	$\dfrac{1+as}{s(1+T_1s)(1+T_2s)^2}$	$1 + \dfrac{T_1(a-T_1)}{(T_1-T_2)^2}\,\epsilon^{-t/T_1} + \left[\dfrac{T_2-a}{T_2(T_1-T_2)}\,t + \dfrac{2T_1T_2-aT_1-T_2^2}{(T_1-T_2)^2}\right]\epsilon^{-t/T_2}$
01.201	$\dfrac{1+as}{s^2(1+s^2/\omega_1^2)}$	$t + a - \dfrac{1}{\omega_1}(1+a^2\omega_1^2)^{1/2}\sin(\omega_1 t + \psi)$ where $\psi = \tan^{-1}a\omega_1$
01.210	$\dfrac{1+as}{s^2(1+Ts)}$	$(a-T)(1-\epsilon^{-t/T}) + t$

* See Section 3.30.

LAPLACE TRANSFORM PAIRS (Continued)

Eq. No.*	$F(s)$	$f(t)$ $0 \leq t$
01.220	$\dfrac{1+as}{s^2(1+T_1s)(1+T_2s)}$	$\dfrac{T_1(T_1-a)}{T_1-T_2}\,\epsilon^{-t/T_1} + \dfrac{T_2(T_2-a)}{T_2-T_1}\,\epsilon^{-t/T_2} + t - T_1 - T_2 + a$
01.221	$\dfrac{1+as}{s^2(1+T_1s)(1+T_2s)(1+s^2/\omega_1^2)}$	$t + a - T_1 - T_2 + \dfrac{T_1^3\omega_1^2(T_1-a)}{(T_1-T_2)(1+T_1^2\omega_1^2)}\,\epsilon^{-t/T_1}$ $+\dfrac{T_2^3\omega_1^2(T_2-a)}{(T_2-T_1)(1+T_2^2\omega_1^2)}\,\epsilon^{-t/T_2} - \dfrac{(1+a^2\omega_1^2)^{1/2}\sin(\omega_1 t - \psi)}{\omega_1[(1+T_1^2\omega_1^2)(1+T_2^2\omega_1^2)]^{1/2}}$ where $\psi = \tan^{-1}T_1\omega_1 + \tan^{-1}T_2\omega_1 - \tan^{-1}a\omega_1$
01.310	$\dfrac{1+as}{s^3(1+Ts)}$	$(T-a)(T - T\epsilon^{-t/T} - t) + \dfrac{t^2}{2}$
01.320	$\dfrac{1+as}{s^3(1+T_1s)(1+T_2s)}$	$\dfrac{T_1^2(T_1-a)}{T_1-T_2}(1-\epsilon^{-t/T_1}) + \dfrac{T_2^2(T_2-a)}{T_2-T_1}(1-\epsilon^{-t/T_2}) + \dfrac{t^2}{2} + (a-T_1-T_2)t$
02.002	$\dfrac{1-s^2/\omega_1^2}{(1+s^2/\omega_1^2)^2}$	$-\omega_1^2 t\cos\omega_1 t$
02.002	$\dfrac{1+as+bs^2}{(1+2\zeta s/\omega_1+s^2/\omega_1^2)(1+s^2/\omega_2^2)}$	$\dfrac{\omega_1\omega_2^2}{\sqrt{1-\zeta^2}}\left[\dfrac{(1-a\zeta\omega_1+2b\zeta^2\omega_1^2-b\omega_2^2)^2+\omega_1^2(1-\zeta^2)(a-2b\zeta\omega_1)^2}{(\omega_1^2-\omega_2^2)^2+4\zeta^2\omega_1^2\omega_2^2}\right]^{1/2}$ $\epsilon^{-\zeta\omega_1 t}\sin\left(\omega_1\sqrt{1-\zeta^2}\,t+\psi_1\right) + \omega_1^2\omega_2\left[\dfrac{(1-b\omega_2^2)^2+a^2\omega_2^2}{(\omega_1^2-\omega_2^2)^2+4\zeta^2\omega_1^2\omega_2^2}\right]^{1/2}$ $\sin(\omega_2 t+\psi_2)$ where $\psi_1 = \tan^{-1}\dfrac{\omega_1\sqrt{1-\zeta^2}\,(a-2b\zeta\omega_1)}{1-a\zeta\omega_1+2b\zeta^2\omega_1^2-b\omega_2^2} - \tan^{-1}\dfrac{2\zeta\omega_1^2\sqrt{1-\zeta^2}}{2\zeta^2\omega_1^2-\omega_1^2+\omega_2^2}$ $\psi_2 = \tan^{-1}\dfrac{a\omega_2}{1-b\omega_2^2} - \tan^{-1}\dfrac{2\zeta\omega_1\omega_2}{\omega_1^2-\omega_2^2}$

02.011	$\dfrac{1 + as + bs^2}{(1 + Ts)(1 + 2\zeta s/\omega_1 + s^2/\omega_1^2)}$ *

$$\frac{\omega_1}{\sqrt{1-\zeta^2}}\left[\frac{(1 - a\zeta\omega_1 - b\omega_1^2 + 2b\zeta^2\omega_1^2)^2 + \omega_1^2(1-\zeta^2)(a - 2b\zeta\omega_1)^2}{(1 - T\zeta\omega_1)^2 + T^2\omega_1^2(1-\zeta^2)}\right]^{1/2}$$
$$\epsilon^{\zeta\omega_1 t}\sin(\omega_1\sqrt{1-\zeta^2}\,t + \psi) + \frac{\omega_1^2(b - aT - T^2)}{T(1 - 2T\zeta\omega_1 + T^2\omega_1^2)}\epsilon^{-t/T}$$

where $\psi = \tan^{-1}\dfrac{\omega_1\sqrt{1-\zeta^2}\,(a - 2b\zeta\omega_1)}{1 - a\zeta\omega_1 - b\omega_1^2 + 2b\zeta^2\omega_1^2} - \tan^{-1}\dfrac{T\omega_1\sqrt{1-\zeta^2}}{1 - T\zeta\omega_1}$

02.011	$\dfrac{1 + as + bs^2}{(1 + Ts)(1 + s^2/\omega_1^2)}$

$$\frac{\omega_1^2}{T}\left(\frac{b - aT + T^2}{1 + T^2\omega_1^2}\right)\epsilon^{-t/T} + \omega_1\left[\frac{(1 - b\omega_1^2)^2 + a^2\omega_1^2}{1 + T^2\omega_1^2}\right]^{1/2}\sin(\omega_1 t + \psi)$$

where $\psi = \tan^{-1}\dfrac{a\omega_1}{1 - b\omega_1^2} - \tan^{-1}T\omega_1$

02.021	$\dfrac{1 + as + bs^2}{(1 + T_1 s)(1 + T_2 s)}{(1 + 2\zeta s/\omega_1 + s^2/\omega_1^2)}$

$$\frac{\omega_1^2(b - aT_1 + T_1^2)}{(T_1 - T_2)(1 - 2\zeta T_1\omega_1 + T_1^2\omega_1^2)}\epsilon^{-t/T_1} + \frac{\omega_1^2(b - aT_2 + T_2^2)}{(T_2 - T_1)(1 - 2\zeta T_2\omega_1 + T_2^2\omega_1^2)}\epsilon^{-t/T_2}$$
$$+ \omega_1\left[\frac{(1 - a\zeta\omega_1 + 2b\zeta^2\omega_1^2 - b\omega_1^2)^2 + \omega_1^2(1-\zeta^2)(a - 2b\zeta\omega_1)^2}{(1 - 2T_2\zeta\omega_1 + T_2^2\omega_1^2)(1 - 2T_1\zeta\omega_1 + T_1^2\omega_1^2)}\right]^{1/2}$$
$$\epsilon^{-\zeta\omega_1 t}\sin(\omega_1\sqrt{1-\zeta^2}\,t + \psi)$$

where $\psi = \tan^{-1}\dfrac{\omega_1\sqrt{1-\zeta^2}\,(a - 2b\zeta\omega_1)}{1 - a\zeta\omega_1 + 2b\zeta^2\omega_1^2 - b\omega_1^2} - \tan^{-1}\dfrac{T_1\omega_1\sqrt{1-\zeta^2}}{1 - T_1\zeta\omega_1}$
$$- \tan^{-1}\dfrac{T_2\omega_1\sqrt{1-\zeta^2}}{1 - T_2\zeta\omega_1}$$

02.021	$\dfrac{1 + as + bs^2}{(1 + T_1 s)(1 + T_2 s)(1 + s^2/\omega_1^2)}$

$$\frac{\omega_1^2(b - aT_1 + T_1^2)}{(T_1 - T_2)(1 + T_1^2\omega_1^2)}\epsilon^{-t/T_1} + \frac{\omega_1^2(b - aT_2 + T_2^2)}{(T_2 - T_1)(1 + T_2^2\omega_1^2)}\epsilon^{-t/T_2}$$
$$+ \omega_1\left[\frac{(1 - b\omega_1^2)^2 + a^2\omega_1^2}{(1 + T_1^2\omega_1^2)(1 + T_2^2\omega_1^2)}\right]^{1/2}\sin(\omega_1 t + \psi)$$

where $\psi = \tan^{-1}\dfrac{a\omega_1}{1 - b\omega_1^2} - \tan^{-1}T_1\omega_1 - \tan^{-1}T_2\omega_1$

* See Section 3.30.

LAPLACE TRANSFORM PAIRS (Continued)

Eq. No.*	$F(s)$	$f(t)$ $0 \leq t$
02.030	$\dfrac{1+as+bs^2}{(1+T_1s)(1+T_2s)(1+T_3s)}$	$\dfrac{b-aT_1+T_1^2}{T_1(T_1-T_2)(T_1-T_3)}\epsilon^{-t/T_1} + \dfrac{b-aT_2+T_2^2}{T_2(T_2-T_1)(T_2-T_3)}\epsilon^{-t/T_2}$ $+ \dfrac{b-aT_3+T_3^2}{T_3(T_3-T_1)(T_3-T_2)}\epsilon^{-t/T_3}$
02.030	$\dfrac{1+as+bs^2}{(1+T_1s)(1+T_2s)^2}$	$\dfrac{b-aT_1+T_1^2}{T_1(T_1-T_2)^2}\epsilon^{-t/T_1} + \left[\dfrac{b-aT_2+T_2^2}{T_2^3(T_2-T_1)}t + \dfrac{bT_1-2bT_2+aT_2^2-T_1T_2^2}{T_2^2(T_2-T_1)^2}\right]\epsilon^{-t/T_2}$
02.030	$\dfrac{1+as+bs^2}{(1+T_s)^3}$	$\left(\dfrac{b}{T^3} + \dfrac{aT-2b}{T^4}t + \dfrac{T^2-aT+b}{2T^5}t^2\right)\epsilon^{-t/T}$
02.101	$\dfrac{1+as+bs^2}{s(1+2\zeta s/\omega_1+s^2/\omega_1^2)}$	$1 + \dfrac{1}{\sqrt{1-\zeta^2}}[(1-a\zeta\omega_1-b\omega_1^2+2b\zeta^2\omega_1^2)^2$ $+ \omega_1^2(1-\zeta^2)(a-2b\zeta\omega_1)^2]^{1/2}\epsilon^{-\zeta\omega_1 t}\sin(\omega_1\sqrt{1-\zeta^2}\,t+\psi)$ where $\psi = \tan^{-1}\dfrac{\omega_1\sqrt{1-\zeta^2}(a-2b\zeta\omega_1)}{b\omega_1^2(2\zeta^2-1)+1} - \tan^{-1}\dfrac{\sqrt{1-\zeta^2}}{-\zeta}$
02.101	$\dfrac{1+as+bs^2}{s(1+s^2/\omega_1^2)}$	$1 - [(1-b\omega_1^2)^2 + a^2\omega_1^2]^{1/2}\cos(\omega_1 t+\psi)$ where $\psi = \tan^{-1}\dfrac{a\omega_1}{1-b\omega_1^2}$
02.102	$\dfrac{1+as+bs^2}{s(1+s^2/\omega_1^2)^2}$	$1 - \dfrac{\omega_1}{2}[(1-b\omega_1^2)^2 + a^2\omega_1^2]^{1/2}t\sin(\omega_1 t+\psi_1)$ $- \dfrac{1}{2}(4+a^2\omega_1^2)^{1/2}\cos(\omega_1 t+\psi_2)$ where $\psi_1 = \tan^{-1}\dfrac{a\omega_1}{1-b\omega_1^2}$, $\psi_2 = \tan^{-1}\dfrac{a\omega_1}{2}$

02.102

$$\frac{1 + as + bs^2}{s(1 + 2\zeta_1 s/\omega_1 + s^2/\omega_1^2)(1 + 2\zeta_2 s/\omega_2 + s^2/\omega_2^2)}$$

$$1 + \frac{\omega_2^2[(1 - a\omega_1\zeta_1 + 2b\omega_1^2\zeta_1^2 - b\omega_1^2)^2 + \omega_1^2(1 - \zeta_1^2)(2\zeta_1 b\omega_1 - a)^2]^{1/2}}{\sqrt{1 - \zeta_1^2}\,[(\omega_2^2 - 2\zeta_1\omega_1\zeta_2\omega_2 + 2\zeta_1^2\omega_1^2 - \omega_1^2)^2 + 4\omega_1^2(1 - \zeta_1^2)(\zeta_1\omega_1 - \zeta_2\omega_2)^2]^{1/2}}$$
$$\times\; e^{-\zeta_1\omega_1 t}\sin(\omega_1\sqrt{1 - \zeta_1^2}\,t - \psi_1)$$

$$+\; \frac{\omega_1^2[(1 - a\omega_2\zeta_2 + 2b\omega_2^2\zeta_2^2 - b\omega_2^2)^2 + \omega_2^2(1 - \zeta_2^2)(2\zeta_2 b\omega_2 - a)^2]^{1/2}}{\sqrt{1 - \zeta_2^2}\,[(\omega_1^2 - 2\zeta_1\omega_1\zeta_2\omega_2 + 2\zeta_2^2\omega_2^2 - \omega_2^2)^2 + 4\omega_2^2(1 - \zeta_2^2)(\zeta_2\omega_2 - \zeta_1\omega_1)^2]^{1/2}}$$
$$\times\; e^{-\zeta_2\omega_2 t}\sin(\omega_2\sqrt{1 - \zeta_2^2}\,t - \psi_2)$$

where
$$\psi_1 = \tan^{-1}\frac{\sqrt{1 - \zeta_1^2}}{-\zeta_1} + \tan^{-1}\frac{\omega_1\sqrt{1 - \zeta_1^2}\,(2b\zeta_1\omega_1 - a)}{1 - a\zeta_1\omega_1 + 2b\omega_1^2\zeta_1^2 - b\omega_1^2}$$
$$-\; \tan^{-1}\frac{2\omega_1\sqrt{1 - \zeta_1^2}\,(\zeta_1\omega_1 - \zeta_2\omega_2)}{\omega_2^2 - 2\zeta_1\omega_1\zeta_2\omega_2 + 2\zeta_1^2\omega_1^2 - \omega_1^2}$$

$$\psi_2 = \tan^{-1}\frac{\sqrt{1 - \zeta_2^2}}{-\zeta_2} + \tan^{-1}\frac{\omega_2\sqrt{1 - \zeta_2^2}\,(2b\zeta_2\omega_2 - a)}{1 - a\zeta_2\omega_2 + 2b\omega_2^2\zeta_2^2 - b\omega_2^2}$$
$$-\; \tan^{-1}\frac{2\omega_2\sqrt{1 - \zeta_2^2}\,(\zeta_2\omega_2 - \zeta_1\omega_1)}{\omega_1^2 - 2\zeta_1\omega_1\zeta_2\omega_2 + 2\zeta_2^2\omega_2^2 - \omega_2^2}$$

02.111

$$\frac{1 + as + bs^2}{s(1 + Ts)(1 + 2\zeta s/\omega_1 + s^2/\omega_1^2)}$$

$$1 - \frac{\omega_1^2(b - aT + T^2)}{1 + T^2\omega_1^2}\,e^{-t/T} - \left[\frac{(1 - b\omega_1^2)^2 + a^2\omega_1^2}{1 + T^2\omega_1^2}\right]^{1/2}\cos(\omega_1 t + \psi)$$

where $\psi = \tan^{-1}\dfrac{a\omega_1}{1 - b\omega_1^2} - \tan^{-1}T\omega_1$

02.111

$$\frac{1 + as + bs^2}{s(1 + Ts)(1 + 2\zeta s/\omega_1 + s^2/\omega_1^2)}$$

$$1 - \frac{\omega_1^2(b - aT + T^2)}{(1 - 2T\zeta\omega_1 + T^2\omega_1^2)}\,e^{-t/T}$$
$$+\; \left[\frac{(1 - a\zeta\omega_1 + 2b\zeta^2\omega_1^2 - b\omega_1^2)^2 + \omega_1^2(1 - \zeta^2)(2b\zeta\omega_1 - a)^2}{(1 - \zeta^2)(1 - 2T\zeta\omega_1 + T^2\omega_1^2)}\right]^{1/2}$$
$$\times\; e^{-\zeta\omega_1 t}\sin(\omega_1\sqrt{1 - \zeta^2}\,t - \psi)$$

where
$$\psi = \tan^{-1}\frac{\sqrt{1 - \zeta^2}}{-\zeta} + \tan^{-1}\frac{T\omega_1\sqrt{1 - \zeta^2}}{1 - T\zeta\omega_1}$$
$$+\; \tan^{-1}\frac{\omega_1\sqrt{1 - \zeta^2}\,(2b\zeta\omega_1 - a)}{1 - a\omega_1\zeta + 2b\zeta^2\omega_1^2 - b\omega_1^2}$$

---

* See Section 3.30.

LAPLACE TRANSFORM PAIRS (Continued)

Eq. No.*	$F(s)$	$f(t)$, $0 \leq t$
02.112	$\dfrac{1 + as + bs^2}{s(1 + Ts)\left(1 + \dfrac{2\zeta_1 s}{\omega_1} + \dfrac{s^2}{\omega_1^2}\right)\left(1 + \dfrac{2\zeta_2 s}{\omega_2} + \dfrac{s^2}{\omega_2^2}\right)}$	$1 + \dfrac{T^2\omega_1^2\omega_2^2(aT - T^2 - b)}{(1 - 2T\zeta_1\omega_1 + T^2\omega_1^2)(1 - 2T\zeta_2\omega_2 + T^2\omega_2^2)}\epsilon^{-t/T}$ $+ \dfrac{\omega_2^2[(1 - a\zeta_1\omega_1 + 2b\zeta_1^2\omega_1^2 - b\omega_1^2)^2 + \omega_1^2(1 - \zeta_1^2)(a - 2b\zeta_1\omega_1)^2]^{1/2}\epsilon^{-\zeta_1\omega_1 t}\sin\left(\omega_1\sqrt{1 - \zeta_1^2}\,t - \psi_1\right)}{[(1 - \zeta_1^2)(1 - 2T\zeta_1\omega_1 + T^2\omega_1^2)][(2\zeta_1^2\omega_1^2 - \omega_1^2 - 2\zeta_1\omega_1\zeta_2\omega_2 + \omega_2^2)^2 + 4\omega_1^2(1 - \zeta_1^2)(\zeta_1\omega_1 - \zeta_2\omega_2)^2]^{1/2}}$ $+ \dfrac{\omega_1^2[(1 - a\zeta_2\omega_2 + 2b\zeta_2^2\omega_2^2 - b\omega_2^2)^2 + \omega_2^2(1 - \zeta_2^2)(a - 2b\zeta_2\omega_2)^2]^{1/2}\epsilon^{-\zeta_2\omega_2 t}\sin\left(\omega_2\sqrt{1 - \zeta_2^2}\,t - \psi_2\right)}{[(1 - \zeta_2^2)(1 - 2T\zeta_2\omega_2 + T^2\omega_2^2)][(2\zeta_2^2\omega_2^2 - \omega_2^2 - 2\zeta_1\omega_1\zeta_2\omega_2 + \omega_1^2)^2 + 4\omega_2^2(1 - \zeta_2^2)(\zeta_2\omega_2 - \zeta_1\omega_1)^2]^{1/2}}$ where $\psi_1 = \tan^{-1}\dfrac{\sqrt{1 - \zeta_1^2}}{-\zeta_1} + \tan^{-1}\dfrac{T\omega_1\sqrt{1 - \zeta_1^2}}{1 - T\zeta_1\omega_1}$ $+ \tan^{-1}\dfrac{\omega_1\sqrt{1 - \zeta_1^2}\,(2b\zeta_1\omega_1 - a)}{1 - a\omega_1\zeta_1 + 2b\zeta_1^2\omega_1^2 - b\omega_1^2}$ $+ \tan^{-1}\dfrac{2\omega_1\sqrt{1 - \zeta_1^2}\,(\zeta_2\omega_2 - \zeta_1\omega_1)}{2\zeta_1^2\omega_1^2 - \omega_1^2 - 2\zeta_1\omega_1\zeta_2\omega_2 + \omega_2^2}$ $\psi_2 = \tan^{-1}\dfrac{\sqrt{1 - \zeta_2^2}}{-\zeta_2} + \tan^{-1}\dfrac{T\omega_2\sqrt{1 - \zeta_2^2}}{1 - T\zeta_2\omega_2}$ $+ \tan^{-1}\dfrac{\omega_2\sqrt{1 - \zeta_2^2}\,(2b\zeta_2\omega_2 - a)}{1 - a\omega_2\zeta_2 + 2b\zeta_2^2\omega_2^2 - b\omega_2^2}$ $+ \tan^{-1}\dfrac{2\omega_2\sqrt{1 - \zeta_2^2}\,(\zeta_1\omega_1 - \zeta_2\omega_2)}{2\zeta_2^2\omega_2^2 - \omega_2^2 - 2\zeta_1\omega_1\zeta_2\omega_2 + \omega_1^2}$
02.120	$\dfrac{1 + as + bs^2}{s(1 + T_1 s)(1 + T_2 s)}$	$1 + \dfrac{b - aT_1 + T_1^2}{T_1(T_2 - T_1)}\epsilon^{-t/T_1} - \dfrac{b - aT_2 + T_2^2}{T_2(T_2 - T_1)}\epsilon^{-t/T_2}$
02.120	$\dfrac{1 + as + bs^2}{s(1 + Ts)^2}$	$1 - \left[1 - \dfrac{b}{T^2} + \dfrac{b - aT + T^2}{T^3}\,t\right]\epsilon^{-t/T}$

$1 +$ (continued from preceding page)

$$\frac{s(1+T_1s)(1+T_2s)}{(1+2\zeta s/\omega_1+s^2/\omega_1^2)}$$

$$\cdots\; \epsilon^{-t/T_1}$$

$$+ \frac{(T_2-T_1)(1-2T_1\zeta\omega_1+T_1^2\omega_1^2)}{T_2\omega_1^2(T_2^2-aT_2+b)}$$

$$+ \frac{(T_1-T_2)(1-2T_2\zeta\omega_1+T_2^2\omega_1^2)}{(T_1-T_2)(1-2T_1\zeta\omega_1+T_1^2\omega_1^2)(1-2T_2\zeta\omega_1+T_2^2\omega_1^2)}\,\epsilon^{-t/T_2}$$

$$+ \left[\frac{(1-a\zeta\omega_1+2b\zeta^2\omega_1^2-b\omega_1^2)^2+\omega_1^2(1-\zeta^2)(a-2b\zeta\omega_1)^2}{(1-\zeta^2)(1-2T_1\zeta\omega_1+T_1^2\omega_1^2)(1-2T_2\zeta\omega_1+T_2^2\omega_1^2)}\right]^{1/2}$$

$$\epsilon^{-\zeta\omega_1 t}\sin\left(\omega_1\sqrt{1-\zeta^2}\,t-\psi\right)$$

where
$$\psi = \tan^{-1}\frac{\sqrt{1-\zeta^2}}{-\zeta} + \tan^{-1}\frac{T_1\omega_1\sqrt{1-\zeta^2}}{1-T_1\zeta\omega_1}$$
$$+ \tan^{-1}\frac{T_2\omega_1\sqrt{1-\zeta^2}}{1-T_2\zeta\omega_1} + \tan^{-1}\frac{\omega_1\sqrt{1-\zeta^2}\,(2b\zeta\omega_1-a)}{1-a\zeta\omega_1+2b\zeta^2\omega_1^2-b\omega_1^2}$$

02.130

$$\frac{(1+as)(1+bs)}{s(1+T_1s)(1+T_2s)(1+T_3s)}$$

$$1 - \frac{(T_1-a)(T_1-b)}{(T_1-T_2)(T_1-T_3)}\,\epsilon^{-t/T_1} - \frac{(T_2-a)(T_2-b)}{(T_2-T_1)(T_2-T_3)}\,\epsilon^{-t/T_2}$$
$$- \frac{(T_3-a)(T_3-b)}{(T_3-T_1)(T_3-T_2)}\,\epsilon^{-t/T_3}$$

02.130

$$\frac{1+as+bs^2}{s(1+T_1s)(1+T_2s)^2}$$

$$1 - \frac{T_1^2-aT_1+b}{(T_1-T_2)^2}\,\epsilon^{-t/T_1} + \left[\frac{T_2^2-aT_2+b}{T_2^2(T_1-T_2)}\,t + \frac{b+2T_1T_2-aT_1-T_2^2}{(T_1-T_2)^2}\right]\epsilon^{-t/T_2}$$

02.130

$$\frac{1+as+bs^2}{s(1+T_1s)^3}$$

$$1 - \left(1 - \frac{b-T^2}{T^3}\,t - \frac{aT-T^2-b}{2T^4}\,t^2\right)\epsilon^{-t/T}$$

02.130

$$\frac{1+as+bs^2}{s(1+T_1s)(1+T_2s)(1+T_3s)}$$

$$1 - \frac{T_1^2-aT_1+b}{(T_1-T_2)(T_1-T_3)}\,\epsilon^{-t/T_1} - \frac{T_2^2-aT_2+b}{(T_2-T_1)(T_2-T_3)}\,\epsilon^{-t/T_2}$$
$$- \frac{T_3^2-aT_3+b}{(T_3-T_1)(T_3-T_2)}\,\epsilon^{-t/T_3}$$

02.201

$$\frac{1+as+bs^2}{s^2(1+s^2/\omega_1^2)}$$

$$t + a - \frac{1}{\omega_1}\left[(1-b\omega_1^2)^2+a^2\omega_1^2\right]^{1/2}\sin(\omega_1 t+\psi)$$

where $\psi = \tan^{-1}\dfrac{a\omega_1}{1-b\omega_1^2}$

* See Section 3.30.

LAPLACE TRANSFORM PAIRS (*Continued*)

Eq. No.*	$F(s)$	$f(t)$ $0 \leq t$
02.201	$\dfrac{1 + as + bs^2}{s^2(1 + 2\zeta s/\omega_1 + s^2/\omega_1{}^2)}$	$t + a - \dfrac{2\zeta}{\omega_1} + \dfrac{[(1 - a\zeta\omega_1 + 2b\zeta^2\omega_1{}^2 - b\omega_1{}^2)^2 + \omega_1{}^2(1 - \zeta^2)(a - 2b\zeta\omega_1)^2]^{1/2}}{\omega_1\sqrt{1-\zeta^2}}$ $\epsilon^{-\zeta\omega_1 t} \sin(\omega_1\sqrt{1-\zeta^2}\,t - \psi)$

where $\psi = 2\tan^{-1}\dfrac{\sqrt{1-\zeta^2}}{-\zeta} + \tan^{-1}\dfrac{\omega_1\sqrt{1-\zeta^2}\,(2b\zeta\omega_1 - a)}{1 - a\zeta\omega_1 + 2b\zeta^2\omega_1{}^2 - b\omega_1{}^2}$

Eq. No.*	$F(s)$	$f(t)$ $0 \leq t$
02.202	$\dfrac{1 + as + bs^2}{s^2(1 + 2\zeta_1 s/\omega_1 + s^2/\omega_1{}^2)(1 + 2\zeta_2 s/\omega_2 + s^2/\omega_2{}^2)}$	$t + a - \dfrac{2\zeta_1}{\omega_1} - \dfrac{2\zeta_2}{\omega_2}$

$$+ \dfrac{\omega_2{}^2[(1 - a\zeta_1\omega_1 + 2b\zeta_1{}^2\omega_1{}^2 - b\omega_1{}^2)^2 + \omega_1{}^2(1 - \zeta_1{}^2)(2b\zeta_1\omega_1 - a)^2]^{1/2}}{\omega_1\sqrt{1-\zeta_1{}^2}\,[(\omega_2{}^2 - 2\zeta_1\omega_1\zeta_2\omega_2 + 2\zeta_1{}^2\omega_1{}^2 - \omega_1{}^2)^2 + 4\omega_1{}^2(1 - \zeta_1{}^2)(\zeta_1\omega_1 - \zeta_2\omega_2)^2]^{1/2}}$$
$$\epsilon^{-\zeta_1\omega_1 t} \sin(\omega_1\sqrt{1-\zeta_1{}^2}\,t - \psi_1)$$

$$+ \dfrac{\omega_1{}^2[(1 - a\zeta_2\omega_2 + 2b\zeta_2{}^2\omega_2{}^2 - b\omega_2{}^2)^2 + \omega_2{}^2(1 - \zeta_2{}^2)(2b\zeta_2\omega_2 - a)^2]^{1/2}}{\omega_2\sqrt{1-\zeta_2{}^2}\,[(\omega_1{}^2 - 2\zeta_1\omega_1\zeta_2\omega_2 + 2\zeta_2{}^2\omega_2{}^2 - \omega_2{}^2)^2 + 4\omega_2{}^2(1 - \zeta_2{}^2)(\zeta_2\omega_2 - \zeta_1\omega_1)^2]^{1/2}}$$
$$\epsilon^{-\zeta_2\omega_2 t} \sin(\omega_2\sqrt{1-\zeta_2{}^2}\,t - \psi_2)$$

where
$$\psi_1 = 2\tan^{-1}\dfrac{\sqrt{1-\zeta_1{}^2}}{-\zeta_1} + \tan^{-1}\dfrac{\omega_1\sqrt{1-\zeta_1{}^2}\,(2b\zeta_1\omega_1 - a)}{1 - a\zeta_1\omega_1 + 2b\zeta_1{}^2\omega_1{}^2 - b\omega_1{}^2} - \tan^{-1}\dfrac{2\omega_1\sqrt{1-\zeta_1{}^2}\,(\zeta_1\omega_1 - \zeta_2\omega_2)}{\omega_2{}^2 - 2\zeta_1\omega_1\zeta_2\omega_2 + 2\zeta_1{}^2\omega_1{}^2 - \omega_1{}^2}$$

$$\psi_2 = 2\tan^{-1}\dfrac{\sqrt{1-\zeta_2{}^2}}{-\zeta_2} + \tan^{-1}\dfrac{\omega_2\sqrt{1-\zeta_2{}^2}\,(2b\zeta_2\omega_2 - a)}{1 - a\zeta_2\omega_2 + 2b\zeta_2{}^2\omega_2{}^2 - b\omega_2{}^2} - \tan^{-1}\dfrac{2\omega_2\sqrt{1-\zeta_2{}^2}\,(\zeta_2\omega_2 - \zeta_1\omega_1)}{\omega_1{}^2 - 2\zeta_1\omega_1\zeta_2\omega_2 + 2\zeta_2{}^2\omega_2{}^2 - \omega_2{}^2}$$

Eq. No.*	$F(s)$	$f(t)$ $0 \leq t$
02.210	$\dfrac{1 + as + bs^2}{s^2(1 + Ts)}$	$t + a - T - \left(a - T - \dfrac{b}{T}\right)\epsilon^{-t/T}$

	$$\dfrac{1 + as + bs^2}{s^2(1 + Ts)(1 + 2\zeta s/\omega_1 + s^2/\omega_1^2)}$$

$$t + a - T - \frac{\zeta}{\omega_1} + \frac{1 - 2\zeta T\omega_1 + T^2\omega_1^2}{(1-\zeta^2)(1 - 2T\zeta\omega_1 + T^2\omega_1^2)}\,\epsilon^{-t/T}$$

$$+ \frac{1}{\omega_1}\left[\frac{(1 - a\zeta\omega_1 + 2b\zeta^2\omega_1^2 - b\omega_1^2)^2 + \omega_1^2(1-\zeta^2)(2b\zeta\omega - a)^2}{(1-\zeta^2)(1 - 2T\zeta\omega_1 + T^2\omega_1^2)}\right]^{1/2}$$

$$\epsilon^{-\zeta\omega_1 t}\sin\left(\omega_1\sqrt{1-\zeta^2}\,t - \psi\right)$$

where
$$\psi = \tan^{-1}\frac{T\omega_1\sqrt{1-\zeta^2}}{1 - T\zeta\omega_1} + \tan^{-1}\frac{\omega_1\sqrt{1-\zeta^2}\,(2b\zeta\omega_1 - a)}{1 - a\zeta\omega_1 + 2b\zeta^2\omega_1^2 - b\omega_1^2} + 2\tan^{-1}\frac{\sqrt{1-\zeta^2}}{-\zeta}$$

02.212	$$\dfrac{1 + as + bs^2}{s^2(1 + Ts)(1 + 2\zeta_1 s/\omega_1 + s^2/\omega_1^2)(1 + 2\zeta_2 s/\omega_2 + s^2/\omega_2^2)}$$

$$t + a - T - \frac{2\zeta_1}{\omega_1} - \frac{2\zeta_2}{\omega_2} - \frac{T^3\omega_1^2\omega_2^2(aT - T^2 - b)}{(1 - 2T\zeta_1\omega_1 + T^2\omega_1^2)(1 - 2T\zeta_2\omega_2 + T^2\omega_2^2)}\,\epsilon^{-t/T}$$

$$+ \frac{\omega_2^2[(1 - a\zeta_1\omega_1 + 2b\zeta_1^2\omega_1^2 - b\omega_1^2)^2 + \omega_1^2(1-\zeta_1^2)(2b\zeta_1\omega_1 - a)^2]^{1/2}}{\omega_1[(1-\zeta_1^2)(1 - 2T\zeta_1\omega_1 + T^2\omega_1^2)]^{1/2}[(2\zeta_1^2\omega_2^2 - \omega_1^2 - 2\zeta_1\omega_1\zeta_2\omega_2 + \omega_2^2)^2 + 4\omega_1^2(1-\zeta_1^2)(\zeta_1\omega_1 - \zeta_2\omega_2)^2]^{1/2}}\,\epsilon^{-\zeta_1\omega_1 t}\sin\left(\omega_1\sqrt{1-\zeta_1^2}\,t - \psi_1\right)$$

$$+ \frac{\omega_1^2[(1 - a\zeta_2\omega_2 + 2b\zeta_2^2\omega_2^2 - b\omega_2^2)^2 + \omega_2^2(1-\zeta_2^2)(2b\zeta_2\omega_2 - a)^2]^{1/2}}{\omega_2[(1-\zeta_2^2)(1 - 2T\zeta_2\omega_2 + T^2\omega_2^2)]^{1/2}[(2\zeta_2^2\omega_2^2 - \omega_2^2 - 2\zeta_1\omega_1\zeta_2\omega_2 + \omega_1^2)^2 + 4\omega_2^2(1-\zeta_2^2)(\zeta_2\omega_2 - \zeta_1\omega_1)^2]^{1/2}}\,\epsilon^{-\zeta_2\omega_2 t}\sin\left(\omega_2\sqrt{1-\zeta_2^2}\,t - \psi_2\right)$$

where
$$\psi_1 = 2\tan^{-1}\frac{\sqrt{1-\zeta_1^2}}{-\zeta_1} + \tan^{-1}\frac{T\omega_1\sqrt{1-\zeta_1^2}}{1 - T\zeta_1\omega_1}$$

$$+ \tan^{-1}\frac{\omega_1\sqrt{1-\zeta_1^2}\,(2b\zeta_1\omega_1 - a)}{1 - a\zeta_1\omega_1 + 2b\zeta_1^2\omega_1^2 - b\omega_1^2}$$

$$+ \tan^{-1}\frac{2\omega_1\sqrt{1-\zeta_1^2}\,(\zeta_2\omega_2 - \zeta_1\omega_1)}{2\zeta_1^2\omega_1^2 - \omega_1^2 - 2\zeta_1\omega_1\zeta_2\omega_2 + \omega_2^2}$$

$$\psi_2 = 2\tan^{-1}\frac{\sqrt{1-\zeta_2^2}}{-\zeta_2} + \tan^{-1}\frac{T\omega_2\sqrt{1-\zeta_2^2}}{1 - T\zeta_2\omega_2}$$

$$+ \tan^{-1}\frac{\omega_2\sqrt{1-\zeta_2^2}\,(2b\zeta_2\omega_2 - a)}{1 - a\zeta_2\omega_2 + 2b\zeta_2^2\omega_2^2 - b\omega_2^2}$$

$$+ \tan^{-1}\frac{2\omega_2\sqrt{1-\zeta_2^2}\,(\zeta_1\omega_1 - \zeta_2\omega_2)}{2\zeta_2^2\omega_2^2 - \omega_2^2 - 2\zeta_1\omega_1\zeta_2\omega_2 + \omega_1^2}$$

* See Section 3.30.

LAPLACE TRANSFORM PAIRS (Continued)

Eq. No.*	$F(s)$	$f(t)$, $\;0 \leq t$
02.220	$\dfrac{1 + as + bs^2}{s^2(1 + T_1 s)(1 + T_2 s)}$	$t + (a - T_1 - T_2) + \dfrac{b - aT_1 + T_1{}^2}{T_1 - T_2}\,\epsilon^{-t/T_1} - \dfrac{b - aT_2 + T_2{}^2}{T_1 - T_2}\,\epsilon^{-t/T_2}$
02.220	$\dfrac{1 + as + bs^2}{s^2(1 + Ts)^2}$	$t + a - 2T + \left[\dfrac{b - aT + T^2}{T^2}\,t + (2T - a)\right]\epsilon^{-t/T}$
02.230	$\dfrac{1 + as + bs^2}{s^2(1 + T_1 s)(1 + T_2 s)(1 + T_3 s)}$	$t + a - T_1 - T_2 - T_3 + \dfrac{T_1(T_1{}^2 - aT_1 + b)}{(T_1 - T_2)(T_1 - T_3)}\,\epsilon^{-t/T_1}$ $+ \dfrac{T_2(T_2{}^2 - aT_2 + b)}{(T_2 - T_1)(T_2 - T_3)}\,\epsilon^{-t/T_2} + \dfrac{T_3(T_3{}^2 - aT_3 + b)}{(T_3 - T_1)(T_3 - T_2)}\,\epsilon^{-t/T_3}$
02.230	$\dfrac{1 + as + bs^2}{s^2(1 + Ts)^3}$	$t + a - 3T + \left[\dfrac{b - aT + T^2}{2T^3}\,t^2 + \dfrac{2T - a}{T}\,t + 3T - a\right]\epsilon^{-t/T}$
03.040	$\dfrac{(1 + as)(1 + bs)(1 + cs)}{(1 + T_1 s)(1 + T_2 s)(1 + T_3 s)(1 + T_4 s)}$	$\dfrac{(T_1 - a)(T_1 - b)(T_1 - c)}{T_1(T_1 - T_2)(T_1 - T_3)(T_1 - T_4)}\,\epsilon^{-t/T_1}$ $+ \dfrac{(T_2 - a)(T_2 - b)(T_2 - c)}{T_2(T_2 - T_1)(T_2 - T_3)(T_2 - T_4)}\,\epsilon^{-t/T_2}$ $+ \dfrac{(T_3 - a)(T_3 - b)(T_3 - c)}{T_3(T_3 - T_1)(T_3 - T_2)(T_3 - T_4)}\,\epsilon^{-t/T_3}$ $+ \dfrac{(T_4 - a)(T_4 - b)(T_4 - c)}{T_4(T_4 - T_1)(T_4 - T_2)(T_4 - T_3)}\,\epsilon^{-t/T_4}$
03.130	$\dfrac{1 + as + bs^2 + cs^3}{s(1 + T_1 s)(1 + T_2 s)(1 + T_3 s)}$	$1 - \dfrac{T_1{}^3 - aT_1{}^2 + bT_1 - c}{T_1(T_1 - T_2)(T_1 - T_3)}\,\epsilon^{-t/T_1} - \dfrac{T_2{}^3 - aT_2{}^2 + bT_2 - c}{T_2(T_2 - T_1)(T_2 - T_3)}\,\epsilon^{-t/T_2}$ $- \dfrac{T_3{}^3 - aT_3{}^2 + bT_3 - c}{T_3(T_3 - T_1)(T_3 - T_2)}\,\epsilon^{-t/T_3}$

03.130	$\dfrac{(1 + as)(1 + bs)(1 + cs)}{s(1 + T_1s)(1 + T_2s)(1 + T_3s)}$	$1 - \dfrac{(T_1 - a)(T_1 - b)(T_1 - c)}{T_1(T_1 - T_2)(T_1 - T_3)}\ \epsilon^{-t/T_1} - \dfrac{(T_2 - a)(T_2 - b)(T_2 - c)}{T_2(T_2 - T_1)(T_2 - T_3)}\ \epsilon^{-t/T_2} - \dfrac{(T_3 - a)(T_3 - b)(T_3 - c)}{T_3(T_3 - T_1)(T_3 - T_2)}\ \epsilon^{-t/T_3}$
03.140	$\dfrac{(1 + as)(1 + bs)(1 + cs)}{s(1 + T_1s)(1 + T_2s)(1 + T_3s)(1 + T_4s)}$	$1 - \dfrac{(T_1 - a)(T_1 - b)(T_1 - c)}{(T_1 - T_2)(T_1 - T_3)(T_1 - T_4)}\ \epsilon^{-t/T_1} - \dfrac{(T_2 - a)(T_2 - b)(T_2 - c)}{(T_2 - T_1)(T_2 - T_3)(T_2 - T_4)}\ \epsilon^{-t/T_2} - \dfrac{(T_3 - a)(T_3 - b)(T_3 - c)}{(T_3 - T_1)(T_3 - T_2)(T_3 - T_4)}\ \epsilon^{-t/T_3} - \dfrac{(T_4 - a)(T_4 - b)(T_4 - c)}{(T_4 - T_1)(T_4 - T_2)(T_4 - T_3)}\ \epsilon^{-t/T_4}$
03.230	$\dfrac{(1 + as)(1 + bs)(1 + cs)}{s^2(1 + T_1s)(1 + T_2s)(1 + T_3s)}$	$t + a + b + c - T_1 - T_2 - T_3 + \dfrac{(T_1 - a)(T_1 - b)(T_1 - c)}{(T_1 - T_2)(T_1 - T_3)}\ \epsilon^{-t/T_1} + \dfrac{(T_2 - a)(T_2 - b)(T_2 - c)}{(T_2 - T_1)(T_2 - T_3)}\ \epsilon^{-t/T_2} + \dfrac{(T_3 - a)(T_3 - b)(T_3 - c)}{(T_3 - T_1)(T_3 - T_2)}\ \epsilon^{-t/T_3}$
03.240	$\dfrac{(1 + as)(1 + bs)(1 + cs)}{s^2(1 + T_1s)(1 + T_2s)(1 + T_3s)(1 + T_4s)}$	$t + a + b + c - T_1 - T_2 - T_3 - T_4 + \dfrac{T_1(T_1 - a)(T_1 - b)(T_1 - c)}{(T_1 - T_2)(T_1 - T_3)(T_1 - T_4)}\ \epsilon^{-t/T_1} + \dfrac{T_2(T_2 - a)(T_2 - b)(T_2 - c)}{(T_2 - T_1)(T_2 - T_3)(T_2 - T_4)}\ \epsilon^{-t/T_2} + \dfrac{T_3(T_3 - a)(T_3 - b)(T_3 - c)}{(T_3 - T_1)(T_3 - T_2)(T_3 - T_4)}\ \epsilon^{-t/T_3} + \dfrac{T_4(T_4 - a)(T_4 - b)(T_4 - c)}{(T_4 - T_1)(T_4 - T_2)(T_4 - T_3)}\ \epsilon^{-t/T_4}$
nn.00(n + 1)	$\dfrac{s^n}{(1 + s^2/\omega_1^2)^{n+1}}$	$\dfrac{\omega^{2n+1}t^n}{2^n n!} \sin \omega_1 t$

* See Section 3.30.

LAPLACE TRANSFORM PAIRS (*Continued*)

Eq. No.*	$F(s)$	$f(t)$	$0 \leq t$
11.001	$\dfrac{s}{1 + 2\zeta s/\omega_1 + s^2/\omega_1^2}$	$\dfrac{\omega_1^2 \epsilon^{-\zeta\omega_1 t}}{\sqrt{1-\zeta^2}} \sin\left(\omega_1\sqrt{1-\zeta^2}\,t + \psi\right)$ where $\psi = \tan^{-1}\dfrac{\sqrt{1-\zeta^2}}{-\zeta}$	
11.001	$\dfrac{s}{1 + s^2/\omega_1^2}$	$\omega_1^2 \cos \omega_1 t$	
11.002	$\dfrac{s}{(1 + s^2/\omega_1^2)(1 + s^2/\omega_2^2)}$	$\dfrac{\omega_1^2\omega_2^2}{\omega_2^2 - \omega_1^2}\left(\cos \omega_1 t - \cos \omega_2 t\right)$	
11.002	$\dfrac{s}{(1 + s^2/\omega_1^2)^2}$	$\dfrac{\omega_1^3}{2}\, t \sin \omega_1 t$	
11.002	$\dfrac{s}{\left[1 + s^2/(\omega_1 + \omega_2)^2\right]\left[1 + s^2/(\omega_1 - \omega_2)^2\right]}$	$\dfrac{\omega_1^4 + \omega_2^4 + 6\omega_1^2\omega_2^2}{2\omega_1\omega_2}\left(\sin \omega_1 t \sin \omega_2 t\right)$	
11.002	$\dfrac{s}{(1 + 2\zeta_1 s/\omega_1 + s^2/\omega_1^2)(1 + 2\zeta_2 s/\omega_2 + s^2/\omega_2^2)}$	$\dfrac{\omega_1^2\omega_2^2 \epsilon^{-\zeta_1\omega_1 t} \sin\left(\omega_1\sqrt{1 - \zeta_1^2}\,t - \psi_1\right)}{\sqrt{1 - \zeta_1^2}\,(A^2 + 4AB\zeta_1\omega_1 + 4B^2\omega_1^2)^{1/2}}$ $+\ \dfrac{\omega_1^2\omega_2^2 \epsilon^{-\zeta_2\omega_2 t} \sin\left(\omega_2\sqrt{1 - \zeta_2^2}\,t - \psi_2\right)}{\sqrt{1 - \zeta_2^2}\,(A^2 + 4AB\zeta_2\omega_2 + 4B^2\omega_2^2)^{1/2}}$ where $A = \omega_1^2 - \omega_2^2 \qquad B = \zeta_2\omega_2 - \zeta_1\omega_1$ $\psi_1 = -\tan^{-1}\dfrac{\sqrt{1 - \zeta_1^2}}{-\zeta_1} + \tan^{-1}\dfrac{2B\omega_1\sqrt{1 - \zeta_1^2}}{-A - 2B\zeta_1\omega_1}$ $\psi_2 = -\tan^{-1}\dfrac{\sqrt{1 - \zeta_2^2}}{-\zeta_2} - \tan^{-1}\dfrac{2B\omega_2\sqrt{1 - \zeta_2^2}}{A + 2B\zeta_2\omega_2}$	

11.002	$\dfrac{\omega_1^2 \omega_2^2}{(1 + s^2/\omega_1^2)(1 + 2\zeta s/\omega_2 + s^2/\omega_2^2)}$	$\dfrac{\omega_1^2 \omega_2^2}{[(\omega_1^2 - \omega_2^2)^2 + 4\zeta^2 \omega_1^2 \omega_2^2]^{1/2}} \left[\cos(\omega_1 t - \psi_1) + \dfrac{1}{\sqrt{1-\zeta^2}} \epsilon^{-\zeta \omega_2 t} \sin(\omega_2 \sqrt{1-\zeta^2}\, t - \psi_2) \right]$
		where $\psi_1 = \tan^{-1} \dfrac{2\zeta \omega_1 \omega_2}{\omega_2^2 - \omega_1^2}$
		$\psi_2 = -\tan^{-1} \dfrac{\sqrt{1-\zeta^2}}{-\zeta} - \tan^{-1} \dfrac{2\zeta \omega_2^2 \sqrt{1-\zeta^2}}{\omega_1^2 + 2\zeta^2 \omega_2^2 - \omega_2^2}$
11.011	$\dfrac{s}{(1 + T s)(1 + s^2/\omega_1^2)}$	$\dfrac{-\omega_1^2}{1 + T^2 \omega_1^2} \epsilon^{-t/T} + \dfrac{\omega_1^2}{(1 + T^2 \omega_1^2)^{1/2}} \cos(\omega_1 t - \psi)$
		where $\psi = \tan^{-1} T\omega_1$
11.020	$\dfrac{s}{(1 + T_1 s)(1 + T_2 s)}$	$\dfrac{1}{T_1 T_2 (T_1 - T_2)} (T_1 \epsilon^{-t/T_2} - T_2 \epsilon^{-t/T_1})$
11.020	$\dfrac{s}{(1 + T s)^2}$	$\dfrac{1}{T^3}(T - t)\epsilon^{-t/T}$
11.020	$\dfrac{s}{(1 - T^2 s^2)}$	$\dfrac{1}{T^2} \cosh \dfrac{t}{T}$
11.021	$\dfrac{s}{(1 + T_1 s)(1 + T_2 s)(1 + s^2/\omega_1^2)}$	$\dfrac{T_1 \omega_1^2}{(T_2 - T_1)(1 + T_1^2 \omega_1^2)} \epsilon^{-t/T_1} + \dfrac{T_2 \omega_1^2}{(T_1 - T_2)(1 + T_2^2 \omega_1^2)} \epsilon^{-t/T_2} + \dfrac{\omega_1^2 \cos(\omega_1 t - \psi)}{[(1 + T_1^2 \omega_1^2)(1 + T_2^2 \omega_1^2)]^{1/2}}$
		where $\psi = \tan^{-1} T_1 \omega_1 + \tan^{-1} T_2 \omega_1$
11.030	$\dfrac{s}{(1 + T_1 s)(1 + T_2 s)(1 + T_3 s)}$	$\dfrac{[(T_2 - T_3)\epsilon^{-t/T_1} + (T_3 - T_1)\epsilon^{-t/T_2} + (T_1 - T_2)\epsilon^{-t/T_3}]}{(T_1 - T_2)(T_2 - T_3)(T_3 - T_1)}$

* See Section 3.30.

LAPLACE TRANSFORM PAIRS (Continued)

Eq. No.*	$F(s)$	$f(t)$ $\qquad 0 \leq t$
11.030	$\dfrac{s}{(1+T_s)^3}$	$\left(\dfrac{t}{T^3} - \dfrac{t^2}{2T^4}\right)\epsilon^{-t/T}$
11.030	$\dfrac{s}{(1+T_1 s)(1+T_2 s)^2}$	$-\dfrac{\epsilon^{-t/T_1}}{(T_1-T_2)^2} + \left[\dfrac{1}{(T_2-T_1)^2} - \dfrac{t}{T_2^2(T_2-T_1)}\right]\epsilon^{-t/T_2}$
11.031	$\dfrac{s}{(1+T_1 s)(1+T_2 s)(1+T_3 s)}$ $(1+s^2/\omega_1^2)$	$-\dfrac{T_1^2\omega_1^2\epsilon^{-t/T_1}}{(T_1-T_2)(T_1-T_3)(1+T_1^2\omega_1^2)} - \dfrac{T_2^2\omega_1^2\epsilon^{-t/T_2}}{(T_2-T_1)(T_2-T_3)(1+T_2^2\omega_1^2)}$ $-\dfrac{T_3^2\omega_1^2\epsilon^{-t/T_3}}{(T_3-T_1)(T_3-T_2)(1+T_3^2\omega_1^2)}$ $+\dfrac{\omega_1^2\cos(\omega_1 t - \psi)}{[(1+T_1^2\omega_1^2)(1+T_2^2\omega_1^2)(1+T_3^2\omega_1^2)]^{1/2}}$ where $\psi = \tan^{-1}T_1\omega_1 + \tan^{-1}T_2\omega_1 + \tan^{-1}T_3\omega_1$
12.021	$\dfrac{s(1+as)}{(1+T_1 s)(1+T_2 s)(1+s^2/\omega_1^2)}$	$\dfrac{\omega_1^2(T_1-a)}{(T_2-T_1)(1+T_1^2\omega_1^2)}\epsilon^{-t/T_1} + \dfrac{\omega_1^2(T_2-a)}{(T_1-T_2)(1+T_2^2\omega_1^2)}\epsilon^{-t/T_2}$ $+\dfrac{\omega_1^2(1+a^2\omega_1^2)^{1/2}\cos(\omega_1 t - \psi)}{[(1+T_1^2\omega_1^2)(1+T_2^2\omega_1^2)]^{1/2}}$ where $\psi = \tan^{-1}T_1\omega_1 + \tan^{-1}T_2\omega_1 - \tan^{-1}a\omega_1$
12.030	$\dfrac{s(1+as)}{(1+T_1 s)(1+T_2 s)(1+T_3 s)}$	$\dfrac{a-T_1}{T_1(T_1-T_2)(T_1-T_3)}\epsilon^{-t/T_1} + \dfrac{a-T_2}{T_2(T_2-T_1)(T_2-T_3)}\epsilon^{-t/T_2}$ $+\dfrac{a-T_3}{T_3(T_3-T_1)(T_3-T_2)}\epsilon^{-t/T_3}$
22.002	$\dfrac{s^2}{(1+s^2/\omega_1^2)^2}$	$\dfrac{\omega_1^3}{2}(\sin\omega_1 t + \omega_1 t\cos\omega_1 t)$
22.002	$\dfrac{s^2}{(1+s^2/\omega_1^2)(1+s^2/\omega_2^2)}$	$\dfrac{\omega_1^2\omega_2^2}{\omega_1^2-\omega_2^2}(\omega_1\sin\omega_1 t - \omega_2\sin\omega_2 t)$

22.021	$\dfrac{s^2}{(1+T_1s)(1+T_2s)(1+s^2/\omega_1^2)}$	$\dfrac{\omega_1^2}{(T_1-T_2)(1+T_1^2\omega_1^2)}\,\epsilon^{-t/T_1} + \dfrac{\omega_1^2}{(T_2-T_1)(1+T_2^2\omega_1^2)}\,\epsilon^{-t/T_2}$ $- \dfrac{\omega_1^3 \sin\,(\omega_1 t - \psi)}{[(1+T_1^2\omega_1^2)(1+T_2^2\omega_1^2)]^{1/2}}$ where $\psi = \tan^{-1} T_1\omega_1 + \tan^{-1} T_2\omega_1$
22.030	$\dfrac{s^2}{(1+Ts)^3}$	$\left(\dfrac{1}{T^3} - \dfrac{2t}{T^4} + \dfrac{t^2}{2T^5}\right)\epsilon^{-t/T}$
22.030	$\dfrac{s^2}{(1+T_1s)(1+T_2s)^3}$	$\dfrac{\epsilon^{-t/T_1}}{T_1(T_1-T_2)^2} + \left[\dfrac{T_1-2T_2}{T_2^2(T_2-T_1)^2} + \dfrac{t}{T_2^3(T_2-T_1)}\right]\epsilon^{-t/T_2}$
33.002	$\dfrac{s^3}{(1+s^2/\omega_1^2)(1+s^2/\omega_2^2)}$	$\dfrac{\omega_1^2\omega_2^2}{\omega_1^2-\omega_2^2}\,(\omega_1^2\cos\,\omega_1 t - \omega_2^2\cos\,\omega_2 t)$
33.021	$\dfrac{s^3}{(1+T_1s)(1+T_2s)(1+s^2/\omega_1^2)}$	$\dfrac{\omega_1^2}{T_1(T_2-T_1)(1+T_1^2\omega_1^2)}\,\epsilon^{-t/T_1} + \dfrac{\omega_1^2}{T_2(T_1-T_2)(1+T_2^2\omega_1^2)}\,\epsilon^{-t/T_2}$ $- \dfrac{\omega_1^4 \cos\,(\omega_1 t - \psi)}{[(1+T_1^2\omega_1^2)(1+T_2^2\omega_1^2)]^{1/2}}$ where $\psi = \tan^{-1} T_1\omega_1 + \tan^{-1} T_2\omega_1$

* See Section 3.30.

BIBLIOGRAPHY

1. Ahrendt, W. R., and Taplin, J. F., *Automatic Feedback Control*, McGraw-Hill Book Co., Inc., New York, 1951.
2. Alexanderson, Edwards, and Bowman, "The Amplidyne Generator, a Dynamoelectric Amplifier for Power Control," *Gen. Elec. Rev.*, Vol. 43, March, 1940; *Trans. AIEE, Supplement*, Vol. 59, December, 1940.
3. Black, H. S., "Stabilized Feedback Amplifier," *Bell System Tech. J.*, Vol. 13, January, 1934.
4. Bode, H. W., *Network Analysis and Feedback Amplifier Design*, D. Van Nostrand Co., Inc., New York, 1945.
5. Brown, G. S., and Campbell, D. P., *Principles of Servomechanisms*, John Wiley & Sons, Inc., New York, 1948.
6. Bush, V., *Operational Circuit Analysis*, John Wiley & Sons, Inc., New York, 1929.
7. Chestnut, H., and Mayer, R. W., *Servomechanisms and Regulating System Design*, John Wiley & Sons, Inc., New York, 1951.
8. Churchill, R. V., *Modern Operational Mathematics in Engineering*, McGraw-Hill Book Co., Inc., New York, 1944.
9. Doherty, R. E., and Keller, E. G., *Mathematics of Modern Engineering*, John Wiley & Sons, Inc., New York, 1936.
10. Edwards, C. M., and Johnson, E. C., "An Electronic Simulator for Nonlinear Servomechanisms," *AIEE Preprint*, 50–47, January, 1950.
11. Evans, W. R., *Control System Dynamics*, McGraw-Hill Book Co., Inc., New York (to be published).
12. Evans, W. R., "Control System Synthesis by Root Locus Method," *AIEE Preprint*, 50–51, January, 1950.
13. Farrington, G. H., *Fundamentals of Automatic Control*, John Wiley & Sons, Inc., New York, 1951.
14. Fich, S., *Transient Analysis in Electrical Engineering*, Prentice-Hall, Inc., New York, 1951.
15. Gardner, M. F., and Barnes, J. L., *Transients in Linear Systems*, John Wiley & Sons, Inc., New York, 1942.
16. Goldman, S., *Transformation Calculus and Electrical Transients*, Prentice-Hall, Inc., New York, 1949.
17. Guillemin, E. A., *Communication Networks*, Vol. 2, John Wiley & Sons, Inc., New York, 1935.
18. Hall, A. C., "A Generalized Analogue Computer for Flight Simulation," *AIEE Preprint*, 50–48, January, 1950.
19. Hall, A. C., *Analysis and Synthesis of Linear Servomechanisms*, Technology Press, Cambridge, Mass., 1943.
20. Harris, H., "The Analysis and Design of Servomechanisms," *OSRD Report 454*, December, 1941.

21. Hazen, H. L., "Theory of Servomechanisms," *J. Franklin Inst.*, Vol. 218, September, 1934.

22. Herst, R., "A Basic Approach to Servomechanism Design," *Elec. Mfg.*, December, 1949.

23. Herst, R., "Seven Basic Types of Servomechanisms Analyzed," *Elec. Mfg.*, May, 1950.

24. Herst, Stovall, *et al.*, "Designing Servomechanism Systems," *Elec. Mfg. Reprint*, 1952.

25. Ince, E. L., *Ordinary Differential Equations*, Dover Publications, Inc., New York, 1944.

26. James, H. M., Nichols, N. B., and Phillips, R. S., *Theory of Servomechanisms*, Vol. 25, McGraw-Hill Book Co., Inc., New York, 1947.

27. Johnson, E. C., "Sinusoidal Analysis of Feedback Control Systems Containing Nonlinear Elements," *AIEE Preprint*, 52–154, April, 1952.

28. Kochenburger, R. J.: "A Frequency Response Method for Analyzing and Synthesizing Contactor Servomechanisms," *AIEE Preprint*, 50–44, January, 1950.

29. Korn, G. A., and Korn, T. M., *Electronic Analog Computers*, McGraw-Hill Book Co., Inc., New York, 1952.

30. Lauer, H., Lesnick, R., and Matson, L. E., *Servomechanism Fundamentals*, McGraw-Hill Book Co., Inc., New York, 1947.

31. Levy, H., and Baggott, E. A., *Numerical Solutions of Differential Equations*, Dover Publications, Inc., New York, 1950.

32. Lewis, J. B., "The Use of Nonlinear Feedback to Improve the Transient Response of a Servomechanism," *AIEE Preprint*, 52–19, May, 1952.

33. Lin, S., "A Method of Successive Approximations for Evaluating the Real and Complex Roots of Cubic and Higher-Order Equations," *J. Math. Phys.*, Vol. 20, No. 3, August, 1941.

34. Liu, Y. J., *Servomechanisms—Charts for Verifying Their Stability and for Finding the Roots of Their Third and Fourth Degree Characteristic Equations*, Massachusetts Institute of Technology, Cambridge, Mass., 1941.

35. Marcy, H. T., "Parallel Circuits in Servomechanisms," *Trans. AIEE*, Vol. 65, 1946, pp. 521–529.

36. McDonald, D., "Analog Computers for Servo Problems," *Rev. Sci. Instr.*, Vol. 21, February, 1950.

37. McDonald, D., *Nonlinear Techniques for Improving Servo Performance*, Cook Research Laboratories, Chicago, 1950.

38. Minorsky, N., "Directional Stability of Automatically Steered Bodies," *J. Am. Soc. Naval Engrs.*, Vol. 34, May, 1922.

39. Nyquist, H., "Regeneration Theory," *Bell System Tech. J.*, Vol. 11, January, 1932.

40. Oldenbourg, R. C., and Sartorius, H., *The Dynamics of Automatic Controls*, American Society of Mechanical Engineers, New York, 1948.

41. Ragazzini, J. R., Randall, R. H., and Russell, F. A., "Analysis of Problems in Dynamics by Electronic Circuits," *Proc. IRE*, Vol. 35, 1947.

42. Restemeyer, W. E., "Operational Methods in Servomechanism Design," *J. Aeronaut. Sci.*, Vol. 12, July, 1945.

43. Routh, E. J., *Dynamics of a System of Rigid Bodies*, 3d ed., Macmillan & Co., Ltd., London, 1877.
44. Scarborough, J. B., *Numerical Mathematical Analysis*, Johns Hopkins Press, Baltimore, 1930.
45. Smith, E. S., *"Automatic Control Engineering,"* McGraw-Hill Book Co., Inc., New York, 1944.
46. Stovall, J. R., "Transducers, Sensing Elements for Servos," *Elec. Mfg.*, April, 1950.
47. Thomson, W. T., *Laplace Transformation*, Prentice-Hall, Inc., New York, 1950.
48. Tschudi, E. W., "Transfer Functions for R-C and R-L Equalizer Networks," *Electronics*, Vol. 22, May, 1949.
49. Weiss, H. K., "Analysis of Relay Servomechanisms," *J. Aeronaut. Sci.*, Vol. 13, No. 7, July, 1946.
50. Weiss, H. K., "Theory of Automatic Control of Airplanes," *NACA Tech. Notes 700*, Washington, 1939.

INDEX

(Numbers in *italics* refer to the Bibliography)